TRANSSEXUALS

Life From Both Sides

by

Lynn Hubschman

DIANE Publishing

Manufactured in the United States of America

CONTENTS

PART TWO

FOREWORD

There is something mysterious about a person who wishes to change genders; more precisely stated, a person who is driven, obsessed with the need to switch genders. Why would anyone go through the torment and anguish of trying to live a life totally different, opposite of what nature, biology, call it what you will, apparently intended, to face the questioning, the ridicule, the frank abuse so frequently encountered, and finally the mutilating surgery required? The drive to evolve into the opposite gender has to be enormous, to be able to cope not only with the inevitable external stresses, but with the internal doubts, indecision, vacillations, and the fear and shame that so often shatter the equipoise of a transgendered individual.

Even those of us professionals who have worked with these people as patients or clients retain our wonder and even amazement at the process, and when transformation is near completion (is it ever totally complete?) join in their joy and pleasure, at least as much as we can, for total empathy is impossible. What makes the journey possible is hope. If ever there is a tribute to the role of hope in overcoming despair, it should be made in these cases.

This book brings needed information about the world of the transsexual (DSM IV can never excise the word from our vocabulary) to all those who are interested: to the spectator who has an intellectual or even a voyeuristic need to know more, to the gender confused, to the transgender person who has set upon this path, to their families and friends, and finally to professionals who wish to deepen their understanding or perhaps to learn the many practical ways to help the transsexual.

So many questions arise. When should hormones be administered? When should they be withheld? What are the ways in which they can damage or help the process of transformation? What is involved in the surgery and what does it cost; who are the surgeons and what are the health facilities available; what are the legal issues; how does one change one's identity so that transactions with agencies or bureaucrats can be made more smoothly?

These and many more issues are described in Lynn Hubschman's book. I had the pleasure of working with her at Pennsylvania Hospital for fourteen years and have always admired her mix of compassion and the hard-headed practicality that allowed her to be direct and forthright while at the same time understanding and truly concerned about the transsexual patient.

Over the years, we saw, treated, or consulted about many people who were uncertain and confused about their gender. Not all were transsexuals. It was our job to help those who were genuinely transsexual and who wished to make changes (not all wanted a complete surgical transformation) to make decisions that would enable them to feel more fulfilled and perhaps happier. We tried to be helpful to all those who came to us with gender problems, to find them professional help, perhaps to accept themselves better even without hormones or surgery. Often there were disappointments and heartaches. We feel that we owe all those patients a debt. To see them cope with the confusion surrounding their sense of identity, their inner core, who and what they were, was a lesson in living, coping, and adapting that had to make us better people ourselves. Lynn and I had the good fortune of observing and knowing these people. She has been able to capture the feeling of being their therapist, counselor, and just plain helper and to distill their concerns and issues in a way that will enlighten all those with an interest in the subject.

Harold I. Lief, M.D.
Emeritus Professor of Psychiatry
University of Pennsylvania

PREFACE

In my thirty-three years as a social worker, almost fifteen were spent as Director of Social Work at Pennsylvania Hospital in Philadelphia, Pennsylvania, where transsexual surgery has been performed for over twenty years.

When patients seeking transsexual surgery came to the hospital, few people knew about the diagnosis and staff were frequently curious or hostile. Since my background was in family counseling and sex education, I began to study the issue. I eventually began working with the patients and those close to them. From these, now twenty three years of practice in this field, as well as experience as the coordinator of the Gender Identity Clinic at the hospital, I have come to understand and appreciate the people who are in this most central and difficult human condition.

Over the years I have appeared on many television talk shows to share my knowledge. Often I have brought patients with me to address various topics related to being transsexual. As a result, I have had the opportunity to better educate the public so they can understand and express empathy for people who are in this situation. The questions that are raised time and time again prove to me that there are always more people to inform. In addition, individuals who suffer alone, or who live in parts of the world where professionals or programs are nonexistent, need information. The many letters I would receive after each television appearance demonstrated this lack of resources.

As a result of the number of years I have worked in this field and the countless transsexuals and their families and loved ones I have been fortunate to work with, I have decided to write this book to explain in simple terms what this issue is about.

This book covers the history and definition of transsexualism, along with standards for surgery. Medical procedures are briefly reviewed. Most of the book is devoted to first-person accounts from people who are transsexual. I wanted them to tell about their life experiences in their own words. The group includes males and females; all are post-operative. A few short pieces by family members are also included. I have tried to reach a broad spectrum regarding age and educational background as well as differing attitudes. At the end, there is a list of those doctors who provide services for transsexuals.

While no one book can cover every possible question or issue, this one attempts to review, in plain language, what I have learned in my years working in this exciting, never boring field.

While I am indebted primarily to my patients and their openness, their families' love and attempts at understanding are equally appreciated. Even when a family could not deal constructively with this issue, we all learned. My own development and respect for the struggle, as well as knowing the intense drive and strength it takes to go through such a life, is constantly being renewed. My work with these courageous individuals has enhanced my professional role and offered me insight into some of life's basic assumptions.

My wish is that this book will open peoples' eyes, hearts, and, most importantly, minds: allowing the public to take another look at a group of people who exemplify the challenge and wonder of the human condition.

INTRODUCTION

Transsexual and Gender Identity Clinics have made tremendous strides in the past forty years in the identification, treatment, and, if necessary, surgery for Gender Dysphoria. However, the opposition to this vital and necessary treatment has become more strident in the past ten to fifteen years in the United States. Religious groups, government agencies, and third-party medical insurance agencies persist in labeling these patients as emotional aberrations rather than bona fide medical problems. Many states forbid the surgery in state-funded hospitals.

The surgeons involved in transsexual transformation surgery have achieved tremendous results so that the neogenitalia created is cosmetically and physiologically appealing to the recipients. In far too many cases, the surgery is denied for lack of funding rather than for any medical or surgical consideration.

Lynn Hubschman and her contributors are to be commended for assembling this outstanding series of patient accounts and surgical techniques. Hopefully, the text will enlighten and persuade some of those opponents and authorities who have so vehemently denied this therapy and surgery its proper position in American medicine.

Since 1969, I and my colleagues at the Pennsylvania Hospital in Philadelphia, Pennsylvania have performed transsexual surgery in more than 160 patients of both sexes. With the proper screening and pre-operative therapy, we have never regretted any of the surgeries. More importantly, none of the patients have experienced serious psychological or medical complications post-operatively.

Hopefully, in the future this type of treatment and surgery will be confined to appropriate medical centers that will continue to do the necessary screening, evaluation, and surgery. In the past, too many susceptible patients have been victimized by unscrupulous practitioners and "surgical mills" that have only been interested in money and not in the patients.

Terrence R. Malloy M.D.
Chief, Section of Urology, Pennsylvania Hospital
Professor of Urology, University of Pennsylvania
Vice-Chairman, Division of Urology, University of Pennsylvania Heath Care Systems

ACKNOWLEDGEMENTS

This book could not have been written without the information graciously offered by all the professionals, organizations and their representatives, friends, colleagues, and of course, the people who entrusted their life histories to me. Knowing how difficult it is to share the type of information required for a book of this nature, my appreciation and regard for each person who wrote a piece is heartfelt. In the three years plus that it took to put all of this together, I have come to know the tedious, lonely process of such a venture. I do not write well, and I do not enjoy writing, but I have always known that this information needed to be shared. While a broad spectrum of material is included, it is meant to be used by anyone who has any interest in the subject matter. There is information for patients and family members, professional counselors, physicians, and students.

Every attempt was made and much energy and time were expended in attempting to have all the information both up-to-date and inclusive, with a variety of opinions expressed. Things change rapidly in this field. New techniques, new standards, and new addresses are all part of the ever-moving picture. There were many people behind the scenes who helped tremendously: from searching for a journal article to granting permission to reprint some material.

I am always in debt to my group at Pennsylvania Hospital in Philadelphia, where I served as Director of Social Work for almost fifteen years. They taught me about the field and were there for whatever I or my patients needed. Many of my peers contributed to this manuscript by supplying and reviewing data. Among them are: Leonard Kryston M.D., Richard Nemeroff M.D., Terrence Malloy M.D., and Harvey Rosen M.D. Nancy Chierici Krell R.N. was also of great assistance.

Of special mention is Harold Lief M.D., who served as a colleague and mentor for many years. I consider him a dear and personal friend. Others who must be acknowledged are: Dallas Denny M.A. of AEGIS, Phyllis R. Frye Esq. of ICTLEP, James Green with the FTM group, Brenda Johnson with the Fort Lauderdale support group,

Sheila Kirk M.D., Vanessa Murray IFGE, and Bean Robinson Ph.D., Executive Director of the Harry Benjamin Association. Special thanks to Anne Lawrence M.D. for her Web page, telephone time, and allowing me to use her valuable resources. Judy Van Maasdam M.A., Coordinator of the Gender Dysphoria Program in Palo Alto, CA is especially thanked for all her years of friendship and open sharing of knowledge. She was always ready to supply whatever I asked for as this journey progressed.

While society's views change, people develop, and attitudes frequently fluctuate, some things remain constant. I use both the word transsexual and the newer term transgender in the same way. Whatever the words, my hope is that the goal to bring as much light on the subject as possible will be achieved. For all the people listed above, I think I can safely say that is the only end.

In ending this page, my deepest thanks go to my daughters, Jody and Tracy, who kept my spirits and energy going with their constant support and push to see this to completion, a mother's dream full circle. The final acknowledgement is to my husband Emil, whose patience, love, and belief, to say nothing of his computer skills, are indeed the wind beneath my wings.

This book is dedicated to:

DANIEL
ALINA
AMELIA

Mes chers petits qui font mon coeur chanter et danser.

ACTUAL LIFE STORIES

The following accounts are written primarily by my clients and their families. A few are written by people whom I have come to know in other ways. Their experiences and feelings about being transgendered are told in their own words; except for some minor editing, the words are reproduced as they were written. As the reader will see, there is a wide variety of personalities, attitudes, values, and coping skills. As in any population, the label "transsexual" does not denote one mold of person, but rather a varied tapestry. The people who are involved with and care about transsexuals are also a broad cross-section of society. These stories express the primary message of the book: the experience of transsexuals and their world.

EVA'S STORY
MALE TO FEMALE

I grew up in a fairly normal family — well, no one's family is normal, despite what the Republican Party tries to tell us. But I had a mom, a dad, and a sister, and we all got along pretty well. I was lucky enough to be raised in a nice neighborhood (on the Philadelphia Main Line), with enough money to keep us comfortable.

I was an average student at a nice public school system; terrific at some subjects, moronic in others, and incredibly lazy. I wasn't friendless — there were a few brave souls unafraid to be seen with me in public (I'm still close to some of those people, more than 25 years later). The vast majority of my fellow students, however, made it their life's work to pound me into the ground, both emotionally and physically. Kids are like sharks: they sense fear, or blood, and they go in for the kill. To this day I have all the instincts of Joan Crawford on a bad career day, and the fact that I cannot have children of my own is a source of endless delight to me.

Second grade was when I caught on to what the problem was. We were in line for something or other and the teacher was separating us into boys and girls. It struck me: oh! I'm a girl — that's what's going on! Of course, I was pretty startled, but it didn't really throw me. It was my little secret. I felt like some kind of double agent. Like many transsexuals before and since, I laughed to myself over hit songs like "Both Sides Now," "Do It or Die," and "Georgie Girl". ("Don't be so scared of changing and re-arranging yourself—it's time for jumping down from that shelf!").

I found drag queens utterly fascinating but at the same time a bit unsettling. To this day, I can enjoy a performance by Lypsinka or the late Divine, but in the back of my mind a voice says, "there but for the grace of modern surgery...."

From the time I started watching TV, Christine Jorgensen jokes were being bandied about. When I first heard about the possibility of a sex-change operation, I knew it was for me. I didn't understand the difference between transsexual and homosexuals until I read Jan

Morris' Conundrum; I just figured that gay men were really women (a lot of people still think that way, unfortunately). It wasn't until I was older that I realized that who you are and who you sleep with are two totally different subjects.

Through my teen years I was seen by the world at large as a very effeminate gay man. I'm sure the people who chased me, threatened me and beat me up wouldn't have cared much that I was a transsexual; multisyllabic words would have been lost on them. I was a pretty poor imitation of a man, never a very convincing actor (actress?). I was short, thin, with a high voice and unintentionally effeminate mannerisms. I still recall standing in front of my mirror trying to practice walking like a guy. I never quite got the hang of it, thank goodness.

In college I had the same experiences many gay men have — I was told by the men's hockey team that if "we catch you in the bathroom we'll beat your fucking face off, faggot." This was long before you could press a civil liberties suit; no doubt the college officials would have sided with the hockey team. So I did what gays (and Jews and light skinned blacks) did for years; I tried to pass, make friends, avoid trouble. I learned to run, to "fight dirty" and keep everyone off balance with jokes.

There's a movie in which someone whistles at Marilyn Monroe and says, "to wear a dress like that, you gotta start laying plans when you're about 13." I'm no Marilyn Monroe, but I did start laying plans real early; I knew by the time I hit puberty that I was going to have a sex change. I stayed in the soprano section of the choir, keeping my upper registers open. I never cross-dressed, because I knew sooner or later I'd be wearing women's clothes as my own (besides, I knew how silly I'd look). I find skirts more comfortable and flattering than trousers. But if I were a man, I'd be happily lining up at Brooks Brothers (or, if I could afford it, Ungaro).

And I stayed a virgin. This aggravated the hell out of my doctors later on — if I were smart, I would have lied and said more people had gone down on me than on the Titanic. But why bother? No terrific guys ever approached me; I had enough problems as it was; I didn't want to get involved in a gay relationship that would — necessarily — have to end badly when I became a woman. Thank goodness I didn't have a wife, boyfriend, and/or child to deal with when the time came.

The toughest part wasn't making a decision that was made for me before birth, as far as I'm concerned. The really hard part was telling others without sounding like a lunatic. "I'm a woman trapped in a man's body" does not — you will agree — sound like the statement of a sane person, unless you're Shirley MacLaine.

My family and friends had always assumed I was gay, so it's not like I was expecting to give anyone a heart attack. I chickened out and told my parents through letters. My father refused to believe me until I actually went through with the surgery. My mother, of course, blamed herself — don't they all? — but soon came around and was very supportive. Today when she hears my old name, she draws a blank. "I can't remember you ever having been anything but my daughter," she says. Obviously, she and I are very close friends. My sister and grandmother also adjusted amazingly well. My grandfather never came around, but then, he and I never particularly cared for one another.

Telling my friends was more embarrassing than traumatic. I sat in a car with my high school pal Eric, and I figured he thought I was gay or bisexual. "It's not the first thing you'd think of, or the second. It's the third." He looked at me, horrified; "Animals?" "It's the fourth thing!" I yelled. "It's the third thing most people would think of!" Few of my friends were terribly taken aback. Only one dropped me like a brick, which is not a bad average by any means.

I started cross dressing in the summer of 1977, the weekend of the New York blackout, while Son of Sam stalked the streets — not a good omen. Making matters worse, it was the 1970s, when everyone looked awful. Platform shoes, double-knit polyester, glitter makeup, Farrah hair. I had no idea about women's clothing; I knew how to tie a half-Windsor, or pick out a blue blazer, but I'd never been taught what every young woman should know. As a result, I walked around for a couple of years looking like I was going to Carmen Miranda's Bat Mitzvah.

The hardest part of cross-dressing was dealing with the psychiatrists I was forced to see. I mean, psychiatrists are all very well and good for those who need advice; all I needed was a simple OK on a piece of paper. I'd taken a few years of psychology in college, so I knew the language as well as they did. "You seem to be suffering symptoms of maladaptive repression," one guy told me. "But doctor," I chirped, "aren't the symptoms of maladaptive repression concomitant to those of adaptive sublimation?" They hate it when you do that. Another doctor leaned forward and whispered, "What do you think of when you masturbate?" I winked at him, "You." It's a miracle I ever got that OK.

Of course, that year of cross-dressing was, to put it mildly, socially uncomfortable; I was neither upstairs nor downstairs nor in my lady's chamber. I concentrated on school and friends and made no attempt to have a romantic life. I felt as though everyone was staring at me; and since I was the only known transsexual on campus, they were staring at me.

I socialized mostly with gay friends; living in Baltimore (where I went to college), I danced nightly at the Hippo, the local gay disco. Days I hung around in Fell's Point with the John Waters crowd. My closest friends were know locally as The Bright Young Things: Keith, Michael, and David (extremely attractive gay men), and Laura and Joy (two other straight women). I'm still good friends with all except Joy, who died of cancer a few years back. We dressed in thrift-shop clothes, both for the elegance and the economy. A 1940s suit or 1930s frock could be had for a few dollars in some of the downtown shops, because the disco look was too dreadful to contemplate.

It took years before I — like so many before me — got over my youthful style and turned into my mother. In my case, though, I didn't mind, as my mother has perfect, quiet but expensive taste in clothes. Today I'm most comfortable in a suit, or a simple midlength skirt with a blouse or sweater. I'm too angular to look good in frills and am too old for miniskirts; so simple lines and good materials are my standbys.

I was operated on shortly after my 21st birthday. I woke up after surgery violently throwing up as a result of the anesthesia; my grandmother was sitting at the foot of my bed and saying, "So, I hope you don't regret it." I regretted just about everything at that point, but within a few days was hobbling weakly about, receiving visitors and the tasteless get-well cards I'd requested (having asked my mother to send "It's a Girl!" announcements to my friends).

One thing I was not prepared for was the chemical shock; the doctor hadn't explained to me that I'd be essentially going through puberty and menopause at the same time. "It's like living with a teenager again," my mother said. I stayed with her for a month, getting my strength back and trying to choke down some food (I was down to about 95 pounds).

After taking a semester off, I returned to my old college as a woman (I still can't believe I had the gall to do that). The students reacted great; they thought I was fascinating. The professors were another story entirely. Despite two years as one of the stars of the drama department, I was blackballed by the department head. "Don't bother auditioning, you won't be cast," he told me. "Your presence onstage would be too disruptive." I — and some of my champions — protested, but I never acted in college again.

A lot of my experiences were, of course, hilarious. I remember one sweet little old lady describing her plastic hip joint and pacemaker to me, adding, "Isn't it amazing what modern surgery can do?" I politely agreed. I appalled my doctor by finding the fact that I had a prostate infection amusing. He shook his finger at me — "a prostate infection is nothing to laugh about, young lady!" His statement failed to curb my amusement.

After college, I suddenly had a lot of decisions to make. For the first 21 years of my life I'd been working steadily and single mindedly toward one goal. Now that I'd achieved it, what was I to do with the rest of my life? It was as though I'd been given a huge box of Whitman's chocolates and had to choose. I'd never really thought seriously about a career; when I was young, girls grew up to be wives and mommies; men got office jobs and supported their families.

I moved to within commuting distance of New York (I'm basically not a city gal) and, for about six years, worked as an actress: summer stock, Off-Broadway, commercials, extra parts in films. I was just successful enough to keep going, but not successful enough to support myself without taking the occasional temp job. For awhile, I enjoyed it — summer stock was great; my reviews as a comedy and musical comedy actress were amazing. One friend told me that seeing me in "Lion in Winter" was like seeing Sandra Dee as Lady Macbeth. What I did to Sadie Thompson, I wouldn't wish on my worst enemy's dog.

But by the time I reached my late 20s, the charm began to wear. One night — 3:00 in the morning, rather — I was standing on the set of a commercial, holding up a can of Brand X tomato soup for the techies to light for the next shot. I'd been on the set for a 15-hour, three-commercial shoot (non-union, of course). I was frantically thinking, "I've got to make friends with the director I've got to make friends with the camera crew I've got to call my answering service I've got to call my agent...." Gee, I realized, this isn't fun anymore! So I cancelled my union dues, threw out my resumes and got out the New York Times classified section.

For the next couple of years I took the typical temp jobs: secretary, receptionist, etc., then landed a minor copywriting job at a small ad agency. After four years of that, I wrote for a trade magazine, and when that went under, I began to freelance. I now write for maybe half a dozen magazines, and have had two books published, biographies of

Jean Harlow and Theda Bara. Another book is due out soon. So, while I am hardly rich, I did stumble into a career I enjoy.

I recently read an article about how men react to their girlfriends' plastic surgery. As soon as a man discovers his lover had her hair bleached, her nose bobbed, or her lipo sucked, he somehow feels cheated; to paraphrase an old song, "I don't care what you are today— I know what you used to be."

I am one of the lucky transsexuals who can pass as the opposite sex. I was born with small genes; I'm slightly built, with a naturally high voice and feminine features. Had I been born with Tom Selleck's genes, my life would've been a lot tougher. I know there's a whole political argument now that says it's not important to pass. But the world judges you on your appearance, that's a harsh reality. I really don't know what to tell male-to-female transsexuals who are large, hulking and have bass-baritone voices. They'll have a tough life if they have the surgery; they'll have a tough time if they don't. That's a tragedy. One of the very few advantages female-to-male transsexuals have is that they can work out, cut their hair, grow a beard and moustache and look terrific.

A few years ago, I began getting quite annoyed about the portrayal of transsexuals on TV and in movies. Even liberal TV shows like "Night Court" and "The Golden Girls" used "sex change" as a punchline, and we were portrayed as either jokes or pathetic freaks on "Chicago Hope," "Prime Suspect," and the films "Soapdish," "Silence of the Lambs," and "Ace Ventura." We were — still are — treated like blacks before the 1930s, gays before Stonewall.

I am furious that transsexualism is still listed as a mental illness, when research has shown beyond all reasonable doubt that it results from pre-natal exposure to hormones.

I started marching with the transsexual contingent in the Gay Pride Parade, being more open about my past, and even appeared on Donahue. In my innocence, I thought there was going to be a serious, intelligent discussion; but it seems that Mr. Donahue wanted a freak show. A letter I wrote to the gay publication NYQ pretty much sums up my feelings on the subject:

Thanks for the cover story on Tula [a well-known transsexual]. It's always reassuring to see the gay community stand up for the transsexual community, especially since not all transsexuals are gay. Michael O'Brien's story was a breath of fresh air, particularly after GQ's condescending article in January and The New York Times reference to us as the "sequins and lamé" contingent at last year's Gay

Pride Parade (despite the fact that we looked more like a bunch of drab suburban housewives).

Transsexuals are still pre-Stonewall. We have no political lobby or effective, palatable spokesperson. It's understandable, really; most of us simply want to fade into the wallpaper after surgery. But this is self-defeating. The few transsexuals who do go public tend to be the misfits, the emotional cripples.

Transsexualism is a neuroendocrinological disorder — nothing more, nothing less. It is no more or less shameful than dyslexia or diabetes, yet we're one of the few minority groups that it's still universally permissible to bash. We are still classified as mentally ill by the American Psychiatric Association; we are routinely fired from our jobs, denied the right to marry, used as the butt of jokes.

Let's take a tip from the gay community; it's time for us to out ourselves, to show people that we are not pathetic freaks — that we're out there leading happy, productive lives. Transsexualism is only a shameful secret if we make it so.

I've been researching the history of transsexuals and found that we have a lot to be proud of. Native Americans have always revered their transsexual population. The Chevalier de Leon was a war hero in 18th century France before being given permission to live legally as a woman. We number among our members world renowned writer Jan Morris, surgeon and tennis pro Renee Richards, restaurateur Rachel Harlow, and inventor Wendy Carlos.

Christine Jorgenson was not, as her New York Times obituary said, the first person to have a sex change. She was merely the first person to have a sex change and a press agent. At least one male-to-female operation took place as early as 1923 in Berlin; but our real godmother is the Danish painter Lili Elbe. Lili Elbe was a true pioneer and deserving of recognition. She was born Einar Wagener in the 1880s and by the early 1910s was married and living the life of a wealthy bohemian, traveling through Europe with his artistic friends. Wagener began cross-dressing in the 1920s, under the name Lili Elbe. His wife, Gerda, was by this time a platonic friend and often used him as a model, and Lili even began a romantic involvement with a very forward-thinking actor named Claude Lejeune. By the late 1920s, Einar was living almost full time as Lili and began looking for a surgeon. Of course, everyone thought he was crazy and submitted him to the most barbaric treatments, but nothing changed his mind, although he was pushed near to suicide several times.

Finally, in 1930, Lili contacted a Dr. Werner Kraus (possibly a pseudonym) in Dresden, who agreed to perform a series of highly experimental operations. Three surgeries were performed, all of which remain veiled in mystery. Lili recovered, with the support of her ex-wife, friends and now-fiancé Claude. Photos of her at the time bear a striking resemblance to Dorothy Parker.

"...It is so lovely to be a woman here among women," she wrote to Gerda from her clinic, "to be a female creature exactly like all the others..." She went through periods of paranoia which will be familiar to all transsexuals: "Other women could be ugly, commit every possible crime. I, however, must be beautiful, must be immaculate, else I lost every right to be a woman," she wrote. On a happier note, she told her diary, " I feel like a bridge builder... I am not nervous anymore. If sooner or later I should succumb physically, I am quite reconciled. I shall at least have know what it is to live."

Lili did succumb physically, on September 12, 1931. In a fourth and final operation, Dr. Kraus attempted to transplant ovaries and a womb into Lili, so she and Claude could have children. She died of blood poisoning shortly thereafter. Her story was told in Niels Hayer's 1933 book, Man Into Woman, published by Jarrolds of London and long out of print. It's a heartbreaking, inspiring, and groundbreaking book, well worth the search.

Despite the fact that I'm turning political in my old age, I have a lovely life right now and have (I hope) retained my sense of humor. I have a lot of friends — some who know Bay's Little Secret, some who don't. I'm close to my family and have a satisfying (if precarious) career. And socially, I'm in the same boat with every other straight, single woman in her late thirties.

I date occasionally, have had a couple of long-term relationships; but Mr. Right still hasn't shown up (for that matter, neither has Mr. Partially Correct for Half Credit). And of course, I have the additional handicap of my past — not many men are willing to date a gal with a draft card. I didn't tell my last boyfriend (mostly because we had other problems to work out) and regretted it. The longer it went on, the sillier I felt about his not knowing; I had to hide old photo albums and letters; I couldn't make jokes. I didn't go through all this so I could lie.

Next time around, I intend to tell the guy before we wind up in bed. That way it will be his decision whether to go ahead or run screaming for the hills. I'm a realist above all, so I know I have very little chance of ever getting married. That's no big tragedy. I have a lot of friends who trapped themselves into hellish relationships because they were terrified of being alone. The hell with that; as my wise old auntie says, "it's better to be alone than to wish you were."

Unlike so many of my friends, I don't dread the approach of age. Being a little old lady is not the worst thing that could happen to you. I like myself, and if I had to go through what I went through in order to become who I am, then I don't have a single regret.

FRED'S STORY
FEMALE TO MALE

My family is wonderful. Although they thought there was something wrong with me — that I was probably going to be homosexual — they loved me just the same as all their other children, maybe even a little bit more. In my family, after a baby was born and it was time to leave the hospital, everyone went to Grandma's before they went home. In my case, there were two of us, since I have a twin sister. When my mother put us in my grandmother's arms, she looked us over, took my foot in her hand and told my mother in Italian, "This one should have been a boy." That wonderful, wise old lady knew, before me or anyone else, that God had made a mistake. My immediate family treated me, luckily, the way I wanted to be treated. If a pole had to be climbed to fix the clothesline, it was me doing the climbing. I did a lot of chores that would have normally been given to a boy instead of a girl. I always had the freedom to be me. My sister depended on me to take care of her, as if I was a brother.

I was very boyish in appearance. I was small with short hair; jeans and sweatshirts were my favorite clothes. I guess "tomboy" would have been the best way to describe me. Emotionally I was very confident; actually, I didn't know I was different. I was always just a kid. My grades were average because I never really applied myself. My street smarts were excellent, though.

I grew up in an old, tough place. We lived on the same block my mother grew up on; my father had grown up not far from there. All the kids I grew up with and their parents were born there, too. So everybody knew everybody else. It was a great, very close community. As children, we had so much to do, beaches, great parks, major movie houses, amusement areas, all right in our backyard. I never had a problem with anyone, and if someone did have a problem with me, I was never aware of it.

I didn't know I was a 'girl'. I didn't know that the shape of your body or what was under your clothes mattered. I guess I became aware when I couldn't play with my friends on a baseball team because I was a girl; this was 1960. It was about that time I started asking God, at bedtime, to let me wake up a boy. Gender? I didn't even know what it was.

If 'puberty' means menstruation, luckily it came very late. I was almost seventeen and had heard the 'stories'. Although initially I was upset, it became a very small annoyance in my life. Not until my early twenties, when I started to feel betrayed by my body, since I felt this shouldn't be happening to me, did it become a problem.

I didn't know at the time, but the private high school that I attended had a very large gay population. I always knew that my attractions were for women and it felt so natural that I really never thought anything was wrong with it. After leaving the school in my senior year, I found out that half of the 'Gay' population was in love with me and the other half hated me, mainly because I made no bones about who I was, what I was and how I was going to live my life. My first sexual experience, at sixteen, was with a girl, who had chased me for the prior two years. I finally asked her what she wanted, which was me, and our relationship lasted eight years. I had then, and still do now, a naivete about women; I never know when a woman is coming on to me. I've had many a laugh over this "problem."

I've been told throughout my life that I am very charismatic. I am a very confident person and always have been. I love myself. I think I'm a great person and I know the world would be a better place if there were more people like me. I also think that everyone should feel this way about themselves.

I've always loved life and enjoyed it for all it was worth. I love to laugh, and I am very rarely angry or depressed. I started a career early in1972 and although I had no formal training, I quickly became very good at it. I still work for the company today. My teens and early twenties were great. I had a good job, lots of friends, money in my pocket and a long-term relationship. I lived my life under an umbrella of homosexuality. Being small and popular, I was viewed as "cute" by my co-workers, but I was well-respected because of my working ability. I was the only female on a shift of forty workers. Everyone knew where I stood sexually and a lot of good-natured kidding took place, but I can take it as well as give it and I never had any problems.

It was in my mid-twenties that I started to become dissatisfied with my physical being. The menstruation began to bother me and I went to my doctor. I started taking hormones and I loved it. The periods stopped, I got stronger and most of all, facial hair. I still wear a mustache today. Three years later I had my breasts removed and then freedom! Although I was small to begin with, now I could wear my athletic T-Shirts and look like I should, with a flat muscular chest. It was just before my operation that I told my mother. I told her that I was legally changing my name and legally changing my sex. I'm a pretty tough nut, and although I love my mother very much, I told her that if she didn't like it, well it was just too bad, I had to live my life for myself. I couldn't live my life for her; if she wouldn't accept me, then I was 'outta there' and she could chalk me up for dead. I guess I figured, the best defense is a good offense. The only thing she could say was that she loved me and she didn't want to lose me. It's been almost ten years since that conversation. So much has happened, and although she claims to have accepted me, there are still mistakes on her part — the use of "she" and "her" when talking or referring to me.

In 1971 my older brother was getting married. My sister-in-law-to-be told my mother that she was going to ask me, along with my sister, to be in the wedding party. I came home and my mother gave me this whole big spiel about how much she loved me and how much she needed a favor from me. Of course I said "Sure Mom, anything." Big mistake. The next day my sister-in-law to be came by and asked me. I nearly fell over, since she was well aware of my social standing. She told me she didn't need my answer right away and then ran off. For the next three months my mother did everything from cry to threaten to beg. I do like my sister-in-law and I finally broke down. I figured it was only one day, and of course there were conditions: number one: no make-up of any kind; and number two: no complaints of any kind about my hair. All parties agreed.

It was 1971 and so I did what all my male friends were doing: for the first time in my life I let my hair grow. By the time the wedding came I had a great head of hair. My girlfriend was jealous.

The gown was bad enough (I felt like I was in drag), but we had these little lacey things to wear on our heads. After the ceremony I took mine off. When it came time to go into the hall for the reception, I struggled to put it back on. Being the shortest in the group, my partner (a cousin of the bride, who I knew all my life) and I were to be introduced first. The introduction was read, the doors were opened and we weren't there. The doors were closed, the MC said they would try this again and the intro was read once more. We ran to the door and as it was opened my partner stepped on the gown. We both went sprawling to the floor. He got up, tried to pull me up, still standing on the gown and down we went again. What's really funny about this whole thing is that, since my sister-in-law's family grew up with my family, ninety-five percent of the people in the hall knew me and had never seen me dressed this way. Everyone went wild. The applause was deafening. The MC was so shocked that he said, "But this is not the bride!!!." Three years later my sister was married. She knew better. I wore a suit.

I found that 99% of the people I know took my 'change' very well. There were a few who found it hard to call me "he" or "him". I got through to a couple of these people simply by telling them to look at me when they want to say "her". If they can look at me and still say "her," since I surely don't look like a "her," then they really have a problem and I will forgive them. Not one of these people let me down. My only real concern is dealing with people from my past whom I haven't seen in more than 10 years. My organization just merged with another and some employees were moved to the same area I'm located in. I walked into the men's room, and standing at the sink was a guy whom I used to work very closely with 15 years ago. My first reaction was to clap him on his back, shake his hand, joke about the fact that he left us 15 years ago and, because of the merger, he is back. He recognized me (except for the moustache I look the same), and we laughed and talked as if nothing was amiss. Not until I left the men's room did I realize that the last time he saw me I didn't use the men's room. It didn't matter to me and it didn't matter to him.

The people I get concerned about are those who like to have something on others, who like to know things about people. I'm sure there have been or will be people in my life who will wait until I walk away and then say, "He was once a girl," or "He is not really a man." But it really doesn't matter, because if I never make another friend in my life because of my transsexuality, I will still have enough friends and people who care for me to last a lifetime.

I love women, God's most wonderful gift to the world. I see them work a full day at their jobs, and then go home and take care of children, cook, clean and run their households. I don't think women get enough credit and they surely don't get enough pay. I don't think a price can be put on rearing children and running a household, and I think all men should help. I cook and clean with the best of them and I'm fortunate to know other men who do, too. I'm not pro-abortion but I surely am pro-choice.

When the woman who later became my wife decided that she liked me, we started a relationship. From the very beginning, my invitation to dinner, I was taken by surprise at just how much she liked me. Our first date took place the day after I taped a national TV show about transsexuality. When she made her feelings known to me, I told her there was something important that I had to tell her about myself. I wasn't expecting to tell her so soon in our relationship, so I was having a hard time of it. I was pacing back and forth, and today we laugh over the thoughts that were flying through her head. Things like . . . he's married, he was in jail once, and oh, my God, he's dying. What I did was take her hands in mine and told her that the day, before I taped a TV show about transsexualism; that I wasn't a genetic man. This young, wonderful and beautiful woman simply said, "Fred, should that matter to me? I love you." We will be married one year on September 21st. It's been the best year of my life.

As this woman and I began to talk about marriage, I decided that I wanted to tell her mother about me. The main reason was that she really liked me and I didn't want someone else to tell her — I wanted her to hear it from me. My wife didn't think it was really necessary and wanted to wait, but I knew that the more her mother liked me, the more I had to lose.

My wife sat her mother down and went through the same thing I had gone through telling her. My mother-in-law says that she had the same thoughts my wife had had. We all laugh about this today.

At first, my mother-in-law flipped out: "I knew something was wrong with him! I knew he was too good to be true!" I stayed away from her house for four days, and then my wife asked if it would be all right if I came by. She said yes, that she wanted to talk to me.

We talked for four hours. She asked me questions about everything from children to sex. We talked about me, we talked about her, and we talked about our future. The final result of our conversation was her statement, "You are everything I want in a husband for my daughter."

Today I am a most lucky man, with not only a wonderful, beautiful wife who loves me, but also a wonderful, beautiful mother-in-law who loves me too. My wife and mother-in-law are the only people in their family that know about my transsexuality.

In 1987 my previous10-year relationship was over. My lover and I grew apart, not unlike many other people, and went our separate ways. Since I was alone and intended to take a rest from long relationships, I decided to seek out other people with my disability — being born without male genitalia. The only organization I could find was one put together by male-to-female transsexuals. They were a group of about 60 ladies; there were also three female-to-male people, but I never got to meet any of them. The president of the organization passed my name and address on to a guy like me who was trying to start a female-to-male group and he wrote to me. I was pleased to hear from him and we got together. Through him I met quite a few female-to-males.

Unfortunately, I found that 99% of the transsexuals I've met are not the kind of people I would have for friends. I'm not saying that they are not nice people, I just like my friends to be successful and confident and somewhat happy. I have talked and will talk to anyone who feels they can benefit from my life. I have and will help anyone I possibly can. Almost all the people I've met through the group have problems. I can't relate to them because my life has been very different. I want everyone to stand up for themselves, to live their lives happily despite their 'disabilities'. Most of these guys' lives have been terrible. They can't work, have no real friends, no family, and mostly, no confidence. You see, I don't really think that I am any better than anyone else, and if I can make it. anyone can. With a firm belief in yourself you can do anything.

It's hard for me to relate to people who don't believe in themselves, and people tend to resent me for my confidence, if they lack their own. I'll give an example of someone in the group whom I have a hard time with.

This guy has been living off the state of New Jersey for almost 20 years. The state pays for all his medical bills, paid for all the operations and even pays his fare back and forth to get his hormone shots (of course he takes a cab). He has been fighting the state to pay for his phalloplasty. He's on welfare, and has gone to school full-time for quite a while to become a physical therapist. Although he can at this time get a job, he doesn't, because, he says, in his field with the required close contact he will have with people, his not having a penis will be evident and therefore harmful. Of course the state doesn't want to shell out more than $60,000, after all the money they spent on this guy. To tell you the truth. I think they really did enough already. I feel this way for two reasons. One, he is really taking advantage of the state, which hurts everyone. Two, no one is going to tell me the penis makes the man. No one, not doctors, lawyers or transsexuals, is going to tell me that I am not a man because I don't have a penis. The essence of all of us is in our minds and our hearts, not in our physical bodies.

CRYSTAL:
NOT YOUR AVERAGE AMERICAN GIRL

He knelt before me with his head of white-grey hair bowed down. He looked amusing wearing my stockings, garter belt, and bra. But I had enough business savvy to not even smile at the sight. Except for the ones who enjoy humiliation scenes, tricks hate to see you making fun of them, and this guy was paying me eighty bucks, after all.

I caught a glance of myself in the full length mirror. My long hair, recently bleached blond, flowed onto smooth shoulders above my hormonally-developed breasts. Though my boobs were small, they looked sexy filling out the material of the sheer A-cup bra. As usual, my makeup was very whorish, just the way that most of these guys liked it. I couldn't wait until I was done with this scene, when I could turn my attention to the other mirror, which sat behind the big one. It had about half a gram of cocaine left on it.

The thought of the dope woke me up. The room was dark and it was very quiet outside. There were no car engines, no garbage trucks or sirens, and no click-clack of the high heels of streetwalkers. It was definitely not the city. I ran my hand over my face to wipe off the beads of perspiration and felt my moustache. I heard the loud snoring of an ex-GI in the bed next to mine, and I was back to reality. No more makeup or women's clothes. No more female hormones or electrolysis. No more turning tricks. And definitely no more drugs.

I lay in a bed in the ward of a Veteran's Administration drug rehabilitation program. It had been two years since I had lived as a woman, and only one month since I had kicked dope. I knew it would be a while before I got back to sleep, because questions were flooding into my head. Most of them started with "Why?"

Why was I dreaming about this now? I thought I was happy being a man. But then, if I was so happy, why did I become such a junkie? And why did I ever want to be a woman in the first place? How could this have happened to such an average middle-class kid?

As I lay there pondering the hows and whys, I realized how scattered my life was. If it were on film, you could clip segments from various spots and they would seem like scenes from very different movies. I found them hard to reconcile with the man who was lying in this ward bed in August of 1988.

Through dozing and waking states I recalled bits and pieces of my life. I had no idea how to deal with these memories. I didn't think I'd find it easy to talk about having lived as a woman with a bunch of fellow veterans. And I would have even more trouble admitting that I wasn't sure all of that was behind me.

"Oh shit," I thought, the tears starting to roll down my cheeks in the still darkness, "How did I ever get into this?"

Twenty years earlier I had lain in bed, my face wet as I silently cried and listened to my parents yell at each other from the other end of the house. My stomach was knotted into a ball of anxiety, my throat choked shut with self-pity and fear, and my body raced with uncontrollable shivers. What made it worse was that I couldn't hear what they were yelling.

Those fearful nights, which occurred at least once a week, are the most persistent memories of my childhood. Mostly, my father wasn't around when I was awake. His new business needed a lot of attention, so I only saw him on weekends and first thing in the morning. His absence didn't bother me greatly. The fights with my mom aside, he just made me nervous, as did most men. I was my mama's boy through and through. It was pretty distressing when my parents split up around my tenth birthday; it only increased the distance between Dad and me. Though I still loved my father, I had no idea how to relate to him.

My mother was another matter. I really admired her. She was independent, resourceful and strong, and she always seemed to land on her feet. When she got divorced, she went back to college, learned to program computers and got a job working for a San Francisco insurance company. She learned to fix things on her own, rather than depend on men. She jogged and kept in great physical shape. She also skied and later won races when she joined a ski club. It was during a skiing trip that she met John, who became my stepfather right when I started high school.

High school! It seems hard to believe I ever went to a typical middle-class school like Aragon. I spent much of high school in a daze, deep in my own daydreams and fantasies of being popular, which I was not. Since I grew up excruciatingly shy, socializing with my peers was not easy, so I did what I could to try to fit in. With my emerging identity as a hippie. I found myself smoking pot by the end of my sophomore year. To my dismay, most of my fellow dopers were bullies with long hair who also liked to get high. Once they sensed how timid I was, I became a target for harassment. I learned how to run instead of fight.

At sixteen years old, I had to shamefully acknowledge myself a sissy. I had never fought in my entire life, and that wasn't my only inadequacy. I didn't know and wasn't interested in anything about cars or sports. This is not to say I was into playing with Barbie dolls or having tea parties; I just had no interest in "boy stuff".

My self-image was a mess. I was a gutless coward, mostly afraid to talk to girls even though I wanted to, painfully shy, and not even man enough to stand up for myself. Plus, I was ignorant of cars and sports, both practically and conversationally. I failed almost every known litmus test of masculinity.

As I looked back over my teenage years, I realized that I couldn't find any one thing that stood out, nothing that might have clearly presaged what happened later. Yet I did find little telltale signs of a hidden gender problem. For one thing, when puberty clobbered me I became very shy around girls. As a male I had no idea how to relate to women. I went all the way through high school and several years after without ever dating. In fact, for almost four years after high school, the few girls I had sex with were prostitutes.

I was very shy around guys. My shyness was at its worst during physical education in high school, when I had to undress and shower in front of the other boys. I just hated them seeing me naked. In retrospect, I guess I felt the same as any young teenage girl would have about being naked in front of boys.

My sex life with females was nil since I was afraid to approach them, but that wasn't true with guys. When I was thirteen, I had gay sex with a neighbor boy, but it only happened a few times because neither of us fancied ourselves as "faggots." For the next four years I had sexual fantasies of women only, but I got so frustrated by the time I turned eighteen that I became willing to experiment again.

I moved in with Dale a couple of months after I graduated high school. He was 28 and worked in the same building as me. He was very confident, self-assured, and good with cars, and he was basically the man I wanted to be. I really looked up to him.

I don't know how long he'd had his eye on me, but he waited until I was safely eighteen before making his move. One night, not even a month after my birthday, he broached the subject of bisexuality after I went into his bedroom to talk. Our conversation got to the possibility of having past lives, and he told me that he thought he might have been a Roman because Romans were bisexual. He had been laying on his bed, and at this point he had his erect penis out and was slowly stroking it. I didn't have the nerve to take the cue that night, but a few nights later I allowed myself to have sex with him.

I went with it for a couple of weeks; I was so horny at that point that it took a while for me to care that I was doing this. After four times in bed with him, I got scared and called it quits. I was repelled by his attempts to kiss me. That made the whole thing too "gay" for me. For years after, I was out to prove that I wasn't homosexual. If anyone asked where I was from, I said "the Bay Area" instead of San Francisco because of the city's reputation.

Soon after this brief affair ended, I began to alter my consciousness on a very regular basis. Getting stoned during the day, all day, became the norm for me. It was a great way to keep from thinking about what I had done, and to keep from worrying about what I was going to do. I liked getting high and didn't consider my motives for doing it.

I wanted to run from my life, a life that became more uncertain every month. My stepfather and my mom had split up right before I graduated in January of '76, and their split affected me even worse than the first divorce. At this point I knew I needed a drastic change. High school had been such a nightmare that going to college was out, at least for a while. I couldn't go on working in my dad's shop as I'd done for most of 1976. Shop work was so boring. Besides, I'd damaged my back at work while trying to be macho.

I was desperate to be one of the guys, but had no idea of how to build up a sense of identity. I knew deep down I was a sissy, and maybe a "homo" as well, but I wasn't about to let anyone see that, including myself. I wasn't sure of who I was, what I was good at, or how to take care of myself. I had a lot to prove. I'm certain that was what led me to the recruiter's office, and so in February of 1977 I found myself at Lackland Air Force Base for basic training.

Somehow I managed to survive Basic, and I was sent to an Air Force base in rural Illinois for technical school. It was there where my drug and alcohol intake surpassed any level that I'd ever reached before. I got stoned on pot my first night there. After all of the culture shock I had been through, it was wonderful to be high again. My party-dude identity blossomed, and the acceptance I was gaining from my drug brothers and sisters made me feel like I was fitting in somewhere. This was a first for me. My uncertainty about my masculinity faded under the pleasant spell of dope, which also gave me the courage to be outgoing and less inhibited. I was a wild and crazy guy.

After six months I graduated from tech school and was sent to a base in Arizona. After being there for three months, I knew my job well enough to do it stoned, and I became quite jaded. I began to get stoned all of the time. I went to work stoned, got stoned on lunch break, and really pulled out the stops when I got off. I became very well-adjusted to my pothead identity. For a while, life seemed great, except for my lack of a sex life.

My foray into cross-dressing happened slowly. Since I'd only had sex with women twice at that point in my life, both of them prostitutes, and since I was still very shy around women, I had little to improve my self-confidence. I had no idea how to talk to females, which made asking them out on a date impossible. So I increasingly relied on self help, although my fantasies only carried me so far. The more I masturbated, the more difficulty I had achieving orgasm.

For some reason, I found the stories of cross-dressing in men's magazines to be intensely exciting, so I decided to get some lingerie. I made the bold move of going to a department store and buying a beautiful powder-blue babydoll ensemble. I had made up a story for the salesclerk, who smiled and told me that my girlfriend would love it. That night I had an intense orgasm wearing these clothes, and it became part of my masturbatory ritual. I cross-dressed for a few months until the guilt of what I was doing overcame me, and I threw everything out.

Yet my desire to dress up in women's underwear couldn't be thrown away; it could only be suppressed for a few months. Before too long, I found myself at K-Mart all over again. It soon became easy for me to shop for lingerie, and eventually I quit telling the stories as I made my purchases. I found that being stoned all of the time helped with these phases of dressing and denial. Drug use made the suppression of cross-dressing possible because it took my mind off of the clothes, and it also helped buffer my feelings of guilt when I did cross-dress.

It was difficult to feel close to anybody the whole four years I lived in Phoenix. My deep, dark cross-dressing secret made me feel different from the other guys. Not only was I unable to put it behind me, it got more powerful every year. When I moved off base into my own apartment, I carried things even further. I attempted wearing makeup once or twice, and had sexual fantasies of turning into a girl. My feelings of guilt were intense.

I separated from the military in early 1981, knowing that it had failed to make a man out of me. After four years I felt just as lost as when I decided to go see the recruiter. I tried my hand at a few construction jobs, most notably as an electrician, but I was too unstable and too drug-saturated to hold one for long. In the year and a half that I spent in Phoenix after my honorable discharge, I had done nothing except work a little, collect unemployment and welfare, learn to play rock guitar, and take an awful lot of drugs.

By summer of 1982, I had a deepening sense of doubt about myself. I doubted that I was capable of taking care of myself, that I'd ever be a hit with the girls, or that I'd ever find my place in life. Aside from my vague, unrealistic fantasies about being a musician, I had no idea of who or what I was or what I wanted out of life. The only thing I knew for sure was that I'd never find out in the Arizona desert. That's when I asked my mother for the money to come back to San Francisco, and when I got the money order, I left Phoenix for good.

I lived with Mom for a few months, but she was going through financial difficulty, so she reluctantly kicked me out so she could move in a rent-paying housemate. Fortunately a good friend invited me to live with him and his girlfriend. Even more fortunate, in my mind, is that he smoked pot and snorted cocaine a lot, and he didn't mind sharing. Life was good for the time being, but I was still very lonely until I met Annie while attending a Johnny Winter show at a local night club. She was quite attractive and intelligent, and best of all, she seemed interested in me. I gave her my phone number and hoped for the best. I didn't hear from her for a while, though.

For a few weeks I had been doing some electrical work at a dance club in the Tenderloin, a poverty stricken part of downtown San Francisco. The neighborhood amazed me. I had never seen anything like it, largely due to my sheltered upbringing. One day I went into the bar next to where I was working to make a phone call, and I got the surprise of my life.

Initially the place seemed like most other bars I had been to. Many of the patrons were women; some of them were quite beautiful, I noticed, as I stepped into the phone nook. As I listened to the phone ring, I noticed how tall some of the women were, and that a few of them had markedly unfeminine traits. One of the girls had a five o'clock shadow underneath her makeup. "What the hell is this?" I thought.

One of the prettier girls smiled and blew a kiss at me as I left. I began to suspect that she wasn't always a girl. Perhaps I was even more sheltered than I thought I had been! I smoked some pot as soon as I could so I wouldn't have to think about what I had seen.

A few weeks after this encounter, Annie called me up. We spent three hours on the phone, and we made several such calls that week. She was clearly as lonely as I was. After our third call, we went on a date that weekend and, after dinner and a movie, we ended up in her bed.

I felt vindicated as a "normal" guy as we lay together after our love-making, and I noticed some very powerful feelings in me. I had been so lonely for so long, and I found myself blurting out that I loved her. I was so happy when she said that she loved me too.

At that point, I became overwhelmed with emotion. I had been lugging my secret around for five years, and I was sick of it. Speaking hesitantly and with grief, I told her of my cross-dressing. I was crying by the time I finished. She asked me if I still wanted to do that stuff, and I told her of course not. Her reply was that it didn't matter — she still felt the same way about me. I loved her even more after that, and I started to have hope that maybe I could be "normal" after all.

To make a long story very short, we got engaged and moved in together. During this time, aided financially by my grandparents, who sent me $500 a month, I enrolled into a computer science degree program at the junior college in San Bruno. I tried hard to be in the mainstream, where I believed I belonged. I was worried that my interest in cross-dressing wasn't dead, and was due to make a comeback. But I believed that a heterosexual relationship would keep me from returning to that guilt-ridden activity.

My worry was well justified because I was getting the urge to cross-dress again. After many months of not dressing up, I began putting Annie's lingerie on while she was at work. Eventually, I brought up the idea of incorporating cross-dressing into our sex life, which started a big fight. I decided that I wanted to be married to her more than I wanted to dress up, so I managed to smooth it over.

On January 21, 1984, Annie and I became husband and wife. For over four months, I was the perfect husband and college student. I made straight As and completely sublimated my urge to dress up. Unfortunately, I couldn't suppress it forever, and I found myself in her closet again. I was torn by this compulsion. The adult magazines I read suggested that there was nothing wrong with it, but Annie had other ideas about that. I decided to go to the college library and research the topic of transvestism, hoping that I could be cured. I checked out <u>Transvestites and Transsexuals: Mixed Views,</u> by Deborah Feninbloom, and studied it.

I was not encouraged by what I read, which said that transvestism is much more common than is often believed, that it's not sick or harmful, and that very few people are cured of it. There was also some stuff on transsexualism, but I didn't pay much attention to it. It didn't seem to apply to me.

By August of 1984, my obsession had reached critical mass. I had been teased for months by images of that bar I'd walked into a year and a half before, and of the "women" I had seen in there. Dressing up in private had lost some of its appeal, and I had a compelling urge to go check out that bar from a participant's point of view. I made the decision to tell Annie, and I'll never forget that conversation I had with her.

I told her that I had been dressing up and that I was having powerful feelings that I didn't understand. I didn't know what I wanted, I told her, and I needed to find out.

"I don't know," she sighed resignedly, "I suppose it would be better to know, once and for all, rather that playing a charade. I just can't believe you're gay!"

We made love almost every night.

"I didn't say that," I explained. "The truth is that I don't know what the hell I am. I'm trying to find out".

"And what is it you want to try?"

"I...I'm not sure," I began. "I've been thinking of going out in public — dressed as a woman. Probably to that bar I told you about...."

"And do what? Let someone — a man — pick you up?"

"Maybe...I don't really know for sure. I just have a feeling that by going through with this I can get it out of my system."

"Oh, my God." She sighed. "Better we know for sure."

In less than two weeks, I found myself back at the bar, only this time I was wearing a wig, full makeup, and a dress. "Awkward" would be an apt description of how I felt, with "nervous" grappling for second place. I wasted no time in ordering a drink, downing it, and ordering another, all within five minutes. During a lull in the action, the bartender came over and asked me my name, to which I almost told him my real name, but finally settled on something feminine that sounded close. He told me I was beautiful, and I just about melted right there. It felt so good to hear that.

Hours later, the bartender and I were laying naked on a floor-level mattress in his upper Tenderloin studio. He had just orgasmed, but I had not even gotten turned on. I wasn't disgusted — I just wasn't excited. After a few more minutes of trying, I reached the conclusion that this scene really did nothing for me sexually. Thus, I changed back into my male attire and went home to my wife.

I thought I was free of it, yet what I read in that library book stayed with me. I had suspected that my cross-dressing was more than an erotic thing, and my trip to the drag bar confirmed it. Not only was there a big satisfaction in being attractive as a female, but even though I was nervous and new to the bar, I had felt at home sitting there on the barstool. I don't know why presenting myself as a woman could have felt so natural so quickly, but I couldn't deny that it did. For awhile, the unsatisfying sex with the bartender helped me to avoid thinking about further excursions, but all it took was Halloween and the annual Exotic Erotic Ball to give me the excuse I needed to get in drag again.

Annie could see the writing on the wall. Not long after Halloween we were in marriage counseling. After a few ugly sessions together, the therapist, Lanie, agreed to see us individually in her San Francisco office. Somehow, all of that hadn't affected my classwork. Since I was still getting straight As in college, I decided that I had the time to get an electric contractor's license. Maybe I could make twice as much in computers, but contracting is such a masculine job. The exam prep school was also in the city, so I ended up driving into San Francisco two nights a week. And I was drawn to the Tenderloin each night on the way home where I gawked at prostitutes and wondered which ones used to be men.

Life continued like that until mid-April 1985, when I saw a review of a film called "Before Stonewall". Since the accompanying photo was of a drag ball in the 1950s, I decided I had to see it. The film turned out to be a documentary about homosexual life and lifestyles in the years before the drag queens started a riot outside of the Stonewall Inn in Greenwich Village during the Summer of 1969. Though I really couldn't say that I identified as gay, I left the theater somehow feeling a sense of belonging that I'd never known. I made a decision.

Within a month I had left my wife and moved into a tiny studio in the Tenderloin. I started to go to the bar all of the time, and I befriended a bartender there, a gay man who, at the time, was going through a transgender phase. Though "Mary" eventually decided she was happier as a he, I still think of him as "she" sometimes, because that was how I met her.

Mary eventually became a good friend who passed on makeup and other transformation secrets. Being well along in the process, she gave me the courage to go ahead with my transition. For one thing, she took me to her doctor to get started on estrogens. She told me I didn't have to worry about a letter from a therapist or anything, all I had to do was say that I'd been on hormones in the past.

The same week that I started hormones, I also began electrolysis, a painful hair-by-hair extermination of my beard with electricity. I was not comfortable with this process, spending most of the sessions gasping and twitching with pain. I finally got the doctor to write me a prescription for Percodan, and it became tolerable. With enough pills and booze I barely felt the discomfort.

By September I began going out cross-dressed at night all of the time, and I spent less and less time appearing as a man. Women's clothes had started feeling more natural to me. and I eventually got to the point where I quit thinking of it as drag. If anything was drag to me, it was men's clothes. By then I had taken the name of Pamela in honor of the first girl I ever had a crush on. Without much of a plan, practically on a series of impulses, I was on the path to becoming a woman.

While my transition to womanhood was exciting, I had few people to talk with about it. My mom seemed rather uncomfortable about the subject, and my former friends became just that — former. There was only one person whom I could relate to at all: that was Damien, a gay male friend I had met through my mother two years before. One day I decided to call him, and he cheerfully invited me to come over for tea and sympathy.

After I got to his place, I told him about my identity change and everything I was going through. Damien was very supportive and enthusiastic about it. It was a joy to be able to talk about this with someone I had known for awhile and who wasn't uncomfortable about it. For some reason, the subject of prostitution came up. I made a joke about needing money so badly that I'd sell my body if I could. He took me quite seriously and put me in touch with a woman who ran an escort agency out of Marin County. I already knew something about it since some of my new friends were prostitutes, and I was already willing to have sex with men because that's what a real woman does, so I decided that it wasn't such a scary idea and called the woman who owned the agency. Besides, I needed the money.

Unfortunately, upon meeting me, she told me that I didn't pass well enough as a female to work as a woman for her agency, but that she would hire me as a male. As an impoverished student eager to make money, and confident that hormones would eventually help me pass, I agreed, and so "Sean" was born. Soon I was making good money for doing relatively little. I cost $70 for a hand job, $100 for oral sex, and that was it. I never had to spend more than 45 minutes with a trick unless he wanted to pay double, and once they got off they usually wanted me gone quickly, which was fine with me. There were times that whoring as a man messed with my head, but I rationalized it by telling myself that I was still a woman inside, even if my clients didn't know it. Still, I knew it wouldn't be too long before I got sick of pretending to be a man, so I made the most of it.

Life was quite interesting at that point. I was taking the final classes I needed to get my AA degree in computer science — evening classes so I could stay up until three AM, turning tricks and snorting cocaine. In the afternoon I did calls as "Sean" for the agency. Then, if it wasn't a school night, I put on makeup and went to the bar to get dates as Pamela. Sometimes I even did some homework. My grade point average was about 3.8, so I figured I could afford to slack off a little. I was having too much fun, making too much money, and doing too much dope to worry about being little miss perfect valedictorian.

Eventually the escort agency folded, partly due to Rock Hudson's untimely death and the resulting hysteria about AIDS, which had a predictable effect on the prostitution business. I concentrated on not failing my classes, and I eventually graduated with honors. Up to that point I had been supplementing my whoring income by doing housecleaning, but it was work I had to do as a male, and I was getting sick of it. Not long after my graduation, I made some heavy decisions.

I was done with selling out who I was. If I had to sell myself, it was going to be for a hell of a lot more money, and on my own terms! The hormones had given me respectable A-cup sized breasts, and my beard had been thinned by electrolysis and slowed by hormones. I was ready to be a full-time woman, and I decided that prostitution would allow me to be who I was and would finance the expensive process of transition.

So what if I was eligible for a degree in Computer Science? A lot of good it would do me as a TS. I'd been reading the want ads, and nobody wanted a programmer with only a two-year degree — much less an obvious former man in a dress. I was in no shape for two more years of school, either. Becoming a woman was just too turbulent, and more important to me.

I couldn't take just any straight job. Hormones and everything cost so much that I would have to go back to being a man if I couldn't make enough money. That left me with only one thing I was capable of doing and that I didn't mind too much, so I changed my name to "Crystal" and seriously entered the world's oldest profession.

Unfortunately, I barely had an idea of what I was doing, outside of working for an escort service. I couldn't very well go down to the library and look under "W" for "whore." I wasn't friendly enough with the other working girls to ask them for help, either. I started to regret that I'd spent so little time at the Black Rose, the main working girl's bar in the Tenderloin.

The Rose intimidated me. Some of the best looking girls were regulars there, and though many were friendly to me, I sometimes felt less than beautiful around them. It was difficult for me to deal with that kind of competition, so I eventually took out an ad in a local sex tabloid and started doing incall and outcall hooking. This led to the wildest six months of my life.

I could go on for a hundred pages and not relate all of the fascinating times I had as a call girl. The most important thing I did during those six months, however, was breaking my last taboo, IV drug use, because I had trouble dealing with the isolation and loneliness of being both a transsexual and a prostitute. During that time I also met Nola, a transsexual who is still my best friend today.

During the next six months, Nola and I became lovers in a lesbian context, but I found myself eventually wanting to be her husband, partly because I got jealous of the men she had sex with. The main reason that I wanted to be her husband, though, was that I could no longer cope with being a transsexual. My self-esteem could not handle the nasty unsolicited comments I got on a daily basis just because I only passed as a woman about 25% of the time. So at the end of September 1986, I went back to being a man full-time.

The next two years were a wasteland of addiction for me. I was not at all happy with myself for being a traitor to my identity. Sure, it was easier not to have to do the work to present myself as a woman, and nobody yelled anything at me on the street during that time, but I saw my surrender as being cowardly. I became quite the pitiful junkie to compensate.

During those two years, the urge to be pretty, to let out my female side came upon me several times, and I gave in to the feeling almost every time. In early 1988, I even went so far as to go out cross-dressed in public, but it wasn't the same. Without the conscious possession of a female identity, it felt like I was in drag. I didn't feel like I was wearing the clothes I was meant to wear. Rather, it felt unnatural and uncomfortable, and it didn't take me long to become discouraged. Thus, I turned to drugs to distract myself from that letdown and the fear that I'd never be free of this problem.

By March of 1988 I had become a full-blown heroin addict, which distracted me from my urge to cross-dress, from my uncertain gender identity, and from most everything else in my life. Though I'd developed a moderate habit as Crystal, which worsened after I went back to living as a male, it is instructive that my addiction got really bad after my attempt at gender relief transvestism had failed. With my life locked into working as a man, with my uncertainty as to whether I could be happy as a TS, I turned to the needle and spoon with a vengeance.

By August of 1988, I checked into a drug recovery program. It hurt to have split from Nola. I'd hoped we'd soon be back together, clean and sober, and living as man and wife, but it didn't turn out that way. The day that I left Nola for the VA hospital in Menlo Park, I had no idea we'd never have that kind of relationship again.

My life changed in that program. Some changes I was expecting, but many I wasn't. After a week of detoxification, I was physically well and more emotionally balanced. I was starting to have hope for my future. I continued to improve physically and my mind got clearer as the weeks went on, but I started to become troubled by mid-September. I couldn't get my transsexual days out of my mind, and the obsession got strong enough that I thought I should write about it. That's when I started the notebook which eventually turned into an unpublished autobiography, from which much of the following material is drawn. I thought that if I knew the hows and whys of my problem, I would be able to understand and maybe cure myself. Becoming a woman was the furthest thing from my mind in September 1988.

DIARY 9/29/88

Oh my God!! Here I am, one year later, in a drug and alcohol recovery program, and reading this book again. I want to cry for myself and for Pamela/Crystal. It seems so unfair that I felt so trapped, and still feel somewhat trapped even today. I think that deep down I still have some conflicts, but I tell everyone to whom I relate my story that I am glad to be a man. I know that I needn't live up to other people's ideas and expectations of what a man is, but it's still hard to go against society's rules. I still have a lot of those traits, such as sensitivity, that made me want to be a woman, and on some level, they make it difficult for me to be a man.... If I was more feminine-looking, I might very well still be on hormone therapy and contemplating surgery. I still feel like I don't fit in.

DIARY 10/5/88
It hurts sometimes, having to keep this secret for fear of rejection by people I like and respect. Obviously, fitting in is important to me because there are so many references to it in this diary. Even Crystal fit in her small world, as limited as it was. I can outwardly fit in here or anywhere I choose to, but my inner turmoil persists. Crystal still lives inside of me and probably always will, for she is the gentle, sensitive, kind, feminine side of my nature.... In one way, it comforts me to be able to fool everyone into thinking of me as a slightly nutty regular guy, but it also feels phony sometimes and I hate that. At times, Crystal rears her beautiful but confused head, and I find myself longing for the old days. Those days seem comfortable, familiar, exciting, thrilling and full of wonder, and it seems easy to dismiss or forget the difficulties, self doubt, sadness and despair that also existed for me back then.

DIARY 10/12/88
Talking with my friend, Lawrence, I realized why I think of Crystal as separate. She can't come out when Chris is around. Lawrence asked to hear her voice and she just couldn't speak . This realization almost brought me to tears. Crystal is locked up in prison. She is buried but not dead, and that hurts a lot sometimes. I wish that Crystal felt more free to come and go as she pleased, but I can understand why she does not. Crystal would flip out at the state of my body: hairy arms, legs and torso, rapidly growing dense whiskers, and a voice low and rough from a couple of years of effort. There are not enough estrogens in me for Crystal to feel secure enough to come out and take over.

DIARY 10/24/88
Here and there I've been noticing signs of Crystal wanting to break out and be herself. A few times, I've found myself walking and gesturing as Crystal and wished I could continue. I miss the natural grace and elegance of her movements, but I find them difficult to do as a man. Whether people interpreted me as a woman or as a drag queen, I would (and did) feel more comfortable and less misunderstood when I looked like Crystal and when I behaved like her.

I left that drug program because I became quite emotionally agitated due to my returning gender issues. I was so distracted that I forgot to get my work passes signed — a dischargeable offense — so they discharged me. God was on my side, however. In less than two weeks after leaving that program, I had money and a place to live back in the Tenderloin. A week after that, I got a part-time job as an office manager for a small business. And I stayed clean and sober by going to support groups.

Despite my run of good fortune, I was becoming very depressed and despondent. Even while I was still in the rehab program, I wanted to see a therapist about my returning gender dysphoria. I knew that I had to start talking about my problem soon and deal with it in one way or another. While my earlier diary entries were introspective and analytical, those of late October through mid-November were full of despair. I wanted so badly to be a woman again and subconsciously knew I had no choice, but I was so afraid of what it would be like. Despite my anxieties about being a TS, my desire to kill myself got so strong that I took the drastic step of getting on hormones again.

> DIARY 10/30/88
> It's not fair. It's not fair. It's just not fair. I could fill this book with that sentence and variations on it, but knowing "it's not fair" provides very little comfort in the face of reality. There are times when prayer seems but meaningless words in the face of my problem. It's hard for even me to understand how gender became a big problem, but it definitely is. How could I go almost 27 years being happy — I thought — as a man, and within the space of a year, be so miserable with my gender that I want to be a woman? And after living for over a year as a transsexual and concluding that, not passing very well as a female, I'd never be successful at it, why do I still wish I was female? There are no easy answers to these questions and maybe no answers at all. I suppose that if I couldn't become a woman, I would wish for a third gender classification, none, where I could dress and act as I please without the fear of being avoided or attacked by people. I am not ashamed of my desire to be a woman, but I am fearful of the rejection and censure by people I like, respect, and care about.

Insanity is doing the same thing over and over again, and expecting different results. I don't think there is anything different I could do if I were to be "queen" again, so I doubt I could change the way other people react to Crystal, but I still want to be her. Yet I feel like I'm hurting myself just as much by keeping her locked inside. On one hand I have the pain for other people's insensitive or cruel reactions and my ensuing self-doubt, and on the other hand I have the pain of keeping Crystal locked away when she screams to be let out. It seems like I am forced to choose between two negative alternatives, and I hate and resent being stuck in this position. I wish I could be ignorant of gender issues like I used to be. I wish I could be like the overwhelming majority of males who never even considered the possibility of being dissatisfied with their natural born gender. I know it would be wrong to kill myself, but sometimes I wish I was dead.

DIARY 11/2/88
I went to the Tenderloin Self-Help Center and attended their gender support group tonight. I have mixed emotions about it. In a way, it was a relief to talk with other gender dysphorics about my conflicts, but being with them reminded me of the seriousness of taking hormones and living as a woman. My thoughts are too vague to reflect further on this right now.

DIARY 11/14/88
(first estrogen shot in over two years)
It's Monday night, about ten to midnight, and I feel awful. Though I have some misgivings about being on hormones again, I am glad for the most part. It's just that I hate this feeling like I don't fit in anywhere. I wish it wasn't so easy for me to act like a typical man, because I feel like I'm betraying Crystal and damaging her sense of identity. At the same time, it is very difficult to let her out because it doesn't yet feel safe for her.

DIARY 1/18/89
Well, here I am, two and a half months later. I'm two months into hormone therapy and electrolysis — and showing it! My breasts are developing much more quickly than they did the first time, and I have been getting thermolysis with a single-minded persistence, about two hours a week. Obviously I've made my choice. After a lot of soul-searching, I have decided that I AM CRYSTAL, that I have always been her, and that all I have been doing is keeping her down for the last two years. I've had plenty of doubts so far, but I feel right about my decision. I'm being true to me.

January to October was a roller coaster of emotions, but it was mostly good times. Soon after I got laid off from my office manager position, I was offered a job in a Tenderloin drag bar. It was my first straight job working as a woman and it brought me out of my shell; plus, I learned how much of a flirt and an exhibitionist I was. I also started doing some hooking again. Electrolysis and hormones weren't cheap, and I was barely scraping by. I knew I needed a "real job" soon.

Since January I had been looking for a programming job. I finally landed one at the end of April, about a month after I started bartending. I left that bartending job with a few regrets because I loved working as a woman and being able to let my personality run free; but I knew this new job had a real future, and I would eventually be able to work in my career as a woman.

For the most part, life was good in the first nine months of 1989, although you'd never know it from reading my journal, because I usually wrote when I felt bad. It usually helped to see my pain and fears written down instead of floating around inside of me as bad feelings, and it was often the first step in getting over them. I was grateful that those despairing moments kept getting fewer and further apart.

DIARY 3/16/89
The last two days have been an emotional teeter-totter, one that has been mostly down. Yesterday I wished I was dead for a while, and my pain led me to doing some out-and-out crying. It felt good to be able to cry when I needed to, and it's somehow a comfort that I sound very much like a woman when I do cry. (I hope this doesn't become an incentive for me to cry more often.) Today I was thinking of how my gut-level instinct differs from my intellectual view of my gender identity. On these occasions, though my heart tells me I am a woman trapped in a man's body, my mind tells me that all I am is a freak: a man in a dress who is deluding himself. Yet I snapped out of it at today's Self-Help Center support group. When a fellow attendee expressed the same misgivings, I was sincerely able to say "I'd rather be a transsexual woman than a man who cowardly denies who I am."

DIARY 6/6/89
Sometimes it's almost easy to accept being an obvious TS. But at other times, like right now, it's almost impossible to accept anything. So I have to think, think, think and remind myself: 1) There isn't a problem I have that getting loaded won't make worse. 2) If I get loaded I'll still have my problems and feel even more hopeless. 3) Suicide is a crime against God and against life. Unhappiness seems to come easily to me. I will never be a natural born female; I don't pass very well right now, and I fear I shall never pass well enough; I fear I may never learn to deal with rejection; I fear I will end up hating myself for wanting what I cannot have.

DIARY 7/3/89
I wish I could just take my situation in stride more often. I want to be able to say, "Okay, I wasn't born a woman and I wish I was. I can't change wanting to be a woman because that's destructive to me; I'd be living a lie trying to deny my female identity; I'd be headed for suicide, because I've tried such denial before." And knowing all that, to be able to say, "Okay, you are a transsexual and you can't change that. And maybe you'll never be accepted as a woman by most people. "And then to be able to say, "That's okay. I'm a good, worthwhile person. And I love myself — period." I wish I could believe all that most of the time, but it's rare that I can. I hope that as the hormones further feminize my looks, and as I recover further and become more spiritual, it will be easier to believe these things and be clean and sober and sane and happy.

DIARY 9/8/89 "So Much for Serenity Tonight"
There's just no telling when I'm going to be sucked into self-pity. I can be feeling good about myself, only to have something small and seemingly insignificant knock me down. For instance, someone at a meeting last week slipped and called me "he" by accident. It launched me into hours of depression. Fortunately, there was another meeting right after that one. Sharing my dilemma and my pain helped a lot. Tonight, my self-pity was caused by going down to The Rose. Seeing so many flawless-looking TSs and queens and being ignored by the guys there made me feel insignificant and third-rate. I started feeling like a plate of dog food sitting next to a juicy steak, so I didn't stay long. The problem is, what can I do about this? I may never look as good as many of them. Accepting this fact is hard sometimes.

By the end of 1989, I was ready to move into living as a woman full-time. Back in July, I had decided on a target date in December because of how well my electrolysis was proceeding. I had switched electrologists and my new one used a better method. The thermolysis was ruining my skin, wasn't proving very effective, and hurt too damn much. The new method was much less painful, and in two months I saw appreciable results that seven months of thermolysis hadn't accomplished. My new electrologist, Jason, estimated that he'd be mostly done with my face and neck in late October. And true to his word, by early November I couldn't have grown any kind of beard even if I'd wanted to.

I had been looking forward to Halloween for five months, ever since I learned of the annual costume party at work, because I saw it as the last groundwork I had to lay for my transition. It was the perfect excuse for coming to work as myself and giving everyone a preview of the Crystal to come. I hoped that when they saw how good I looked as a woman — and I was starting to look pretty good — more of my coworkers would be able to accept my transition. It went exceedingly well. Lots of people complimented my looks, some said I looked better as a woman, and my supervisor, a man, even told me I had good legs. It was very gratifying to feel so validated, even though they didn't know I was serious about it.

Encouraged by how well it went, a few days later I told my departmental manager that I was a transsexual. I sat in a chair in front of her desk, nervous as a hooker in church, and bared my soul to her. She had always been friendly and unimposing to me, but she was the boss so I was scared anyway. I gave her a short explanation of my gender conflict and how I had wanted to be a woman for a long time, but had lacked the resolve until recently. And now my therapist and I thought I was ready to start living as a woman full-time.

My manager didn't seem extremely surprised, nor were very many who knew me, because my personality and mannerisms didn't change much no matter which role I was in. I suppose that she and others had previously assumed I was gay. (I'm sure that there are still those who think that, since a lot of people confuse sexual orientation with gender issues.) Though she had no previous experience with someone like me, she was very supportive. She told me she'd get back to me after she discussed my case with the divisional manager. That was on a Friday, and by the time she got back to me on Tuesday, my nerves were frazzled by four days of suspense and morbid fantasies. Most of these fantasies involved being told that I wouldn't be permitted to work as a woman which then caused my going back to drugs or killing myself or both.

To my great relief, she told me that all her manager asked her was what she thought of me. When she told him I was a valuable employee and that she personally liked me, she said he had no problem with my transition on the job. All that was left to decide was how to break the news to the division. I looked forward to my "first day on the job" with much anticipation. I knew I was doing the right thing.

We decided to announce my transition by sending an e-mail message over the computer system. It went directly to the people in our department and to the managers and supervisors of the other departments, so that they could inform their staff as they saw fit. I worked on that e-mail message during my spare time for several weeks, and with my manager's help, we edited it to the following:

> Dear Fellow Employees,
>
> As of tomorrow, Chris will no longer be working for the Installations Department. Instead Crystal will be assuming Chris' duties as a programmer.
>
> Perhaps you have heard of the term "transsexual" before. It refers to a person whose gender identity (psychological sex) does not match their anatomical sex and who is undergoing medical therapy to make their body more closely match their mind.
>
> I am a transsexual. I have had these feelings of identifying with the opposite sex for years, but only recently have I been able to accept them and the fact that a change of sex is appropriate in my case. It has been a great relief to find myself after years of confusion and self-doubt, but I do not expect life to be a bowl of cherries from here on out. So what I want most is to adapt to my new gender role with the least amount of controversy and difficulty as possible.
>
> I will need your understanding to do this. I will continue to do my job and maintain a friendly, cooperative, professional relationship with my coworkers. Some people may not approve of my transition, and that is perfectly okay with me. I don't expect everyone to like what I'm doing.
>
> You may be wondering what to call me, how to relate to me, and so on. "Chris" or "Crystal" are fine with me, and I would greatly appreciate being referred to in the feminine ("she," "her", etc.) because that is how I think of myself.
>
> If you'd like to ask any questions please feel free to do so. Transsexualism is still a rare phenomenon and a lot of misinformation exists about it.
>
> Thank You.

My changeover to working as a woman went smoothly. My coworkers handled it very well and were mostly supportive. I now rarely have to correct a few of them who still call me "he". To my delight and gratitude, most everyone quickly caught on, and some even took to correcting others on my behalf. It didn't take more than a few months for the change to settle in. I am mostly accepted as another of the women in the office.

It is very fulfilling to live as a woman and work in the field of my choice. I don't regret my career as a prostitute, and would probably go back to it if I weren't permitted to work anywhere else in my preferred gender role. Being a whore wasn't so bad, but I am glad to have a job that challenges me and that I love so much. Besides, if I was whoring for a living, it would be tough to stay clean and sober because of all of the drugs around that scene. I can't look down on other TSs (or anyone else) who does such work. Many of them can't find other jobs because society usually won't give "freaks" like us a chance. So I am very grateful to have my job, my recovery, my identity, and most everything else that I have today.

It took me a long time to do it, but I found myself and liked what I found. I am not the same person I was when I left my wife in 1985. My changes have been physical, emotional, and spiritual. I look a lot more like I want to look, I have a healthier attitude, and I feel a peace I have never known. I have confidence in myself, a career with a future, a mind no longer clouded by drugs, money in the bank, and most importantly, a sense of who I am. I no longer fear the future. It has been a long, rocky road to where I am today, but if I had it to do all over again, I don't think I'd change very much. Hindsight is 20/20, and though it is tempting to fantasize what things could be like if I knew then what I know now, I am glad to be where I am today. If I could change my past, I may not have ended up as well off as I am.

Life still throws me some surprises. I assumed that I'd be attracted mostly to men, but I got into a lesbian relationship after four months of living full-time as a woman. I have turned out to be almost completely lesbian in my orientation, which I am very well-adjusted to. Even more unexpected for me was, in the summer of 1992, deciding that I did NOT want the rest of the sex change surgery. I'd had my testicles removed in May of 1991 so that I could greatly reduce my intake of estrogen, and having the testosterone influence removed was like a godsend. Then, in early 1992 I found the love of my life: a woman who helped me to see that I didn't need to get the operation to be happy. I had a fantastic sex life with her, and she opened my eyes to the reality of spiritual androgyny.

While I still call myself a transsexual, I no longer believe myself to be a woman, neither in the conventional sense nor the same way that other transsexuals may see themselves. I am not "trapped in the wrong body." God gave me this body and these feelings for a reason. I am NOT a mistake. I really believe that, in the words of a diary entry in 1988 (and talk about out of the mouths of babes!), I am of a third gender status — what some Native American cultures call "dual-spirited."

Unfortunately, since our society obstinately persists in recognizing only two genders, I feel compelled to identify myself as a female, because that label is much closer to what I feel like inside. Yet, the truth be told, I feel like my gender is more fluid. I am integrating my Yin and my Yang, and I am becoming a whole being. I must admit that I sometimes feel like I'm on shaky ground with such a radical concept of my own gender. It's not easy being a Daniel Boone of the gender frontier, but it's easier than just simplistically telling myself I'm a woman because I can no longer wholeheartedly believe that. I'm not exactly a woman, but that doesn't make me a man.

I look forward to the day when our culture allows fluidity of gender. I will not be around to see it — at least not in this body — but I believe that when the time comes when we can let go of our rigid bipolar ideas of gender, we may not have very many transsexuals anymore.

****

It's a trip to reread something I penned almost four years ago — really more like seven if you count when I started on the autobiography — but I don't think I'd change much today, even though I've refined and stylized my scratching since then. I've been published numerous times in book and periodicals, and have a novel, a book of short stories and my autobiography still to publish. While I like my writing more these days, the straightforward flavor of this prose lends even more to its naked honesty and sincerity. It's a real accounting of real life.

I've still got the same computer programming job, almost eight years — seven and a half as Crystal. I'm still a lesbian, too. My lover, Rita, and I have been together over three and half years. I've also been working on fulfilling my musician fantasy of twenty years, too. Rita happens to be an amazing rock guitar player, and while I still play guitar as well, my main job in our band is as lead singer. Our group is called Glamazon, and we've been playing rock clubs in San Francisco for two years now. We produced a CD in summer of 1996, and we're working toward getting signed by a record company so I can quit my day job.

I would not be where I am today, successful, stable and happy, if I had not accepted my transsexual identity and made my peace with it. This holds doubly true for my sanity. I will always be grateful to writer/actress Kate Bornstein (Gender Outlaw, Routledge 1994) for helping me grasp the concept of Third Gender. While our society still can only count to two, learning that I can go further has helped erase all the doubts I had about what sex I really am. I don't have to be a woman or a man! Sure, I need to put something on my driver's license, but until the day I can put a "T" there, it will remain an unapologetic "F". Life is good.

Adapted from Christine Beatty's autobiography, Glamazon.

RYAN'S STORY: FEMALE TO MALE

My recollection of my childhood or pre-adolescence is that it was very confusing and frustrating. I'll call myself Ryan for the sake of confidentiality, but ironically my real name as a young girl and as an adult was very appropriate; it suited me as a "tomboy" and as a man in my later life.

I was born in June of 1950 in a small middle-class town in New Jersey. My sister was born in April of 1949. We were 14 months apart, close in age but very different throughout our entire lives. When we were four and five years old, my mother had a miscarriage. She claims she never knew what sex it was, but my father told everyone it was a boy.

My father and mother met when they were 19 and 18 respectively. They dated for a few years until my father went into the service. While in the service, he was wounded in battle and, as a result, lost his leg above the knee. He married my mother a year after he was discharged.

As a result of his disability, my father was unable to pursue his ambition to be a builder, but instead opened a small jewelry store in town which he owned until he died in 1983. My mother was a housewife for many years; then, when we were older, eight and nine, she started working part-time to help out with the finances. She retired 20 years later. We were a middle class, Catholic, closely-knit family.

The best way to describe my existence for many years is to say that I lived two separate lives. To my mother I was naturally her daughter, whom she very proudly dressed in dresses every Sunday, along with my sister who wore a matching dress. How can I forget Mom's dress — she matched us too. Oh, how I hated it! Especially that itchy uncomfortable — what was the horrible thing called? Oh yes, a "crinoline"! This, and the fancy ponytail on the top of my head, were pure torture for me.

After church on Sundays, I would quickly run into my bedroom, rip off those horrible clothes and put on my dungarees. I couldn't wait to get outside to help my father. I was always with him doing the more masculine duties and chores of those times. I don't think he thought I was strange for being by his side. He accepted that I was a tomboy, as everyone else did. In retrospect, though, it was much more serious than people thought, and really evident that I wanted to be a boy. My relationship with my father was great when I was young because he needed me to help around the house. His handicap, which prevented him from doing all the chores himself, gave me an outlet for me to be myself.

Every Saturday morning while my father was dressing for work, I'd watch him tie his tie. I'd put on one of the other ties and he would make a tie knot for me so I could wear it around the house. I would always make sure that I would know how to make it again. After he left for work, I'd go into my room, put on a shirt with the tie and look in the mirror. Then I'd slick back my hair, put on the pants, insert a rolled up sock down them to give the impression of a penis, don socks and loafers and dance in front of the mirror. I also had my own toy shaving kit; I'd watch my father shave, then after he left for work I'd go into the bathroom, lather up and shave. Wow, I thought, this is great!

My parents never discouraged any of my behaviors or actions. I think they were very content to have two daughters: one who stood by mom's side and one who was there to help dad.

At Christmas time, especially when we were young, (around ages five and six), my parents bought us toys and dolls, but there were always guns, holsters and trucks for me too. We lived in a neighborhood with many children our ages. I always hung around the boys. We had our own football and baseball teams. We had organized bicycle races too. I beat the boys in everything, not realizing at the time that I had a God-given talent as an athlete. I later received awards in high school and college for being an outstanding athlete. Physically I was bigger than most of the boys and stronger, so they always respected me and accepted me as one of them. In my eyes I was always one of them, I never thought any other way.

My gender was never a problem for me until I started having female friends at school. To me they were "girlfriends" like the boys liked to have. There was one girl I especially remember. Her name was Kathleen, and she gave me palpitations for as long as I can remember, even into high school. I never acted on it, though.

I felt a conflict with my gender when friends started to come over to my house. My bedroom had a masculine decor. I would spend hours building and painting model cars, ships, and airplanes. My shelves were covered with models. So when my friends came over, I would hide everything because I thought that they would laugh at me.

When I reached 7th and 8th grades, most of my friends started going to dances sponsored by our church. Back then it was sweaters and blouses with wrap-around skirts, eye makeup, lipstick and hairspray. I would do the whole nine yards because I wanted to be "cool" like my friends and my sister. Talk about feeling awkward! But I always had a good time dancing with my friends. My night was always complete when my heartthrob Kathleen walked in. I knew I could never slow dance with her, but I was glad she was there.

Throughout my high school years I was very active in school athletics and extra- curricular activities. I socialized with many of the team members. I certainly never dated anyone in high school (anyone male, that is). I was too interested in falling in love with girls. I had my first gay experience when I was a sophomore. Needless to say, this was great for me, as being a gay woman in the 60s (dyke type) meant being very androgynous, which satisfied my needs at the time. My sexual experiences as a gay person were not as female to female, I always felt that my role and my being in the relationship was male. I was the initiator, the aggressor, if you will. I was the stronger one, I liked the feeling of making my partner feel good; this gave me pleasure. I despised the thought of anyone referring to me as a girl because my whole image of myself was that of male, which brings me back to one little thought when I was around 10 year old. I thought that one day I could be "Mr.Universe" with bulging muscles. In the attic of our house, I would hide magazines of body builders and muscle men, occasionally sneak them out and daydream that I would look like these men someday.

When I turned 16, I started going to gay bars (with a false I.D. of course). Back then it was great because I could go to clubs wearing a necktie and a man's shirt. Of course I would leave the house looking somewhat like a girl and don my male clothes once I left town. Going into Philadelphia looking androgynous never presented a problem for me. This was probably because in Philly these things were commonplace in certain parts of the city and because my looks and my size made me rather intimidating.

My parents never questioned me about my friends or my outings. My father never got involved with my social life; I guess he felt it was my mother's responsibility. The only time my mother questioned me was when I came home late. Sometimes she would lock me out and wait up for me, then when she opened the door she'd hit me with her shoe. I don't think she ever overreacted, because she felt that I could always take care of myself no matter where I went or who I was with. I wonder if maybe they knew I was different and were afraid to ask me about anything. In my mind, I was their son and I could take care of myself, so if I got home later than my sister, it was acceptable.

Throughout the next four years, during which time I was in college, I was so involved with my studies and my future career that my sexuality was not a major issue. My major was health and physical education, so I felt very comfortable with people who had similar interests, many of whom, as I later came to realize, were also gay. I enjoyed my college years, as I felt I had a lot in common with my fellow classmates. We played on teams together, we partied together and we discussed our lifestyles.

In my sophomore year I met a woman whom I dated for the remainder of my college years and for the next 13 years after that. She was bisexual, but saw something in me which I didn't care to deal with at the time. She always felt that I was in the wrong body. We talked about it on occasion, and we watched one or two televison shows about people who had been through the operations. I envied them but I knew I couldn't deal with it at the time. I couldn't deal with it for many reasons. I was in a relationship where I was comfortable, my lover and I always felt we had a marriage, and we were comfortable with our sexual lives. She helped me deal with things in my life that made me feel like a whole person. If we had a family social function to attend, such as a wedding, she knew this was a total dilemma for me. We would spend hours trying to find clothes that were not too feminine or masculine to suit the occasion. I loved social affairs, but I wanted to wear a suit or tuxedo. I missed many family functions, especially weddings of cousins, due to my sexuality, which distanced me from them for 20 years.

I believe it was during 1975-76 that I began to go through a difficult time when I didn't know what I wanted in terms of a job. As a result, I panicked and decided to quit my teaching position. I didn't know what I wanted to do. I had considered the military, the FBI and also the NJ State Police Academy. I was running and I knew it. I was running from my job, my lover, my family and myself.

I decided to join the Marine Corps for the next few years. It was an experience, and by the end of my fourth year, I had the top marine position in the Pentagon. I could have had any job in D.C. when I got out, but I just wanted to get back home. I don't know what I thought I accomplished, because there I was without a job. I wasn't happy in a professional position because I was a woman. Had I been a man at the time, when I was teaching, I think I would have gone on for my masters' and moved into a counselor position or become an administrator. I knew I couldn't do it as a woman; I was in the wrong body.

I went on to pursue blue-collar jobs. I am very mechanical and work well with my hands. I went to school on the G.I. bill to learn building trades. I worked as a carpenter for about one and a half years in Philadelphia and New Jersey. I felt comfortable and enjoyed this type of work, but I was still faced with the reality that I was a woman working in a man's job in men's clothes, with customers calling me "he" sometimes and "she" other times. Every day, I wondered how many times this would happen.

In 1982 I finally found steady employment as a service technician with a local utility company. This was great for me because I enjoyed the work, as well as being on my own most of the day. What annoyed me at times, especially with coworkers, was that because I was female there was always doubt as to my capability and workmanship. I had a problem with this because I knew I was more conscientious and skilled than most of my coworkers. It's very difficult to convince people that women can work well, especially in a male-dominated field. In my mind I was the better man, only the others didn't know it.

In 1983, my father passed away suddenly, which left me extremely depressed for a long time. I felt as if my whole existence had come to an end. With everything I ever did, I had always looked to my father for approval, and now he wasn't there. I didn't have any time to mourn because I had to start running his business on a part-time basis four days after his death. I felt like I was burning my candle at both ends. My lover and I were hardly with each other; when we were, it was working in the store. It was a very difficult time and I wasn't ready to handle things. I had to continue my full-time job, run the business, help my mother through her depression, and try to keep my relationship from falling apart. Eventually I closed the business, my mother pulled herself together, and my lover and I ended our relationship of 17 years due to the fact that there was another woman in my life.

I moved into an apartment of my own in 1988 and lived there for a year and half. I felt very confused and alone. I know my family was confused because I kept many things to myself. They couldn't understand why I would move out of my house and leave my friend behind. I was never open about my homosexuality, so I felt frustrated because I couldn't explain my actions.

I was also seeing another woman, my future wife. I'll call her Carey here. This complicated my life at the time because I was trying to cope with too many problems at once.

When I met Carey, I felt my suppressed feelings about having a sex change begin to resurface. I wanted to be normal with her, and for me this meant marriage, family and freedom to be me. I was scared for many reasons, one of which was Carey's reaction to my feelings. I loved her very much and she made me feel like I always needed to feel. I didn't want to lose her.

When I explained my feelings to her, I know she was quite surprised, but as she thought more extensively, it was obvious to her that I was more male than female in many ways. I was aware that it was important to her to identify as gay and that she was quite headstrong in her views concerning her sexuality. What confused me about her was that I knew how she felt about women, and yet most of her previous lovers had been very androgynous. Subconsciously I felt, or at least hoped, that she would accept my masculinity. We were very compatible sexually. We both enjoyed our sex life more than we ever had before. We discussed our future, which seemed at that time to be an insurmountable task.

Unlike any other heterosexual couple, who would simply have been making wedding plans, we had many more problems to deal with before walking down the aisle. We thought of taking the easy way out by running away, possibly to another state, but we both knew it would not work. I began therapy sessions, alone at first, then with Carey for the next year and a half. This helped us deal with our problems. My therapist offered to have sessions with family members to explain what we were going through. Carey and I decided to explain to the family on our own.

Our biggest fear was rejection by our families, which we both knew was a strong possibility. My family was very accepting of my decision. Of course, since they had known me for a lifetime, this did not come as a total shock. It brought us much closer together as a family. Carey, on the other hand, had a more difficult time. Her mother was accepting, although at the time I'm not sure she thoroughly understood what we were talking about. Her sister, who is one year older than Carey, decided that this was not right, it was sick, it was not normal, etc. etc. She would accept her sister in her house, but not me. Carey was not ready for this reaction. She made a very difficult decision which meant not seeing her sister again except for an occasional family function. I knew that her heart was broken because she and her sister had been very close. As a matter of fact, she wanted her sister to be maid of honor at our wedding someday.

As a result of this rejection, we've gone through some trying times in our relationship. I know there was resentment at times and a lot of hurt. Carey has always supported me in spite of all the controversy and for this I will always be grateful.

Carey is really a very strong woman in her convictions and beliefs. She is very loyal to her partner. As a note on the lighter side, I have to tell this short story which we still laugh about today.

When we first started seeing each other, I used to visit her at her apartment as an androgynous woman. I suppose that some people in her complex who saw me thought I was a man and some thought I was a woman. There was an older woman who lived two doors down who greeted us occasionally, and she obviously thought I was a woman. I spoke with her one or two times in the laundry room. A few months passed, and by this time I had moved in with Carey and started living as a man full time. One day there was a knock on the door. I didn't answer it because I was in the bathroom, so Carey answered it. Being the nosy person that I am, I opened the bathroom door to listen. It was the older woman from two doors down. Hellos were exchanged, then the lady said something about using her parking space if we needed it. Carey replied, "Oh, that's okay, I don't need it." The lady replied, "How about the gal who moved in?" Carey said, "What gal?" The lady then replied "You know, the gal that stays here or ahhhhh" as Carey interrupted to tell her there was no "gal" here, there's a man who lives here, though. Now the lady's face was redder than red with embarrassment. I was listening with amusement in the bathroom, trying to control my laughter. The lady left in absolute confusion and as Carey closed the door we both got hysterical. I only wished that I could have been a fly on the old lady's wall at dinner that night.

The point of the story is that Carey always stood by me and was strong in her thinking. I like this about her. She made me see that if you believe in yourself and what you want, you never need to compromise yourself. I never realized that at times I had been doing just that.

I started my hormone shots six months into my therapy sessions. My voice began to change within three months. I began binding my breasts to make me look more masculine. I also knew it was time to do something about my work situation. My therapist came with me to the human resources department and explained the situation. I was asking for a transfer to another division 50 miles away.

I had previously screened various doctors to perform the operations, so while my transfer was being processed, I was arranging dates for my operations. I had both surgeries completed at one time, which included bilateral mastectomies and a total hysterectomy. Both surgeries were very successful with no difficulties. I spent the next few months convalescing and preparing myself for my return to work. Even though I was transferred to another division, certain union officials, due to contractual agreements, were privy to my situation. This was not a problem and the transition was remarkably smooth and pleasant.

I have learned from this whole ordeal that many times we are our own worst critic. If one dwells on the fact that he or she is less of a person than anyone else, this is exactly the message that will be projected. There is an attitude, if you will, that you must project. You have to believe in yourself and never let anyone take from you what is yours. Sometimes I have to play a kind of mind game with myself. I tell myself I am important and I am a complete human being just like everyone else with whom I come in contact.

We as TSs have waited nearly a lifetime to be what we always were, and are now, and no one can take this away. This is especially the case when the time comes to change your lifelong credentials, such as birth certificate, driver's license and name. When you go before the judge to change your name from "Mary" to "John," hold your head high, and when the judge asks why you want to change your name, you reply, "I don't like it, I never liked it". The judge will reply, "Name change granted". Hallelujah! Obstacle #1 conquered. By the way, you can do it without a lawyer for $75.00 in most states.

After my surgeries were completed and I was living as a full-time male, I was able to change my birth certificate. I must admit I cut this a little close because Carey and I were getting married in two weeks and I hadn't received my new certificate. I don't think I had ever been that nervous in my whole life. The priest was waiting for the record, the wedding plans were all finalized, then finally one week before the wedding it arrived.

Carey and I had a beautiful wedding, with all of my supportive family and hers. Only Carey's mother knew my situation; we never told the rest of the family and didn't think it was necessary to do so. Most accepted me without question as they would any genetic male. The reception was wonderful and we spent the next week on a cruise in the Caribbean.

I am a very fortunate person in that the whole transition went smoothly for me. I have always had a supportive wife, family, and friends. This is not always the case, as I experienced when I went to support group meetings. There are many transsexuals who are totally rejected by everyone. Some are not very passable in terms of voice, stature, looks, etc. and the road ahead may be extremely difficult. If you are like this, you may need the support group more if you find total rejection from family and friends.

A NOTE FROM CAREY

When Ryan and I first got together it was as a gay couple. But soon after, he told me he wanted to have a sex change. Needless to say, I was surprised. Ryan was never a feminine woman but I never expected he'd want to change his body. He said that he wanted a different relationship with me, he wanted to marry me and be my husband, not a lover. He said he had thought about it years ago but meeting me brought it out on the surface again. He left the decision up to me because he didn't want to lose me. He felt that he had lived as a woman for so long that if I was opposed to a change, he could stay the way he was.

I gave it a lot of thought and came to the conclusion that I couldn't possibly say no to a person who felt so uncomfortable in their body that they would go through all that it takes to have a sex change. Besides, even though he felt he could stay the way he was, I don't think that at that point in his life he could have done that without some serious repercussions. I felt that whether he realized it or not, in his mind he was ready.

We were both very naive about the whole undertaking. At first we decided we would move far away, to another state, and therefore wouldn't have to tell my family or our friends. Ryan was going to tell his mother, of course, but not the rest of the family. After going to support group meetings, we soon changed our minds. I think what happens at support group meetings is that you start feeling better about yourself and know you're not alone. Then your confidence gets stronger and you feel that people you care about will understand.

Unfortunately, that is not always the case. Ryan's mother and sister understood and were very supportive but my sister and nephew were not. This hurt me tremendously because my sister and I were very close and I missed seeing my nephew. I had to get on with my life, though, and Ryan and I started the long procession of seeing doctors in different states, going to support groups and seeing his therapist every week, which is a requirement of the program. The therapy sessions were really for him; I just came along for support.

It's a very hard road for the partner of a TS because everything is geared for him. In the group sessions I was the only partner there. Topics for partners were very rarely discussed. In fact, more than a couple of the people in the group were left by their lovers when they were going through the change, and sometimes I felt a resentment for my being there. It's bad enough to get rejected by your own family, but to get the same treatment from the group really hurts. Once I wrote an article for the TS newsletter and they wouldn't even publish it.

As time went on, Ryan started on his testosterone shots and the changes started. It's not only physical changes but emotional changes as well. Mood swings, at times low tolerance levels, and highly intensified sexuality. Some TSs even had violent feelings. I guess it's because they're going through puberty at such a fast rate that it's hard to keep up with the changes. It was amazing to watch as Ryan went from one physical change to another. He went through all the operations but the final one. It's an adjustment for everyone, especially family and friends. I think the hardest part was saying "he" instead of "she".

We got married almost two years ago. His whole family came and were very supportive. The part of my family that was at the wedding didn't know about Ryan because they had only met him as a male. I kept him "hidden" until after the operations. That was very stressful as well because my father died during that time and Ryan couldn't be at the viewing and funeral with me.

I think the important thing is not to compromise yourself. You have to brazen it out with your partner. Be who you know you really are and don't let anyone sidetrack you. As a partner, you're probably going to have to be the stronger one, at least for awhile, because he is going to be questioning himself for quite some time. No matter how confident he looks on the outside and how passable you KNOW he is, he's still not quite sure of himself and his actions. It's a shame that TSs can't just be themselves instead of worrying about whether they're acting too feminine and therefore sometimes going to the extreme and acting like a macho jerk.

On a more personal note, make sure you love the person, not the shell. In my case, I had to give up a lot for this relationship, but more times than not it's the TS that deals with most of the rejection. Either way, you both need a lot of support and understanding from each other. We've been together four years and there are still gender issues to deal with. Try to be honest with yourself at the beginning instead of leaving issues in midstream. That's much more damaging to him, because everything is hitting him at one time and his recovery process will be a lot slower when he doesn't have his partner there to boost his ego.

As for the TSs, I know that going through this is not easy and is very self-absorbing, but don't forget your partner. She needs TLC just as much as you do. If she's lost her family, make your family hers, and don't neglect her because you feel that your issues are more important than hers. Her issues might not be physical, but there are emotional ones. Most of the time she's afraid to bring them up because she's thinking of you and what you're going through with the operations, work-related issues, etc. She doesn't want to add to your stress. Don't let her feel that she has to hold it all in, because it festers and can be very damaging to your relationship, sometimes causing its demise.

A MOTHER'S THOUGHTS

My story is one that could be written by a good number of parents in the world today. I am the mother of a transsexual. After having five sons, we finally had a daughter. Her brothers were delighted and she was treated like a queen, but she was never interested in dolls or anything feminine.

When she was nineteen, everything came to a head. I have to say, I was devastated. I couldn't believe it and in my heart I didn't want to believe it, but it was something that had to be faced.

My heart ached for her as much as for myself. She was so unhappy, and we didn't know what to do. She tried group therapy, religion, and whatever she could find, but nothing worked.

Then she heard about the program that she did go into and proceeded to begin the sex change. It took me a long time to adjust to the idea. I told myself over and over that I should never have brought her into the world and I was so sorry I had. As time went on, I learned to control my emotions and feelings. It was very hard because all of the family didn't accept this. There are so many jokes about it. They have no idea of the feelings, emotions, and heartaches that go along with the transition.

I kept telling myself that if she was willing to go through with the pain of surgeries to make her what she should have been at birth, then the least I could do was to be there for her and give her my support. The more time went by, the more I realized and admitted to myself that she never should have been born a girl. I'm only sorry now that she has had to go through so much to become what she should rightly have been from the beginning. She is now a he and almost completely finished with the whole process of transition. He is very happy, which, I have to say, makes me very happy too. It has taken a long time to reach this point and I am so glad I stood by him. We don't advertise what has happened, but we do tell those who should be told and also those people who we know will accept it and agree that it was for the best. I would rather have a live son than a dead daughter, and that's what I would have had if she had gone on like she was. I have never been ashamed at any time.

There are a lot more parents who will be going through all this, and I really feel for them. I also feel for the parents who gave up on their children when they found out they were having problems, because that is the time when their children really needed them. It surely isn't easy but no one ever said life was going to be. So we try and make the best of things. I know I'm glad I did!

If our child had had a birth defect that was very noticeable, we would have done all we could for her because she is ours and we love her. We laugh and we cry over our children and pray we do our best for them. That's all we can do. I love my sixth son as much as the other five. He's alive and well. He's still the same person inside. Nothing changes that! It still isn't completely over but I'm not afraid to answer the phone anymore. How much more can you ask for? I don't miss my daughter because I never really had one, so there isn't anything for me to miss. I pray my new son has a long and happy life ahead of him. He certainly has earned it. To want something so much and to be going through what he is going through — I have to give him a lot of credit for that and I am very proud of him. He's worked very hard for all this to happen and in my heart I know it was meant to be!

A FATHER'S THOUGHTS

I had always thought that discovering that someone you know is a transsexual would come as a shock. Yet when, in the spring of 1991, my 29-year-old son, Alex, told me that my daughter Mary, then 27, had asked him to tell me that she was, my first reaction was that of calm acceptance.

It came as no surprise. Mary had exhibited no feminine characteristics for as long as I could remember. She did not play with dolls, wore only pants, had only boy toys and, in general, acted like a guy. When she rented her own apartment, there was nothing in it to indicate a woman lived there other than a box of tampons. Yet, on a conscious level, I did not have a clue that Mary was transsexual. I thought that she might be gay but saw no evidence of it.

The reader may at this point ask why I refer to Mary by the feminine pronoun. I do so because at this time Mary is still physically a woman and has not yet started hormone treatments or surgery. And, to tell the truth, too many years of conditioning cause me to still refer to Mary as "she". It will change as the physical changes occur.

When I got the news, I at first felt a sense of relief that at last Mary had an identity that she could live with. The sorrow and grief that she suffered so long in silence were followed by guilt — where did I go wrong? — came later, as did anger — why her/me/us?

I immediately called Mary and told her she had our unconditional support. (Her mother and I divorced in 1969 but we still remain friendly and the welfare of the kids always took precedence. I had remarried, and Mary and my wife hit it off very well at the outset. This made the whole process much easier.) Naturally, Mary was concerned about the cost of the very expensive procedure which she rightly was determined to have. I assured her that it would be taken care of and that, with all the other crises that were bound to arise, money would not be one of them. She was relieved and thankful, almost to my embarrassment. I never really considered any other course. Mary is my kid and this is what parents do. Or so I thought. Later I discovered that all parents don't react the same way.

My wife couldn't have been more understanding, and she made it clear that she knew that the cost to us in dollars and emotion was part of parenthood. Mary's natural mother was more than generous in volunteering to absorb as much of the cost as she could and was also most understanding. It may seem that there is much, perhaps too much, discussion of expense. but let's not forget that we're not talking about a nose job here. There is extensive therapy, along with hormone treatments and four surgeries.

The procedures take several years. For this reason, I suspect that many parents balk. This was also a factor in Mary's reluctance to tell us what was going on, and to this day she still expresses guilt that she's placing an undue burden on us. She doesn't realize that kids themselves are an undue burden and that this just goes with the territory.

In 1992, Mary had a complete mastectomy. Until that time, I really wasn't being completely honest with myself and was repressing a profound sense of loss. I had been saying that I wasn't losing a daughter, I was gaining a son, which was denial in its purest form. I WAS losing a daughter — my beautiful little daughter was gone forever. When it hit I was overcome with grief. I wept for hours and was inconsolable until I realized that my child in a woman's body was quite miserable as she was and that she had that rarest of chances to remake herself into what he really is.

Then the emotions came fast and furious. In quick succession there was guilt — what did I do to generate this state of affairs? Obviously, nothing. Being able to come up with a logical and satisfactory answer never absolved the self-made guilt. After doing some research on the subject and speaking with Mary's therapist on several occasions, the situation was put into proper perspective.

Next came anger. Not just anger at fate for dropping a nuke on Mary but for having the fallout land on my head. Not only, "Why Mary, God?" but "Why me?" The anger is largely gone now. To the question "Why?" I can only answer "Why not?"

Fear. Fear of the surgeries and hormone treatments that Mary faces. Fear of how this would be received by the family, friends — his and ours - would she become an object of ridicule and bad jokes or, worse yet, pity? Fear of a change in our financial circumstances so that I couldn't contribute to the treatment. Fear of how Mary was coping with the profound changes she was undergoing. The fear remains but it is controlled. I believe that if we went without fear of this process we would be less than human.

Anxiety. Is it going to work? Is Mary going to be satisfied? There is no answer to this now, but all seems to be going well.

The summer of 1992 was a watershed. Mary took a new apartment which was brighter and more cheerful than her old one and had established a relationship with a woman who knew the entire situation and was more than supportive. The hormone treatments began showing results and Mary became more man than woman. At this point I tried to start calling him David, his new masculine name . He also started proceedings to change it legally. Calling him "him" and "David" was still a major change for me, and more often than not, I was not successful. I enjoyed working with him fixing up the new place as man to man and got a big kick out of giving him a new hammer. Guy stuff.

I feel closer than ever to David now that I can understand his real identity. There was always something tentative in our relationship, in large part caused by my never dealing with the right person. David told me how difficult it was to keep up the charade and do "girl things" on demand. I can't even imagine. I can only feel pain.

I never regarded the multiple surgeries as mutilation of the female body, as they were described by some others. They are simply corrective procedures necessary to David's well-being, although the thought of my kid going through several operations makes me very nervous indeed.

David's voice has deepened and his appearance has changed. There is little question that he is a man, and he is often addressed as "sir". David is much happier and satisfied with his lot, which was, as he told me, intolerable. There is little doubt that on some level I miss my daughter, although the son who replaced her is so much happier, and this is what makes dealing with it so much easier.

JANE'S STORY: MALE TO FEMALE

As a child, physically, I was very delicate and feminine for a boy. This is my perception. My parents deny any memory that this was true, but everyone else made it clear that I did not look the way a boy was supposed to look. Genetically I was completely male. I had no hermaphroditic qualities at all. I was just a pretty boy.

Emotionally, I was a wreck from being harassed on a daily basis because of the way I looked combined with a very feminine body language. I was in an almost constant state of fear. The lack of understanding and support from my parents made it worse. But, there was an unexplained strength that got me through the whole thing.

Intellectually I tested in the top 2%, so my perception of everything that was going on was both confused and precocious. I think my intelligence is the thing that saved me from the depression of my gender problem, because I knew that, one way or another, I'd find a solution.

During puberty, all I thought about was sex. My penis was the focus of my life at around 13-14. I was attracted to both men and women but, because of the way I looked, men seemed most interested in me.

I had several silly sexual encounters at the age of 13 with my best male friend, whom I grew up with. He perceived my femininity in a way that no one else did up to that point, without really knowing it, I'm sure. He was definitely heterosexual, but his emotional/physical attraction to my femininity was very strong. He eventually discovered girls and forgot all about me. I wasn't upset because I didn't really consider homosexual sex as something I wanted. I didn't have a social prejudice; I just didn't like being a boy with a boy. I wanted to be a girl.

My attempts at having sex with girls as a teenager were very frustrating and I finally gave up. They all wanted me because I was so feminine they didn't feel threatened. Unfortunately they didn't realize I wanted what all the other guys wanted; I was just nicer about it.

I went to Catholic school for 12 years. It was a nightmare that I still carry with me. Many of my serious emotional problems, aside from the gender problem, were caused by the fascist attitudes forced on me (and everyone) at Catholic school. I consider the Catholic Church to be one of the most destructive forces on the planet earth today. Christ would be appalled if he knew what they turned his very cool teachings into. But enough of my preaching.... I guess I'm pretty bitter.

My school was gender divided: boys on one side of the building and girls on the other. I remember several incidents where students and teachers, yes, teachers, made public scenes of questioning my gender and pushing me forcibly into the girls' side of the school. I found it interesting that no disciplinary action of any kind was taken against them (or me, for that matter) and my parents were never told. In fact, my parents didn't believe me when I complained to them. One of my theories is that my gender problem was so obvious that everyone was terrified of me, and any disciplinary action would have brought it too much into the public view. At the time I was glad, but now I wish it had been more public; I might have had the courage sooner to do something about it.

I ranked very high in my school intellectually, which has always been a mystery to me in that I was so upset all the time I don't know how I passed any tests. I'm not exaggerating, I really was upset all the time. I was harassed every minute of every day by the other boys and teachers.

The knowledge of how cruel people can be was imprinted on me at a very early age and I carry it with me still.

My becoming aware that I was different is my earliest memory. I was three. I was riding my tricycle and some boy in the neighborhood stopped me on the sidewalk and rearranged some detail on the handlebars of my bike. I didn't like it and put it back the way it was. He got mad and either pushed me or was mean. I remember him saying, "That's the way girls ride a bike". I complained immediately to my parents. My father suggested that I go outside and beat the boy up. This confused me. I was only three and violence did not come naturally to me. I said that I didn't want to beat him up and my father called me a "sissy".

I put two and two together and decided that since I didn't want to beat the boy up, being a sissy was OK with me, and if my father didn't like it, that was his problem. I was disappointed that my father didn't come up with a really workable solution. I didn't beat up the boy and I probably kept riding my bike the way "girls do" but, for the life of me, I can't imagine how many ways there are for three-year-olds to ride a tricycle.

Your reaction to this story might be that I decided to become a girl because I was a pacifist. While this is a perfectly good reason, it wasn't mine. When the boy complained that I was riding my bike the way girls do, I didn't understand what he was complaining about. The way I remember it is: I already felt like a girl.

Whatever tiny differences children of that age are able to distinguish between the genders, I had already latched on to the wrong one, without even knowing what genitals were.

What did I do about it? I didn't tell anyone until I was around eight. One day we were sitting around the playground and everyone was talking about what they wanted to be when they grew up. I said, very matter-of-factly, "I want to be a girl". Well, this caused a sensation in the neighborhood that followed me around for ten years. If I had known that what I said was going to ruin my social life, I would have said "a fireman". But I hadn't yet learned completely how cruel children can be. I learned very fast.

As I said, I was harassed every minute of every day of my childhood. I had a few really nice, loyal friends. I never understood why they didn't treat me badly as everyone else did. I still don't understand it.

While I was in college I finally told my parents I wanted to be a girl. They sent me to a psychiatrist with the pathetic hope that I was sick and could be cured. He disappointed them by explaining my condition as explainable, although not common, and recommending a doctor in a program that led to surgery. My parents were hysterical. I felt happy for the first time in my life. Up to that point I thought I was going to be trapped in the strange-looking body I had forever, with everyone giving me a hard time about not being male enough. Now I realized it wasn't my imagination that I wanted to be a girl, it was OK.

I went a little crazy. I started to feminize myself immediately. I grew my hair long, painted my nails, plucked my eyebrows, dyed my hair, wore makeup, bought girls' clothes and, basically, started to become a girl. Everyone (oops, not everyone) who knew me was really upset. I didn't care. I was on a personal quest, and after 20 years of being tortured I decided I wanted what I wanted. No one was going to stop me. I realize now I should have been more discreet and gone more slowly, but at the time I was out of my mind with freedom and self-awareness. If I hadn't been able to lash out the way I did, I probably would have killed myself.

About the "oops, not everyone". There was a surprisingly large group of friends and acquaintances who supported me emotionally. They thought changing my sex was a great idea. I get very emotional (happy) now when I think about how brave and emotionally mature those people were compared with the obnoxious, violent masses I had to deal with. It was those few people who really got me through it.

I handled the stress, anger, and depression badly. I think the severe reaction to being able to feminize myself "finally" was an overreaction to the stress, anger, and depression of my childhood. The way I see it now, there was nothing else I could have done and, actually, it could have been worse. I didn't drink, I didn't do drugs, what did I do? Well, I fed my intellect with all the music, books, art, and intelligent friends I could find. It did the trick, I guess, and it still works.

The only related experience I can think of is: when I was 18, about two years before I started the change, I was walking through the boys' dorm on campus at about 1:00 a.m. with a couple of my male friends. One of the resident advisors ran down the hall yelling, "Hey you can't have girls in here!" We turned around and said, "What girl?" He pointed to me and said "Get her out of here." We explained that I lived in the dorm and the advisor became the sort of abusive jerk that I had become accustomed to. I was often mistaken for a girl, long before I made any changes in my appearance. Now I realize I'm really lucky to have had that kind of head start.

My parents had sent me to a psychiatrist to get me cured. Instead I went into therapy with the right kind of doctor and went through the long, painful process of the change.

Before surgery I was confused. I was terrified and depressed, and very insecure. But I did manage to have a sense of humor and was an intellectual and creative success.

My first reaction after surgery, at age 24, was to the incredible physical pain. I have heard from others that it wasn't too bad but, for me, it was awful. I had a high level of confidence in my surgeon, which he destroyed quickly. My vagina did not function; it wasn't deep enough. I was very frustrated because the doctors kept insisting it was perfect. My boyfriend did not agree.

Then, disaster struck. I had a perforation which required a by-pass colostomy. I wore a bag for six months. That experience was more traumatic than the original surgery. Then I had the colostomy reversed. Meanwhile, my vagina had closed up significantly so I had an experimental operation (which is more common now) to expand it using a piece of colon. The doctor made a mistake during that surgery and I was in the hospital twice as long as predicted and had a very large scar down the front of my abdomen.

After over a year of surgery and more emotional and physical pain than I thought I could ever endure, everything healed and functioned.

Am I pleased with the results? No. I feel that cosmetically the vagina does not look natural. Some men have noticed; most haven't. It functions well but must be maintained constantly to keep it open. I don't like having to worry about that. In fact, memory is a real problem. Telling people is a real problem. The doctors suggest telling no one. I can't live with this philosophy.

However, I have had several men, who meant a lot to me, dump me after I told them about my sex change. This has hurt me a great deal and has made me look at the whole thing as maybe not worth it. Friends have explained to me that because I look so convincingly female, it is a shock when some people find out I was male. Many transsexuals do not look convincing or it is easier to figure out, so people are more prepared to hear the story. I don't know if I buy this theory, but I do know that I'm tired of men thinking I'm pretty and wonderful and then dumping me when they find out I changed my sex. It seems like I went through all that for nothing.

However, in spite of the physical and emotional pain the operation has caused me, I can honestly say I am very happy. I am comfortable with myself in a way that I don't feel would have been possible without the sex change. This really is the most important thing.

My parents paid for electrolysis, counseling, the initial operation and the colostomy because I didn't have health insurance at the time. Health insurance paid for the colostomy reversal and the vaginal reconstruction. The total cost in 1977 was around $30,000. I assume it would be much more now. I had no cosmetic surgery done, i.e., breast implants. I don't believe in it. I wanted to be completely natural and I am grateful that I was born with the features that made it possible for me to look female.

Who do I tell? Very close friends who, as we become closer, I would have to lie to in order to explain my past. I only tell lovers who express the desire to make a serious commitment. In some cases they took it well and the relationship grew and then died of natural causes. As I said before, others took it badly (there was one very recent example, which is why I sound so bitter about it).

How do I deal with my past life? It's very hard. I'm expected to function as a balanced, self-confident female in a society not very nice to women (more about that later) but I have the memories of a harassed and tortured little boy following me around. Therapy has helped me to deal with the bitterness and anger my childhood produced, but the memories will always be there. I survive emotionally by keeping everything in perspective. After all, I have achieved my life's dream, one I had had since I was three. But there is an up-and-down emotional reaction to my current happiness vs. my unpleasant childhood memories. When women friends talk about their childhoods I feel left out and can barely join in the conversation. There's no way to prevent being uncomfortable with this.

Life is the same because I have always been a very strong personality, very extroverted. I have many of the same tastes and attitudes I had growing up, i.e., I enjoy the same music, art, literature, humor. I have always been a kind of "class clown" and continue to be one as an adult.

My life is different because I feel I am being true to myself. As a boy I felt incomplete, strange, untrusting, insecure. As a woman I feel like myself.

I truly believe that the line between male and female is very thin. I think society, in its various evolutions, has created an artificial gap in the genders. There are many biological differences between men and women but I believe, given the opportunity for a neutral upbringing, that everyone is the same. However, there is not a possibility for a neutral upbringing because of the many obvious and many many many subtle behavioral traits that are taught to children from the moment of birth. I hope that someday scientists will figure it all out, but I don't think they will because I don't think very many people really want to find out the truth. The truth is terrifying for most people.

Has it changed? For me, not much. The only behavioral difference between me as a boy and me as a woman is the clothes I wear. I maintain a very unisexual aesthetic which I am often criticized for by my friends. My hair is shorter that it was when I was a boy in high school. I wear almost no makeup. I never wear high heels — they are very uncomfortable, who are they kidding? I feel that a lot of what makes a woman in society is superficiality. I feel that I have the basics, meaning the primary physical characteristics, and that is all a woman needs to be. The rest is just insecurity, selfishness, ego.... This is my subjective viewpoint based on observing both genders from the inside and outside.

As to dating, love and sex: I was not prepared for the cruel rejection I have received from men I have told about my sex change. Most men have taken it very well. I'd say the ratio is 8 out of 10 have taken it well and been supportive and positive. But the few men who treated me badly as a result of my past have hurt me more than anyone realizes. What it means to me is that the operation didn't make me any better. It didn't make me normal. I may as well be the little boy on the playground who is being beaten up because he wants to be a girl. Of course, I don't really believe this, but in moments of weakness it is hard not to be afraid it's true.

My friends tell me that "everyone gets rejected and it always hurts, sometimes a lot". I know this is true. But I think this hurts more. My reason is that the rejection is not superficial, or even based on incompatible personalities, or the usual stuff that ends relationships. It is based on the essence in me, my "core". To have that rejected after all I've gone through is truly devastating. As a result I am very picky about who I tell. I'm not good at reading most men and have misjudged men many times. If I were better at it, I probably would have been better at being one. They have always been a mystery to me.

Sex is great. It fulfills many needs, most of them not physical. I am amazed at what I feel physically during sex. Emotionally it is a much more intimate experience than I felt it was as a boy. Being entered is a more intimate feeling than entering someone. There is a difference.

Before surgery I was very promiscuous. I would sleep with just about any man (and some women). I think that was part biology (I had a very strong sex drive) and part emotional insecurity. My childhood was so awful, I felt so hated, that as an adult, anyone who wanted me was someone I wanted. It said to me "You're not bad, someone likes you." It was a very immature reaction but I was around 20 after all. There are plenty of 20-year-olds who follow that lifestyle who had wonderful childhoods. What's their problem?

My body. I like it, a lot. People are always telling me how attractive I am. This always surprises me. But it is an amazing feeling to look in the mirror and feel good about what I see.

Orgasm. It's been so long I don't really remember how it felt when I was a boy. I remember it was very intense. But it's very intense now. I think I could say now that it lasts longer and the sensation covers a wider area. Where before it was centered in my penis it now encompasses a large area in and around my vagina. It is not easy to achieve, however.

I was in a relationship with the same man I was seeing at the time of my surgery for 12 years. Toward the end of the relationship I perceived a change in the way he was treating me sexually. After a year of asking and wondering, he admitted that he had always felt he was bisexual (I knew that) but now was feeling more homosexual. He no longer felt a sexual attraction to me, or any woman. I was upset at first because I felt if I hadn't had the surgery we would have stayed together, but now I don't think so. I think the relationship ended for many reasons and that was the easiest excuse to use. Men do that a lot: use the easiest excuse to avoid having to deal with any true, complex emotions.

What would I tell anyone contemplating this surgery, etc — I would say, "Don't do it." My friends and doctors would be disappointed to hear me say this because they consider me well-adjusted and happy, and they are right. But deep in my heart I feel that this surgery is a miracle and the solution to the problem but the world isn't ready for it. I think that if I had stayed male I would have been unhappy, but it would have been an unhappy that fits more easily into the more common problems of the world. Being transsexual and having the label hanging over my head is not easy to live with in the kind of society we live in.

However, for those who are as driven as I was when I was beginning the change, I say "be prepared". I realize that it is impossible to tell someone who is committed to the change to consider alternatives. They don't want to hear it. But the world is a different place now than when I changed. Men are given permission to be surprisingly feminine. There are a large number of macho, insensitive, dull men but a growing number of sensitive, feminine, interesting men. Part of me feels that, given the opportunity, to be one of them is not such a bad compromise.

I would tell families, friends, lovers, employers, etc, to absolutely support their transsexual no matter what. Anyone who has gone through that much emotional pain deserves to be treated nicely, for once in their life. The truth hurts but the truth is a very valuable and rare commodity.

Women's rights is a very hot topic. I feel that society treats women very badly. There are very few exceptions. The only women I know who do not feel society treats them badly are very, very successful women or women who have their heads in the sand.

Men and women are apparently at war. Everyone's favorite game is placing blame. Whose fault is it? Well, it's everyone's. Men blame women for their problems because they can't take responsibility for having created the problems themselves. Women do the same thing but to a lesser degree. The society we live in was created by men. It has changed slightly in the last 50 years due to the growing strength of women's attitudes but it has a long way to go. One of my great disappointments is that a great number of women buy into the destructive and demeaning attitudes that society teaches them. They can't see the truth behind the propaganda. This upsets me.

I sometimes feel I turned in my rights as a first-class citizen for second-class citizenship by changing from a man to a woman. I don't really believe this, of course, but every day there are situations where a man (or woman) treats me in a demeaning way because I am a woman. I feel this is wrong. As I said before, I find men and women potentially alike. I am upset by behavior that undermines the possibility of everyone living peacefully. I see many situations daily that make any honest communication and union between the sexes impossible. Men not granting women the rights they would grant themselves is one of the most shocking and sad situations in the world today.

To continue my tirade from above, I don't like the way society treats women. The easiest part of being female is that I can get away with a lot. Society gives women a lot of freedom in terms of aesthetics that men are only now beginning to be allowed to enjoy. The things I'm talking about are clothing, color, hair, emotions, personality, etc.

I probably would not have the sex change again. If I did, I would have liked to start sooner. I wish I had pushed my parents earlier, like around age 12, into putting me in therapy so I could have started the change earlier and avoided the nightmare of my teen years.

A DAUGHTER TALKS

I never knew my father growing up, and now I suppose I never will....

This was my second response upon hearing the news that my father was now, in fact, a woman. Frankly, my first reaction after my visibly shaken mother said to me, "I don't know how to tell you this, but your father is a woman," was whole-hearted laughter. I guess she thought the news was going to have some profoundly disastrous affect on my entire being, that I was going to fall to pieces after hearing what I suppose is, to many, debilitating information. But in all honesty (and much to my mother's surprise) I did indeed laugh. I don't think it was shock in any form. Just the idea that I would take so much interest in a person I never knew was farcical in my opinion.

Of course, an explanation must accompany every story in order for it to make sense. I suppose I am writing this from a somewhat different standpoint than anyone else in this situation. My parents divorced when I was nineteen months old. Aside from the images captured in old wedding photos, I never knew my father. My mother would always ask whether I wanted to see him, but on every occasion, my answer was no. This was long before his surgery; it had no bearing on my decision. It's just that I never felt it was necessary to contact a person who was never there in all the years that passed; the years that brought so many missed opportunities that I could have achieved, both educationally and recreationally, if I had been supported by more than a single parent. My mother had always been the one to provide for me, to care for me, to love me, and the introduction of a fading image from an old piece of film seemed an irrelevant idea at best.

I found out about "the change" the summer before my junior year in high school. Three months later I met my father, who was now a woman, for the first time. She thought that I could deal with the situation now that I was sixteen, and she said that she wanted me in her life for support and to make up for lost time. In truth, I could have dealt with the change from male to female a long time ago. I believe what was holding her back was that she didn't know how to introduce herself to me. She needed time to understand the ramifications of the situation herself before she could present it to someone else. It was an awkward situation, but not at all as uncomfortable as I thought it could have been. The greatest difficulty came in addressing her because, of course, I could not call her "Dad" and under no condition am I ready to call anyone other than my mother "Mom". So we agreed to the simple solution of calling her by her new first name.

I guess it all comes down to the question of "So, how has this affected your life?" I hope I'm not disappointing anyone by admitting that it really hasn't. I guess I've always been a liberal person, because I believe that one should be true to what feels right for them; and if it makes them a happy, contented human being, then by all means , I support their measures. For me, this situation was more of an issue of being there as a parent, not of being there as a man or a woman. I understand that my father is making an effort to be a parent now, and I am completely appreciative of such actions. However, we've only known each other for three years. Sixteen years have passed us by and that's a lot of irretrievable time. The critical stages of growing up are over and all that is left now is pretty much the easy part. In three more years I will be a member of the business-suit-clad work force, striving for a life of independence, and then where will my relationship to my father be? There is too much catching up to do and I'm afraid we're both running out of time.

Nevertheless, I have never been embarrassed by this situation. When my mother's side of the family first learned of it, I'm sure eyebrows were raised at the prospect of how I was dealing with knowing my father under the circumstances. I never shrank away from the issue, but was always willing to talk about my recent reconnaissance with him. I always felt that if it bothered them, then it was an issue they would have to deal with on their own, because I didn't mind at all. It's true that I haven't shared this part of my life with anyone at college, mainly because I don't believe I know anyone well enough yet. But there are some lifelong friends of mine whom I have told, knowing the implications of my honesty. However, there is a time when being honest expends less energy than a game of charades.

As much as I'm trying to avoid making this a didactic piece of prose, I don't think it would have much merit if I did not give words of advice. First of all, let me tell the children that if you have a parent undergoing a transition of gender, don't be too abrupt at erasing them from your life. If people are trying to tell you that it will negatively impact your life, don't listen to them. You are the only person who can make choices about which direction your life is headed in, and don't let anyone persuade you to think differently. For example, who could ever believe that a child raised all her life by a single mother, only to discover that her father is now a woman, would be a Dean's List student in two majors, maintain a part-time job as a supervisor, and still have the drive to be active in campus and community activities? Certainly not me, but here I am. Furthermore, your parents are still there as just that: your parents. That is their job. It is what they are supposed to do. And if they did not love you, they would not try to make you understand that this is the best decision for them. You mean too much to them to not be a part of their life, part of their struggle, and hopefully part of the support they require.

And now a word of advice to parents having to grapple with explaining to your children what you are feeling: remember to do just that. Be honest and tell them about your emotions and the reasoning behind your decision. I only wish my father had contacted me sooner. I'm not saying I would have understood completely, but it would have laid some sort of foundation. The worst thing you can do is make assumptions about what your children can and cannot understand, because they may infer your reluctance as I did, which was that my father was either too busy to be bothered with me or just had no desire to have me in his life. In order to maintain a happy, healthy relationship with others, it is necessary to be happy with yourself first. However, don't neglect the fact that your children may want to help you or may simply have questions that need to be answered to understand what you are feeling. Don't hide the situation or try to shield them from it. It's best to confront it from the beginning in order to eliminate problems in the future.

In my heart, I believe that if you are a good parent, it does not matter whether you are something different than you were before. It is not an issue of male or female, but rather that you are loving, responsible, and true to your children. If you are capable of maintaining love and caring for both your child and yourself, then you have proved your worth as a human being, regardless of gender.

ANOTHER MOTHER SPEAKS

I suspected that something was going on, but I was not sure what it was. When my daughter first told us about her belief that she was really a boy, the pain that she had endured overwhelmed me. I wanted to "make it all better" and let her know that I was there for her. Her pain and suffering were difficult to watch. They made me feel so helpless.

I found myself reacting on two levels. One was concern for my daughter and one was the grief I felt at losing all my hopes and dreams for my baby girl. I tried to be comforting to my daughter but she also heard my screaming and crying over the loss of my little girl. The years might have been easier if I had explained the grief that I had to go through. I gained a son — but I lost a daughter. My pain created yet another burden for my loving and sensitive child. In my initial reaction, I paced the kitchen and yelled at God "Why me?" Then a deep silence fell and everything went quiet. My next thought was, "Why not me?" I felt a deep peace and acceptance and knew that God would give me the strength I needed. I have never forgotten that moment and the sense of peace.

Another factor I have had to deal with is guilt. Did I do something wrong when I was pregnant that would have caused this? Should I have been more alert when abnormal signs showed up during infancy? There are no answers to those questions. I certainly would have pursued them knowing what I know now. However, we can't go back.

I was filled with grief over losing my daughter but also filled with love for my child. The same loving, caring child was there regardless of whether the external appearance was male or female. My daughter was a beautiful daughter but my son is a handsome son.

The years have been filled with pain and anguish for my son and for me watching his suffering. To finally see him change to my son and become the man he knew he was is a joy. He has blossomed and is on the way to fulfilling his potential.

My son did not have a lot of faith in the love of family and friends accepting him. It was a shock for them to hear the news, but on the whole, what everyone wanted was for my son to be happy and to stay part of our lives. The acceptance of the change from "my daughter" to "my son" was easiest when someone got to spend time with him and recognize that he was the same person they had always known. I was very happy that my son gave us the chance to be there and share his life. One of my greatest fears was that my son would go off and separate himself from the family in order to get a new start. I also feared he wouldn't be able to stand the pain and would end his own life. That would have been an unbearable loss. I feel blessed to have my child, to be supportive, and to love him.

In retrospect I would have done some things differently. I would have pursued the medical questions in infancy and tried to spare him the pain. My son was in his teens when he told us. I wish I had been able to take steps to help him then. I was hampered by the cost and by the fact that teenagers can be fickle. I feared he would change his mind later. I do regret how much of his life has been lost, but I rejoice that in his thirties he has finally been made whole. I will always be sad when I think of my daughter; however, I treasure my wonderful son. I am glad that I have him and can watch him grow and achieve his potential.

JIM'S STORY: FEMALE TO MALE

At a very early age, even before I started school, I remember telling my parents that I felt I was a boy, not a girl. I vividly remember my mom telling me that I should never tell anyone my feelings because they might take me away and I would never see my sisters or the rest of my family again.

I come from a family of two sisters and a mother and father. We grew up very close to my aunt and her family of three boys and two girls. My oldest male cousin was four months older than I was and we got along great. I thank God we were close because I was always the bigger and stronger of the two of us, which really helped my ego while I was growing up.

I was very close to my dad in my early years. We would go hunting and fishing together and sometimes I would go with him, on the road, in this big semi truck. When we would stop to unload produce at the stores, everyone would comment on how much I looked like my dad. That always made me feel good. After all, when people would say you looked like your dad, wouldn't you think they saw you as the little boy you thought you were? I did, and it made me feel proud of myself. As I got older, my dad and I grew further and further apart. It started during my teenage years. All of a sudden he wanted me to be that young lady they kept telling me I was, but I wasn't and couldn't be. I just couldn't make the change. I didn't understand why I couldn't or shouldn't do those things I enjoyed.

I also remember getting into trouble when I would play with my sisters. Whenever they wanted to play with dolls, I would always suggest cowboys and Indians or hospital. Naturally, I was always the Indian so I could scalp their dolls or the doctor so I could do surgery of some sort, amputate limbs or do eye surgery. I wasn't really a mean or destructive child, but looking back, I think it was my way of not having to play with dolls, which I grew to hate. I felt they were being forced upon me, so I came up with ways not to have to play with them. I remember getting Christmas and birthday presents that I had no use for. Guess what they were? Dolls! I always gave them away, but my family never got the picture. One aunt did give me a big hook-and-ladder fire truck that I wanted, when I had my tonsils removed.

I also got a set of boxing gloves. My dad would take my sisters and me down into the garage to settle our fights. The only problem was that since I was the biggest and strongest, I would always get the worst of it, because my dad would always step in, put the gloves on and say "Okay, you're so tough and want to fight, fight me." I got really mixed messages, because even if my sisters were wrong or started something, I always ended up the bad guy.

As we got older, my younger sister would always get into arguments and would then tell her opponents that she'd get her big sister to protect her. She always managed to pick on bigger kids and she knew I wouldn't let anything happen to her. This image of the protective big brother really boosted my ego and reinforced my feelings of being a boy.

I developed physically at a very early age. It was a very difficult time for me. Even though I knew these things happened to girls as they grew up, it wasn't supposed to be happening to me. I never could accept the fact I was a girl and that this was normal for me. In fact, it made me feel like I was more of a misfit and freak than I had felt before.

I was a very likable person, but I couldn't let people like me or get too close because I was afraid they would find out how I really felt, and then it wouldn't be my secret anymore. I was really afraid of that. I always remembered what I was told by my parents at an early age, that I would be taken away from my family if others found out.

I was very active in sports and let myself escape from reality by living in a dream world, which helped me survive in real life. I was always Jim Michael, super athlete, super Marine, super dude. After high school graduation I did join the Marines. I had a strong feeling of patriotism and felt that every young man should serve his country. I was still in such denial of myself that I really believed the Marines' slogan: "WE BUILD MEN." I expected them to do that for me. I was a great marine, but I was never the woman marine they wanted me to be. I always tried to be the tough, squared away marine I had been, in the dream world of my childhood. I was so mentally strong, I made PFC right out of boot camp and found ways to avoid having to wear the woman's dress uniform. I was able to wear fatigues and boots most of the time, which made my day.

During this period of my life, I came to know of the gay life-style and finally felt I might fit in somewhere. I was totally shocked when I found out that gay women didn't feel the same way I did. They liked their female bodies, felt they were female, and enjoyed having someone make love to their female body. The thought of someone wanting me physically, mentally, or emotionally the way I was was something I could not deal with. Once again I felt like a man without a country, or a place to be me. I didn't fit in anywhere.

It wasn't until I was in my mid-20s and out of the service that I met a young woman who knew more about me than I knew about myself. She would allow me to make love to her and accepted me as the man I thought I was, without making me feel guilty or inadequate about it. She also gave me information about contacts to help with the changes in my life that were necessary. Although this relationship didn't last long, and I didn't follow up on anything at this time, it let me know that at least there were people in this world who could or might be able to accept me as a person without regard to my sexual identity.

I didn't really expect to find another person like this again, but then I never would have thought I would have met someone like this in the first place. I consider myself very lucky because I found a very loving, compassionate, unselfish woman whom I've shared the past twenty-three years with. For the first thirteen years it was our secret. Some people thought we were gay, some thought we were good friends, some thought we were more married than the average married couple.

I was extremely lucky, because when I hit the crisis point in my life on turning 41 and really had to make the change or self-destruct, I had more support and understanding than I ever thought possible. My mother-in-law told me how much she loved me and that I didn't have to go through the surgery, that she loved me just the way I was. The big problem was, I didn't love myself. In fact, I felt so inadequate that I had become a real jerk. I don't know how anyone, especially Sara, put up with me those thirteen years. I would get jealous and carry on like a macho jerk. Sara wanted to stop somewhere after work. It didn't matter if it was to visit her parents or other relatives or to stop for a drink with coworkers, female or male. I would go nuts. Although we enjoyed doing things together, I could never understand her need for time to herself, away from me. I had such low self-esteem that I couldn't understand why such a wonderful person would want to be with someone like myself.

I also remember the night I told Sara's father about my plans. We were snowed in, just sitting around getting drunk and talking, when I said I wanted to have a sex change. He looked at me and said "give me one good reason why you think you need to." I didn't have to think at all before I replied, "I guess the only reason is so that I can just be me, if only for one day, to be able to see myself and be the person I feel I am. Maybe that's selfish, but I would like to just be me." He sat in his chair and looked at me and said, "You could have come up with lots of stories, but you didn't. Everyone has that right." He then asked, "When are you going to do it?" Boy, did I back-step. I had his support, but I started coming up with all kinds of excuses: lack of money, the thought of losing Sara, the thought of losing my job. He looked at me and said, "If this is something you feel you need to do then go see the people you need to see, and everything else will fall into place. Stop talking about it and do something. You can make excuses forever and nothing will ever get done. If you need to do this for the reason you said, it doesn't matter if Sara is going to understand and stay with you." This was true. Even though I loved her, I was destroying us both by not being truthful and honest about my feelings and myself.

All of a sudden I realized that I had everything to gain and nothing to lose. I would still be the same person she fell in love with; the only thing different would be my own peace of mind. Little did we know how true that was. I'm not the jealous person, nor the foul-mouthed macho man I thought I had to be in order to be a man. I'm more at peace with myself and a more caring person. I don't have to be that tough guy, and I'm not.

Although I had complete support from Sara's family, including her parents, stepparents, brother, sister-in-law, cousins, aunts, uncles and grandfather, I did not enjoy the same support from my own family, except from two aunts. I had very little contact with my family throughout my actual surgeries and hormone treatments. We did talk on the phone about once a year and exchanged Christmas and birthday cards, but that was the extent of our relationship.

Since my surgeries, it's like a whole new life for me, and us. The first changes occurred after only a few weeks of hormones. My voice deepened and a little bit of facial hair began to grow. Over the past ten years I've lost about as much hair on my head as I've grown on my face! Yes, hormones do cause baldness if it's a pattern in the males in your family. My first surgery was a mastectomy. I woke up after the surgery feeling like a big load had been removed. (It had - 44Ds!) The night before surgery I had read the book Jonathan Livingston Seagull, and after surgery I felt just like Jonathan, free.

It was several years later that I came off the cloud I was on and really looked at my surgery. I had been so gratified and relieved in not having breasts, not to have to wear a bra, being able to go without a shirt, growing hair on my chest, that I hadn't really looked at what the surgery had left me with. When a young boy asked me about my chest, I really looked at it. There were no nipples, and the brown area was egg shaped and much too low on my chest. I realized that if we were ever to have children, especially boys, of our own, I didn't want them to think that their chests would look like this when they grew up. I had a second reconstructive surgery on my chest which left it much more natural-looking, and no one, including my two sons, has ever made comments about it.

My lower surgery did not go as well. I was supposed to have a hysterectomy, vaginectomy, construction of a penis (using my enlarged clitoris) and a urinary hookup. I had a fibroid tumor, though, and lost a lot of blood, so they weren't able to complete all that I was expecting to have done. The surgeon and the program staff had stressed how important it was to have the support of family, spouse, and friends during the sex change process and surgery, yet when the surgery didn't go well, they were very unprofessional in the way they treated my spouse. After sitting in the waiting room through six hours of surgery, with no word as to how it was going, and then seeing me wheeled past on the gurney into intensive care, the only thing the doctor said to my wife was, "Things didn't go well, go on home, they'll keep you posted on how he's doing." The ICU nurses were the ones who told her what had happened and let her in to see me. Actually they had only been able to do the hysterectomy and the vaginectomy.

After six months of recuperation and healing, I went back in to have the rest of the surgeries. Even then, things were handled unprofessionally. After I was given the anesthesia, the doctor informed me that he was not going to be able to do what he had originally planned. Mainly, this meant the urinary hookup which would have enabled me to stand to urinate. I was very upset, but I kept telling myself to stay calm so I could come through the surgery and get on with my life. I am thankful because the penis I have is all mine and is very sensitive, although small. I had never experienced such wonderful satisfying feelings before. On the other hand, I feel we were not treated right by this particular doctor and I never recommend him to anyone else considering this surgery. Life goes on, though, and as I've said, mine (ours) has just begun.

Sara and I have been legally married for ten years. Shortly after our marriage, we decided that we wanted to have children to make our life and family complete. We tried artificial insemination by donor for eighteen months without success. We then tried adoption, through agencies and independent attorneys. After several years of hopes and sorrows, we have two boys, ages five and two, who keep us young and on our toes.

My relationship with my family has changed too. It is unbelievable. We had no face-to-face contact for five years after I began the process of becoming Jim, but for the past five years we have had a closer, more loving relationship than ever before. They now openly accept me as their son and brother and I feel the weight of secrecy has been lifted from them too.

As I've said, life has just begun for us. I'm in my fifties, so please don't give up, whoever you are. There is a wonderful life to live, but sometimes we have to put ourselves in others' hands in order to do so. Once it's done, the wonderful feeling of being able to be you is so powerful that you can overcome all which seems impossible. Keep the faith, have trust, and remember to always be yourself first, last and always.

A NOTE FROM SARA

I met Jim just after my first gay relationship had ended. I met him (her) at a gay bar, and we began a relationship. After a month he asked me to marry him and told me of his desire to have a sex change. I thought I was gay and could not even think of going through a relationship with someone who wanted to change sexes. I was very upset, so Jim let it drop. We got together and he mentioned the surgery several times over the next few years. I always got hysterical and he would drop it, until he finally never mentioned it again. Without him knowing about it, I did begin to read some books and articles about transsexuals, and there were several headlines making sex change disclosures. So when, after 13 years together, he told me he had reached a point where he had to have the surgery, and he hoped I would stay with him but he would understand if I didn't stay, I was ready to give it a try.

I knew I loved the person inside the body. Did it really matter what the body was? We started an adventure, finding the right people to help, the doctors, the money to pay for everything, relating in new ways to family and friends and to each other, laughing, crying, working it all out. After the surgeries and the emergence of Jim the total person, we began another adventure: trying to add children to our family. We now have two vivacious, active boys who will lead us into our next adventure.

A BROTHER SPEAKS

I wasn't surprised when, about fifteen years ago, I learned that my little sister was gay. It was a relief, in a way, because then I didn't feel so alone. We became pretty close after that, partly because we seemed to understand each other's feelings somewhat. I say "somewhat" because she was female and I was male, so I suppose we could never completely understand each other.

Then a few years ago she mentioned to me that she'd thought sometimes about having her breasts reduced. I didn't think too much about it, coming from a rather butch lesbian, and I just cautioned her that that was a pretty serious and probably irreversible step to take, and she should give it a lot of thought.

Apparently she had given it a lot more thought than I realized, because she recently announced to the family, through a very intelligent and soul-baring letter, that she is a transsexual.

Actually, I wasn't very surprised, maybe because the breast-reduction comment had foreshadowed the letter, or maybe because I'm open-minded (at least I like to think I am), or maybe because I'm hard to surprise. I don't know. At any rate, her news didn't matter to me and it mattered very much to me, both at the same time. It didn't matter because she was my sister and I loved her without question, and it mattered very much because she is becoming my brother and I love him without question. It will take a good bit of adjusting on my part, but that is miniscule compared to the hell he must have been living for so many years, having been born with the wrong body.

I intend to help him celebrate his new life in whatever ways seem appropriate, and at this point acceptance and support seem appropriate. Most of our relatives seem supportive, too. Some may have trouble understanding it all, but that will probably not get in the way of my brother's new life.

A SISTER SPEAKS

I can't even remember not having a sister. She's been my sister for most of my adult life. Even in writing this, it is difficult to think of her having lived as a male.

I am a bit over three years older than Ellen, although with her poise and maturity, she has often seemed to be the older sister. For someone who has been through so much, she has a remarkably sane and realistic, albeit a touch cynical, view of life. She has a healthier attitude toward men and romance than most of my girlfriends, or than I, often do.

To go back a bit — we weren't super-close as children. We had different personalities that only partially had to do with being a boy or a girl. I was quieter, and tended to run or cry rather than confront — I took after our mother. Evan had a smart mouth and would rather battle verbally than back down. He was (she is) very talented and intelligent. I remember early attempts at artwork and writing: a comic book called "Super-Broad." Quite good, actually; I wonder if any of them survived.

While Evan was into art and old movies — and did great portraits and caricatures of stars such as Marilyn Monroe, Jean Harlow and Marlene Dietrich — I was into ballet. We shared a love of cats, and certain TV shows: "Lost in Space," "Rocky and Bullwinkle," "Laugh-In" and "Ed Sullivan." So much of my life from about age ten to 17 was taken up with ballet classes, rehearsals and shows, though, I probably didn't notice anything unusual about my sibling.

When I went off to college, Evan was only 14. For the next five years, our lives didn't cross too often. He went off to college too, as a drama major. I came back home after graduate school, nervous about my career path, and just off another broken relationship. I can't recall how the conversation began, but Evan was hinting that he wasn't exactly what he appeared. My first guess, naturally, was "homosexual." Evan said, "No, wrong number of syllables." Then it became clear: "transsexual."

I remember I wasn't shocked. It explained so much: why she hated camp, gym, swimming, but liked to play with Barbie dolls with me. I wondered why I wasn't told sooner. She said I was so hung up with boyfriend troubles. Our mother knew earlier. She is easy to confide in — nonjudgmental, though a worrier. She was great throughout the whole process.

None of us will ever forget Ellen's first steps toward cross-dressing. I was living in New York City with one of Ellen's best friends. The day she came up to shop for women's clothes was Day Two of the Great New York City Blackout of July '77. It was amazing that she even made it to Queens. Ellen adjusted very well to the difficult task of living as a young woman while still in a man's body. I always figured that it was because she was a good actress. She said that she was a good actress because she had to act her whole life.

I understand that many doctors require a preoperative transsexual to cross-dress for two years. Ellen was so stable as a woman, she would be allowed to have the operation after only one year. As I write this, more memories are surfacing (it may be hard to believe, but on cable TV as I am writing this is "The Christine Jorgenson Story." I didn't know it would be on when I began this — the TV listing said "La Cage aux Folles". How apropos).

Anyway — I do remember the young Evan going to a psychiatrist of some sort. I suppose they were trying to straighten out what appeared to be homosexual leanings. Trouble was, she was always one step ahead of the therapist and told him whatever he wanted to hear. Later, when she had to see a psychiatrist prior to surgery, he said she was too well-adjusted. Fortunately, she persevered until she found a legitimate professional who knew what she needed.

I suppose one of the aspects that relatives of transsexuals worry about is: what to tell your friends? I only had a limited window of years when it was necessary to say something. I told the few college friends I planned to stay in touch with, as they would notice the appearance of a full-grown sister. Friends I met in subsequent years only needed to know that I had a younger sister. I did tell my ex-husband when we were engaged — coming from Los Angeles, it didn't faze him a bit. The awkward part was, he really liked her, and she detested him.

The point to remember is — what effect does your sibling's transsexualism have on your life? For me, the main thing is that she can't have children, and I probably won't. I have told friends that my sister had some complications, had an operation and can't have children (well, it's all true, isn't it?). I follow up by saying she never wanted kids — she didn't like children even when she was one. That's all anyone generally needs to know.

One of the positive aspects of the situation for me has been a growing empathy for transsexuals, gays, lesbians and others outside of the mainstream. Although most people now refrain from racial slurs, religious jokes and maybe even gay comments, it appears that transsexuals are still fair game. They are a small, hidden and usually silent minority. I am not aware of knowing anyone other than my sister, yet I often find myself defending the whole concept. Very few people get through life without some emotional or physical trauma. My sister has had plenty of both — and I am very proud of how she has triumphed over it all.

A PARTNER SPEAKS

Being the spouse of a person with gender dysphoria made me feel extremely lonely and scared at first. I felt that no other person could understand what was happening in my heart and mind. This shame and fear kept me from sharing my grief. I didn't want to be labeled as the woman married to the "freak." I was afraid to tell my friends and family, and nowhere could I find up-to-date information. I checked the library and several bookstores; all to no avail. My alternative, then, was professional help, but I quickly learned that few in the field of psychology were understanding of or knowledgable about the problem. Yet, though they themselves didn't know, they were able to point me in the direction of those who did. Now that I know I'm not the only one suffering, I'm no longer afraid.

When I first learned of my spouse's desire to be a woman, I was shocked and very upset. He had never acted particularly feminine during the time I'd known him. I guess I was relieved that he was not gay and didn't have AIDS, but that didn't change the fact that the person I thought I knew so well was really someone else inside. For years after he told me, I tried to deal with it myself. I pretended that it would go away as our marriage went on. I thought that if I were a good enough wife to him, he would get over his obsession. He did not. Our problems only grew worse because he knew it only hurt me to talk about them. I then felt guilty for feeling hurt, and that grew into resentment.

Why shouldn't I be hurt? Why couldn't I cry about it? Was my heart not broken by his words? He wanted to be a woman; not my male lover anymore but my female lover. I just couldn't understand and so I grieved for myself.

After holding all my questions and feelings in, I finally broke down. I began bombarding my husband with every question I could think of regarding his thoughts, feelings, and past history. It took days to get all the questions out and some were still unanswered, but now he understood my feelings and fears and I understood his. This opened up our hearts and allowed us to be honest with each other. It also helped me to finally comprehend his position and how it affected him. His hope that it could work out became mine. I truly believe that because we were so honest with each other, we were able to get through it all.

We explored our sexuality together. This was a tremendous help to me since I was unsure if I could have a healthy sex life with a same-sex partner. I soon learned that I could and it greatly relieved many anxieties. Once again, I cannot help but say just how important total honesty with each other is. Knowing each other so well and so deeply strengthened our bond and made me feel that I could face the world undaunted.

After finally gathering the courage to tell my family and friends, I quickly learned that some had the same selfish fears I originally had. They couldn't understand and were therefore refusing to do so. I was told he was using me, that he only cared about himself. I was given much advice about lawsuits, divorce, and how much money I could get if I left him. Did I know what I was doing? How could I dare to bring shame on my family?

Not all were so quick to chide. Some were very supportive and, though they didn't understand, at least they tried to. I can only say that when it came down to it, I realized that it was my life, not theirs. They feared the change just as I did, but I was the one who had to live with it.

I knew my life would never be the same again, but then, it wasn't the end of the world either. We all fear change because we all fear the unknown. I know I love my spouse very much, maybe even more than before. I still feel afraid at times, but in the same way that any married person does. Am I still attractive to my spouse? Will I be left for another? All of this my spouse comforts me about, and vice versa.

As for dealing with the public — well, if I was concerned that people at church, the grocery store, the doctor's, etc. were going to treat me differently, I'm not now. My life is mine and not everyone has to like it. I'm strong enough to put up with stares and whispers from strangers, although others might not be. My best defense is to stare back and offer them a picture or an autograph. This usually surprises them enough to make them leave me alone. I also know the law is on my side when it comes to rude and harassing persons.

I know that, no matter what, the person I love loves me, and that whatever the outward appearance, it's the inner personality that truly matters. I now find great joy in teaching my spouse what it is to be my sex. We have a great time together shopping for clothing and shoes. We look through women's magazines, discuss hair styles, and even dress each other up. I feel that now I have a friend, as well as a lover, in my spouse. This closeness of sharing and being an active part of my spouse's new life has made what was once dreadful and depressing now a wonderfully new and exciting experience. The more I saw him as her, the more used to it I became. I know now I couldn't see her any other way.

LETTER TO PARENTS AND SIBLINGS

Dear Mom, Dad, Brothers and Sisters,

I want to thank those of you who attended the family meeting and also those of you who wrote to me last November and December. Please accept my apology for taking so long to respond.

Now that you all have a copy of the notes from the meeting, I'd like to add a few things.

Recently I've become disappointed when I found out that almost all of you want me to see a different psychologist, social worker or even a counselor. I know that you want me to change my mind and I certainly don't blame you, because I understand what you're feeling about my situation. It seems as though no one realizes that my psychologist is very well qualified with her many years of experience helping people like me and their families. I am very comfortable with her and can talk to her about anything. To me, that's important. I don't want to have to disappoint any of you any more than I already have, but to be honest with you all, I'm not interested in talking to another therapist of any kind. I am happy with her and will continue to see her. Again, I'm sorry.

One of the things I want to make clear to you is that my decision to match my gender identity to my physical structure is final. There will be no turning back. I am 100% sure that the decision to alter my body is the right decision for me. Please try to accept that. I know it's going to be very difficult to accept, but I'm only asking you to try, please.

You see? All my life I grew up hearing my family, friends and other people talk about gay people being "sick" and that they deserved to die if they couldn't be "normal". I could not even imagine how much worse it would be if the topic of the conversation were to be about transsexuals! That's why I had such tremendous fear of society and fear of breaking the hearts of those who loved me (and still do), especially my family members.

The other thing I want to make clear to you all is that I do believe in God and love Him, but I don't believe in any religions. I have no hard feelings towards Him and have nothing against Him. either.

What I believe about God is that He gave people the intellegence and abilities to help all kinds of people in many different ways. That's why we have doctors, social workers, specialists, biologists, teachers, tax consultants, friends, and so on....

One of the most common questions I've heard is, if God wanted me to be a male physically, why didn't He make me one?? Or why didn't He make me a female genetically?? Why was I born male in a female body??

It's the way my body was formed before I was even born. Apparently, something went wrong in the part of my brain that is responsible for deciding which sex I will be. Maybe my brain cells couldn't make up their minds, so I turned out to be half and half! Since it's not possible to change genetically, doctors and surgeons made it possible to change the physical structure so it would match the gender identity.

If you could go to the library and ask for "The Book of Abnormalities", you'll see true stories with pictures of people who were labelled "abnormal" only because they were different from you. How about those people in the book who were eight feet tall or two feet short; men with female breasts; women with beards and penises, and so many other things about them that makes them "different" from you. All these people were born this way. And because of society, they either committed suicide, lived in hiding all their lives, or found the courage to search for medical and/or psychological help. If alterations were possible, then I feel it would be neccessary to do so in order to make life easier for them, and for me too. Believe me, I've tried all my life to accept and deal with myself the way I am. But it's so hard and depressing to live inside a female body while being male genetically. I'm not happy living this way, never was, and never will be, until the day I begin hormone therapy, after the mastectomy. I want to be "ME", the one person I really am.

I know in my heart that this is deeply painful for you all. It hurts me so much to break your hearts, I never meant to hurt you, never wanted to hurt you. But it hurts me to have to keep pretending to be someone that I am not. I hope that some day all this hurt will melt away, then we can build new and happy memories together as a family.

Those of you who still find it difficult to accept at this time, I'll still love you and you'll still receive birthday and holiday cards from me every year. I will always be thinking about you. When you're ready, God will help you to go through and deal with this situation with me.

Those of you who feel ready to accept now, I would really like to see you often as I go through the processes.

Please remember that you will all always be in my heart no matter what you choose to do about acceptance. I will still love you all just the same.

Love Always,
Paul.

The following poem was included with Paul's letter to his family. Copyright © 1992 by K.A. Kling. Originally published in Issue #27 of the FTM Newsletter, April 1994, by FTM International, Inc. Reprinted by permission.

BODYSOUL

It's becoming an obsession.
Every morning as I wake
That I look into the mirror
To see if I am there...
to see if I am there.
When I'm driving down the highway,
It will take me by surprise
'Cause I look into the mirror
And I am startled by my eyes.
My eyes reflect a different soul
My body doesn't show.
I wish that I could be myself,
The one nobody knows.
I am living with obsession
To be the one I really am
And I look into the mirror
To see if I am there...
To see if I am there.
Can you see me now as I do?
Not the me you used to know.
If you cannot see me hurting
Then I think it's time to go.
My eyes reflect a different soul
My body doesn't show.
I wish that I could be myself,
The one nobody knows...
The one nobody knows.

1992 — K.A.K. (Kitt Kling)

AMY'S STORY: MALE TO FEMALE

The strongest and most consistent part of my transsexualism has been my desire for a feminine body and appearance. Desire for a feminine social role has always been secondary, although I have certainly come to appreciate that role very much as well. But for me, this has been a journey in which the body has led the way.

My earliest memory of transgendered experience is standing in my mother's bedroom closet, feeling the fabric of her dresses, wanting to wear them and to be like her, finally pulling one down from its hanger to fall over me, and becoming sexually aroused. I must have been three or four at the time.

By age six, I was playing with girls my own age, wanting to wear their clothes and engage in their fantasy play. The girl who lived next door had a red ballet tutu that I especially admired, but she told me I couldn't wear it, or pretend to be a ballerina, because I was a boy.

I was allowed to stay home alone sometimes after I reached age eight, and I always used these occasions to dress in my mother's clothes. This was very arousing for me, but I hated getting erections, because I didn't want anything to spoil my fantasy of having a girl's body. By age ten, in addition to cross-dressing at home whenever I was alone, I would remove my mother's panties from the laundry hamper and wear them to school under my boy's clothes. Every night I would lie awake fantasizing that some benevolent adult might learn of my need, find me, and arrange for surgery to remove my penis.

I was a good student, and skipped two years of junior high school, entering high school (tenth grade) at fourteen. My classmates were two years older on average, and being exposed to the company of physically developed young women was delightful and agonizing. I wanted to touch them, and I wanted to be them, all at the same time. I desperately coveted their breasts, their cute clothes, their long hair, their make-up, and their ability to be with one another in what I dreamily imagined to be intimate, sisterly groups. I fantasized constantly about taking female hormones, growing breasts, and having my penis removed, so that I could join them. But all I managed to do was wear my hair as long as my parents would allow, keep my nails long, and shape my eyebrows.

When I read in the local paper about the opening of the gender program at Johns Hopkins, I wrote a long letter to the chairman, pleading for help; but in the end, I didn't send it. I knew that he would only contact my parents, who would never consent to letting me be transformed into a girl, and that I would only be humiliated by the revelation of my shameful secret.

But only a few months later, the pressures became unbearable and I did confide in my mother. I imagined that if she saw my agony, perhaps she would help me, maybe even cooperate with my desires. Her reaction was one of concern, but not of sympathy. She sent me off to a psychiatrist for weekly visits, hoping he could "cure" me. This, of course, did not occur.

When I went away to college at sixteen, I could finally cross-dress in relative freedom in my dorm room. This was always sexually exciting, but, incredibly, I never managed to bring myself to orgasm until age eighteen, because I was never willing to touch my penis. Finally I discovered by accident how to climax by rubbing against a pillow with a pair of panties covering my genitals. About this time I first read Harry Benjamin's book, *The Transsexual Phenomenon*.

I had been scheming for three years, trying to obtain female hormones, and shortly after my eighteenth birthday, I finally succeeded. I persuaded a chemical supply house to sell me 20 grams of chemical grade diethylstilbesterol (DES). At last I had a tool to feminize my body, but it was very crude. I dissolved my DES in vegetable oil and drank it, or rubbed it into my breasts. Soon my skin became smoother, my breasts enlarged, and erections became infrequent and even painful. I was delighted, but also fearful— what if someone discovered what I was doing?

I had no plan, no strategy — only a desperate desire to feminize my body. I was then too ashamed to admit to anyone that I wanted to be a woman. I knew from my reading that I would never be accepted into a gender program; after all, I had been successful as a male, I hadn't played with dolls, and I was sexually attracted to women. Most shameful of all, my fantasies of self-feminization had a sexual component — I would be seen as merely a fetishistic transvestite, not as a true transsexual. I went on and off hormones half a dozen times during my final two years of college, alternating between elation and despair.

I entered medical school at twenty, and tried to bury my feminine inclinations under a male facade. I grew a beard, rode a motorcycle, took up rock climbing and wilderness backpacking. But, inevitably, my true feelings resurfaced. By twenty-two I was back on estrogen. I had a girlfriend in whom I confided, and she let me wear her clothes, and even incorporated my feminine identification into our lovemaking. We broke up when she eventually tired of my obsession. About this time, I re-read Robert Stoller's *Sex and Gender*, an influential book I now regard as poisonous. Stoller's chapter "Transvestites' Women" caused me deep concern. I believed, and my recent experience seemed to confirm, that if I wanted a lasting relationship with another woman, I would have to suppress my transsexual desire. But that seemed impossible.

Following medical school, I started earning my first real salary, and was able to afford some facial electrolysis. All throughout my residency and fellowship training I wore my hair long, cross-dressed in private, and intermittently took hormones. But I could never take the next step of actually living in role. I feared that if I transitioned, I would never be approved for surgery, and would spend the rest of my life impoverished, friendless, and unloved. Faced with that prospect, I tried to reconcile myself to living as a man.

I managed to do so with relative outward success until my late thirties. Of course, not a day passed that I didn't fantasize about being a woman; but to actually live as a woman seemed no more possible than to grow wings and live as a bird.

Eventually my biological reproductive clock chimed, and I began to explore relationships that might lead into parenthood. At 38, I married a sensitive and intelligent woman, with whom I proved to be deeply incompatible, and together we had two children. To my surprise, something about becoming a parent seemed to reawaken my desire to reach a more satisfactory accommodation with my transsexualism. Perhaps my enjoyment of the nurturing role made me realize how much I truly valued femininity. Perhaps creating two new lives, and watching how quickly those lives changed before my eyes, made me aware that all lives, including my own, were precious but transitory, and that now was the time to live fully. Or perhaps seeing the uncanny way my children's behavior mirrored my spouse's and my own, convinced me that sometimes our biology is indeed our destiny, and that I could no longer avoid mine.

At age 42, I resumed taking low-dose estrogen, and tried a variety of strategies for androgynous expression, short of actual cross-living. For a time, I made transsexual self-portraits using the computer to see whether feminizing a "virtual" body might be enough; unfortunately, it was not. Eventually, I was put in contact with an experienced gender therapist, who recognized my condition and encouraged me to experiment with cross-living for short periods in the protected environment of transgender support groups. This was satisfying beyond my imagining; I even discovered that I was quite passable as a woman. After many months of preparation, just before my 45th birthday, I began living full-time in a female role. I completed sexual reassignment surgery some six months later. Now, with the journey of the body seemingly complete, I find that the satisfactions of the place at which I have arrived are wondrous, but often bittersweet.

By most standards I am incredibly fortunate. I have been able to continue to work in a rewarding well-paying professional practice. My colleagues treat me politely, at least to my face. I have two beautiful children who love and accept me, and I am allowed to see them twice a week. My surgery was successful, giving me a functional vagina and preserving my ability to achieve orgasm. I can pass readily in most social situations; sometimes I am even called beautiful. I do not regret the path I have taken, and I surely don't want to go back. But for me, as for nearly all transsexual persons, transition and surgery have been only palliative, not curative. I still cannot put aside for long the terrible alienation and desperate loneliness at the core of my condition, nor deny the wounds they have left. Like most transsexual women, I remain deeply wounded.

Naturally, I am proud of my new womanhood, and of my ability to share that common bond with my non-transsexual sisters. But while I may call myself a transsexual woman, in my heart I often feel that I am not really a woman, any more that I was once really a man. In many ways I am of an alien species, with only my transsexual sisters as kin. That is why, for me, community seems to offer the only salvation, the sole redemptive possibility. That is why the transsexual women's community remains my focus, indeed my obsession. Only among my transsexual sisters have I thus far found real understanding, and the prospect of genuine love. Among them I can, for a time, feel unashamed of my transsexualism. When I see the incredible, undeniable beauty of their faces, some of that beauty reflects back, allowing me to see myself as beautiful too. And when the darkness comes over me, then, most of all, I need the palpable embrace of a true sister: someone to whom I need never lie, who knows my truth without my saying it; someone who will unflinchingly lick the wounds from which I still bleed, the iron-salt taste as well-known to her as to all of us who have bled in this bodily journey. If there is such a one for me, and if I can do this also for her, then perhaps our wounds will slowly heal.

A MALE PARTNER

Transsexual. Growing up in a New Jersey suburb, I don't ever recall hearing that word. Even after years of bartending in Philadelphia. I always thought that if a man dressed in woman's clothing, that meant that they were a drag queen. I never knew about the flip side of that coin.

I lived with a girlfriend for almost eight years. During that time I learned a lot about the opposite sex. Everything from emotions, mood swings and expressions to daily rituals. I also grew up with two sisters, which didn't hurt learning about the female of the species. So I have a pretty good idea of the differences between males and females emotionally and physically. And the only part of Nora that doesn't fall into the female category is a part of her anatomy that she wants to live without and seems very out of place on her.

People don't like Nora for what she is, they like her for who she is. They treat her like a woman, not a male, not gay or a drag queen. She's smart, creative and very outgoing. Her people skills are extraordinary. She's capable of making people feel comfortable in the most uncomfortable situations. I can honestly say that I've learned more from Nora than from any other person I have known. I guess that's what draws me to her?

The nine months prior to meeting Nora were a total blur. I had a really bad break-up with a girl I spent one third of my life with and planned to marry. From there I turned to alcohol and one-night stands for solitude. After months of hangovers and really strange women, I decided that this wasn't getting me anywhere. So I stopped going out drinking and sleeping around. After about a month of keeping to myself, a co-worker talked me into going out after work for a drink. Well, one drink turned into many and I thought I was back where I started.

I walked into the after-hour club and after about 15 minutes I met Nora. We talked and flirted for a while, then met up later for breakfast at a diner. When we finished, I offered to drive her home and she accepted. On the way to her place we talked some more, kissed, exchanged phone numbers and said goodnight. I wasn't unaware of

Nora's situation. I just didn't know if she was pre- or post-op. Her roommate, who I also had a crush on and was a friend of mine, answered some of the questions I had. (All of Nora's girlfriends are very pretty.) We started seeing each other but took the physical part really slow. When we had sex for the first time, I didn't know what to think; I never had sex that way before. Shortly after, she moved in and we got along from day one.

Months went by and we learned a lot about each other. We continued to get along great and enjoyed living with each other. The problem was that I wasn't comfortable with the sex we were having and I was sure I wasn't ready for a relationship. To tell you the truth, I don't think she was really that comfortable with it either in her current condition. The childish teasing, rumors and speculation about my sexual preference didn't help matters. Especially coming from people who called themselves my friends.

To clear up any misconceptions, there is absolutely without a doubt not a homosexual bone in my body. I always thought of Nora as a female. She's tall, beautiful and more feminine than most females that I know.

After about a week of not talking to each other, we finally sat down and talked. She told me that she loves me and wanted to be with me. I told her that I love her but I wasn't ready for a relationship or comfortable with sex. We came up with a solution. We'd still live together and remain friends. Well, we're not boyfriend and girlfriend but we are definitely more than friends. Sometimes sexual tension runs high because I haven't had intercourse in a vagina in almost two years and Nora only wants to have sex with me. I'm not going to lie, sex does mean a lot to me. Sometimes I wish I didn't have these urges. Things would probably be different between us.

I've never gotten along with anyone like I get along with Nora. We don't even fight, we have debates. We have very few differences and we work through any that we do have. Even though it's debatable if we're a couple or not, there is rarely a day when we are not seen together. We care for and respect each other very much. I can't imagine spending my time with anyone else.

Nora will have gender surgery in two months.

ALAN'S STORY: FEMALE TO MALE

When I hear the word transsexual, I think of a lifetime filled with misery. It makes my mind flash back to a painfully tormented existence. It brings back all the frustration, hurt, and anger of being born with a birth defect that few people can understand. I can think of few worse fates in life than being born into this world as a transsexual. It has never been my dream to alter my body through surgery. It has been my nightmare.

The sun was hot. The beach was packed with families vacationing at the shore. I was four years old when the words from a stranger made me realize that I was different from all the other kids playing on the beach. I was accustomed to swimming topless in the pool in our backyard, so it seemed natural for me to remove my bathing suit top while I was playing in the sand with my sisters and cousins. It was then that a stranger came up to me and asked if I was a boy or a girl. I remember feeling embarrassed by the question. Why was I picked out from all the other kids on the beach? Why did that stranger ask me that question and nobody else?

I remember being called a girl by my family and I remember being confused by it. As a child, I really didn't understand the meaning of gender, but I knew that little girls acted a certain way, played with toys that I didn't like, and dressed in clothes that seemed foreign to me. I wanted to play with the toys that boys had. I wanted to wear the clothes that boys wore. I liked the same things that other boys liked. Even though everyone called me a girl, I remember feeling confused because I certainly did not feel like one inside.

I remember going into first grade and wondering why I was forced to wear a uniform when all the other boys got to wear pants and the blue tie that I longed to wear around my neck. I remember crying at my First Holy Communion because I had to wear a white dress and I wanted to wear the white suit instead, and I remember crying to my parents and asking them why I couldn't be a boy. They told me that both boys and girls are special, but not everyone could be a boy. At that moment everything made sense to me. I wasn't different after all.

It was my conclusion that every girl must have had the same feelings as I did. My childish understanding was that every girl wanted to be a boy but there were just so many that are allowed to be born each year. But later, I remember being shocked in grade school when I discovered that girls actually liked being girls and that they never shared the same feelings that I had. Nothing made any sense to me. Why was I different? There must be something wrong with me. Looking back in time, I realize my feelings were justified.

I am the youngest of four children born into an Irish/Polish Catholic family. I was raised in a loving home and was taught the value of family and friends. I was very close to my family but I learned at a very early age not to be too honest with my feelings. As a child I was a typical tomboy. I played softball, climbed trees, played wire ball, and was competitive with the other boys on the street. Society accepts boyish behavior in children, but when a child starts to mature, that same behavior is viewed as abnormal and not to be tolerated.

By the time I started high school, I was becoming more uneasy with the feelings that I had learned to conceal. I had friends in school, but did not allow anyone to know my inner self. Although I attended parties, I never dated or encouraged others to get too close to me.

I was educated enough to understand the meaning of the word homosexual; however, I didn't need to experiment with my feelings within the gay community because I did not fit into that category. At that time there wasn't a name for people who were born like me. As a teenager, I was attracted to a few girls in school. I never approached them, since I could not respond as one who was born a female, but rather as a male who was interested in a heterosexual relationship. I could not respond or act upon any normal teenage flirtations since I was in the wrong physical container.

I felt like an imposter to my family, friends, and to myself. My reflection in the mirror was that of a female; yet my mind, my heart, and my soul were that of a male. Frustration and hopelessness made my life become more isolated. I had no one in whom I could confide. How could I expect someone to understand my feelings when I could not understand them myself? I didn't want to commit suicide because I didn't want to hurt my family, but it was during this time that thoughts of suicide did start to enter my mind. I didn't think I was strong enough to remain in a world where I clearly did not belong.

Finally, there was a shadow of hope. I was sixteen when I saw the Christine Jorgenson Story. My friends laughed about this male who went to Denmark to undergo reassignment and become the woman she felt she was. I was sitting there stunned. I couldn't believe another human being on this planet shared the same painful feelings that I lived. I learned what the word "transsexual" meant, and I knew at that moment my identity and path in life. My friends' laughter would become a vehicle to place me into a marginalized position in a world of prejudiced conditions.

Most teenagers are anxious to complete high school in order to begin the variety of choices in life, which would provide paths into education, business, marriage, and plans for the future. My drive was to complete high school and work hard with a full time job, which would pay my way into New York to gain an appointment with the Harry Benjamin Foundation. There I would be tested, and understood with the possibility of "fitting into" a world in which I felt so alien. My desire was simply validation. Where my peers were in hopes of living and enjoying, I existed in loneliness and isolation in a world of unanswered questions.

In 1974, at the age of nineteen, I went to the Harry Benjamin Foundation for a consultation. They were clear and up front. Any surgical moves to correct my disability would require money that I needed to earn. I remember walking out of that office and feeling hopeless. For years I had waited for this moment, and nothing was accomplished. I realized that I could not get any assistance until I had the thousands of dollars they were asking. I was alone in a strange city, alone with my secret too horrible to tell. I returned home that day feeling alone but not discouraged.

Soon afterwards, I wrote to Dr. Terrence Malloy of Pennsylvania Hospital. An article in the local paper indicated that he was performing the same surgery that was performed in New York. Again, the response to my letter was the same as my visit to New York. I never made an appointment to see Dr. Malloy because I didn't have the finances required for surgery. But, now I had a goal and I had a focus. I was determined to save the money that was needed to have my body in alignment with my mind.

I had very few avenues for entertainment. Membership on a local softball team provided an occasional outlet. Wearing a uniform would always create a safe atmosphere. It made socialization safe. Uniforms make everyone the same, void of personal identity and sexuality.

I became close in friendship but never allowed anyone to get close to my thoughts. They were friends who never knew my personal reality. They never would truly know me. One by one they married or coupled with others. Once again I felt like a misfit, and there was a distance that was growing. I was feeling marginalized by my peers.

In the spring of 1980, my father was diagnosed with lung cancer. There was no doubt in my mind that he could beat it. He was the strongest of men with the heart of a gentle giant. Just months before, I had one brief conversation with him about the feelings that I had had all of my life, and he told me to "follow my heart". A conversation that lasted no more than a few minutes, but a conversation that I would remember a lifetime.

Six months later, at the age of fifty-seven, my father died in his bed. At this time my mother was strong and yet fragile. I saw the spark of life go out of my mother's eyes. It was from the moment of my father's passing that I felt all personal goals had to be secondary to my mother's needs. All my energy and drive had to be used in providing my mom with an emotional foundation. My private goals would be dealt with sometime in the far future. I knew that regardless of the years of repair, this time would be needed for my mom.

Love of child for parent can be so complex. But the complexity is always sobered by death. The times taken for granted prior to death's touch are only a shadow of a relationship. The days, months, and years that followed my father's passing allowed me to realize my father to be a gem. His words, "follow your heart", will always be as powerful as the day he spoke them to me.

My mom's loss was our collective loss as a family, and yet, she carried into each passing day the spirit and joy of her Irish personality. My role was one of a protective child over a grieving parent, never wanting to abandon my mom, and choosing to stay home over socializing with friends. My mom encouraged me to go out and enjoy good times; her support was never abandoning.

I preferred inviting friends to my home, as opposed to going out, for several reasons. Firstly, my mom could be a part of the evening; and secondly, it prevented a situation where I avoided the glances and cutting remarks of those who did not know me but made it their business to determine my sexuality. As a result, I stopped going out. I preferred inviting friends over and socializing at the house where I felt secure and I knew my mom was safe. The emptiness of one's loss makes you very protective over the surviving parent. I always had the fear that when I was away from home, like my father, my mother would leave me through death.

As the years passed by, the feelings that I had had since childhood were continuing to torment me. I was finding it difficult to focus on anything but my gender. One's gender is the very essence of one's being. Gender identity is with us twenty-four hours a day, seven days a week, and is a part of our dreams during a deep sleep.

If I entered a store, my gender would be questioned. When I donated blood to the Red Cross, I would be asked aloud, "What is your gender?" I would go to the rest room and be told that it was a ladies' room and that the men's room was down the hall. Attending certain social gatherings with my family, I was told by people that my attire was not appropriate. A shirt and pants would be my everyday attire of choice. I never compromised my attire, yet this provoked questions from others. I began to dread going out. No matter how a conversation started, my gender always seemed to be an issue. My life was under a microscope. As a result, my daily routine consisted of going to work, coming straight home, eating dinner, and then lying in bed until the next morning. Days, months, years ... a lifetime of this would force any sane person to see suicide as a personal choice or perhaps a personal release from an existence of a false life. The only thing that held me back from suicide was my mom. I could not cause her the pain of another loss.

My mom and I had a good relationship; yet the few occasions when I would generate a conversation pertaining to my gender identity, my mom became confused by the issue. This was the reason why it was rarely discussed. I learned early in life that my questions and issues of gender were to be solved alone and were not open to conversation. This solitary experience had few outlets. If it would be my choice against suicide, it would be necessary to find outlets.

As the years passed, I became a "pro" at shielding my family from my horrible secret, a secret that left me filled with guilt, shame, and anger. I realized that if my family knew my personal reality, they probably would not love me anymore. I did not want to hurt anyone, but I could no longer live with my body and mind in constant conflict. I was becoming a shell of a human and an emotional cripple.

It was in October of 1987 when I had returned home from work that I felt uncertain as to whether or not I could return. I had worked for the same industry for twelve years, never missing a day. But this particular Wednesday I felt all of my pain catching up on me. Totally exhausted, my life was an exercise in survival.

Yes, I remember that Wednesday, when my life hit with the force of bereavement for a life I never had an opportunity to live. I hated how I appeared and how people perceived me. The life I was not able to live emptied my spirit and drained any energy left within me. I had bottomed out of the life I had struggled so hard to live. Yes, I remember that particular Wednesday when the void was filled with pain, loneliness, unanswered prayers, and a desire not to go on.

I felt I was having a nervous breakdown. I told my mom I was sick. It was then that my mom handed me a card for a family therapist. She had obtained this card from my brother and had been holding on to it for a few months, not knowing how to approach me on the subject. At that moment, with thoughts of suicide so overwhelming, I took the card and called to schedule an appointment.

Therapy was the beginning stage of the road to recovery. It is a very slow process to heal a tortured mind. It was a lifetime of pain that took me into a dark hole of hopelessness, and it would be years of personal commitment to therapy that would get me out of that hole I called my life.

When I first went to my therapist, Pat, I expected to be judged the same way I had been in the past. Instead, I found her to be compassionate and caring. In time, I found that I was able to trust Pat as a therapist and as my friend. For the first time in my life I could be totally honest with another human being and not feel guilt or shame when releasing my personal thoughts. Pat would be the healer of my personal spirit. Depression crippled me. Pat slowly began to chop away at the walls of defense that I had built and allowed me to understand that I had a right and a place within this world.

Not only did I have Pat to believe in me, but I also had a friend at work with whom I confided. Anita has been an emotional support since the first conversation I had with her, concerning my gender dysphoria. In a world of loneliness, I found two friends who understood, or perhaps, just liked me without conditions. In August of 1981, it was Anita who drove me to Pennsylvania Hospital to attend a meeting which would be the first step necessary to enter the program for transgendered individuals. There were eight people like myself; Dr. Lief, a psychiatrist; Lynn Hubschman, a family counselor; and a nurse associated with the transgendered program at Pennsylvania Hospital. It was during this session that I was given information about surgical procedures, costs, and whether or not they felt I would be a candidate for the extensive surgery. I remember feeling violated by that last issue. How could it be that these professionals in the field of psychology were going to decide whether I qualified for my true identity? In fact, I thought for the first time in my life that I had a moment of absolute certainty. These three individuals representing the hospital may have come to the table equipped with degrees and published works, but for this particular issue, I was the expert, not they. One by one, we had to give a brief history of ourselves and explain why we felt we needed this surgery. I sat there and listened to the most personal thoughts of others, and they listened to mine.

To expose the most intimate details of your life would be difficult, at best, in the company of friends. But here, with strangers, within a period of two hours, we each had to condense our lives and become vulnerable to all present. I felt I had no right to be listening to the personal stories of others. After each person spoke, the staff quietly discussed with each other whether or not we fit into the category of being a true transsexual. I am certain that each person around that table felt violated. To me, they were the judge and jury, and it was basically a thumbs up or a thumbs down verdict. I felt like I was on the witness stand defending my life. They would be the ones to decide my fate. This was not the type of meeting I had expected, but it was a starting point. This was the initial step in entering the program with Pennsylvania Hospital.

No one was told that they were or were not to be a candidate for the program. In conclusion, we were identified to be an ambivalent group. I found that to be a personal affront. After two hours, eight confessions of people, and a room filled with anxious lives holding the baggage of depression, fear, and confusion, we were proclaimed ambivalent. This did not seem valid. This was my pain, my life, and my journey, where ambivalence plays no part. My journey had begun.

Before leaving the meeting, I scheduled an appointment to take the MMPI test. The MMPI test must be taken by each candidate. This is a psychological test, which assesses the personality of each individual involved with the program, and it must be taken prior to any surgery there.

My therapy with Pat continued and developed into a friendship. The support found in both Pat and Anita could not be measured. Pat gave me professional counseling and Anita gave me unconditional friendship. Looking back, there is no doubt in my mind of the importance of these two friendships. As a result of their support and faith in me, I am alive today, and writing now about my past. Had it not been for their friendship during that period in my life, I would not be looking into a future. They both believed in me, and helped me to believe in myself. They made me feel as though I had a place in this world and that I had importance. Not only did they want me to survive in this life, they wanted me to desire to survive and find value in myself.

My mom could see that emotionally, I was getting stronger. Little by little, I would tell her different things I was experiencing through therapy. I recall sharing with my mom the topic of gender identification. My mom sat and listened to me and tried to be supportive, but her eyes would fill up, and the conversation was cut short.

The program at Pennsylvania Hospital was not only a personal commitment but an exercise in total honesty. I had to approach each person in my life and explain my male identity. It was important that everyone respond to me as a socialized male and use the proper pronouns to support my male gender. My attire had always been male or at the very least androgynous.

In May of 1989 I started hormone treatment. Anita drove me to Dr. Kryston's office for my first injection. Dr. Kryston is a kind and compassionate professional. He made a difficult day much less frightening.

It was morning and I had just gotten home from work. I had an appointment with Dr. Kryston, who, after six weeks, would give me the third injection. I still hadn't told my mom that I was involved in the program at Pennsylvania Hospital, and this would be the day of the conversation. My mom was sitting at the kitchen table with a cup of tea. Casual conversation worked its way into the topic of my gender dysphoria and the Pennsylvania Hospital program. I explained that I was receiving injections to correct my birth defect. I went on to say the things I always wanted to reveal, and to explain that no one was at fault for this condition. For the first time in my life, I felt that my mom was able to understand my problem. My mom's eyes filled with tears, but they were tears different from the past. She said she always thought that she was to blame and never was able to let go of her burden until that conversation. There is no blame in my condition; there is only correction. I thanked my mom for giving me a childhood without conditions. My mom said, "You are my child, and I love you. I don't give a damn what anyone else has to say about this; I'll stand by you".

Anita drove me to Dr. Kryston's that day. This time when he asked, "How are you?", I answered, "I'm great. To me it's Christmas day. My mother loves and accepts me". I left that office feeling as though I could conquer the world. On the way home to my house we stopped for flowers. The flowers were for my mom, with a card which simply read, "To the best mom in the world". I felt happy for the very first time in my life, never knowing that within days the bottom would drop out from my happiness.

It was July 6th, 1989, and I had just completed the midnight-to-eight shift at work. Anita was also working that tour the same week.

As we were walking out to the parking lot to our cars, we were making plans to go out the next night. It had been a couple of years since I had gone out socially, so this was going to be a big step for me. We were actually making plans to go out and have some fun.

I remember driving home from work that morning feeling great about life. I was maintaining an honest relationship with my mom, and I had Anita who was emotionally supporting my decision for surgery.

Normally, when I walked in the back door, my mom was sitting at the kitchen table having her cup of tea listening to WPEN playing songs from the '40's. On that morning, there was no kettle on the stove and the radio was silent.

I walked into my mom's bedroom and saw her lying on her bed. But she lay there motionless—something was wrong. She wasn't breathing. I tried CPR, and then grabbed the phone and dialed 911. I ran to my neighbor's, and pounded on their door. "I need help," I said, "It's my mom, it's my mom".

During the time that I was waiting for the Rescue Squad, I was trying to get my mother to breathe. The Rescue Squad finally arrived, went into the bedroom, and shut the door. The bedroom door finally opened. My mom had died. She had had a cerebral hemorrhage during the night.

Prior to that day, I thought I knew everything about pain, but I realized then that I was just a novice. I was empty. I had no more to give. The shock, the pain, and the loss was overwhelming. At the moment of my mother's passing, plans for my future were quickly swept away. All my emotion was absorbed in the grief of losing another parent. In an instant, the energy and drive that I had built up in preparing for a new life was taken away.

The flowers I had just bought for my mom were still fresh. I never dreamed that within days I would be placing that card that read "To the best mom in the world" under her pillow to be buried with her.

I was an empty shell for nearly two years. After the funeral, when the last click of the gate was sounded, there were fewer visitors at my door. Anita was constantly at my side, giving me support. She literally put her life on hold to get me through a crisis that would take me near the edge of my existence. It was also the love shown to me by my Aunt Betty that would get me through another day.

I temporarily dropped out of the program at Pennsylvania Hospital. I could not continue on a journey that would require the emotional strength that I now lacked.

There are many stages associated with grief: shock, denial, anger, sadness, and finally acceptance. I had weekly sessions with Pat to help me through the process of healing a shattered heart. I was living without my parents, without gender, without hope. It would take over a year of counseling to give me the strength to want to go on with life. If I had decided to wait until I was over my mother's death before re-entering the program, I'd still be waiting today, some three years later. You never get over missing the person that you lose through death. Life goes on, but it is never quite the same.

If mothers are the sweetest flowers that grow, then my mom was the rose that I would have chosen from my garden. She had a smile that would light up a room, and love that would fill a heart. The loss was not only felt by me, but by everyone that her warmth had touched. My life will never be quite the same without my mom and dad. Their physical containers are absent from this world, but their essence lives within me and keeps me strong.

It was August of 1990 when I made an appointment to see Dr. Kryston to continue with hormone treatment. I needed to go on with the program. I needed to correct my birth defect. A birth defect that was so draining that, in time, without surgery it would kill me emotionally.

I was surprised at the people who supported me and I was also surprised at the people who could cut me out of their life, unable even to recognize the shadow of a relationship or friendship once shared.

I confronted my brother-in-law, Tom, who had been my friend since high school. He sat and listened to me. He never judged me. From the moment of that conversation through this day, I no longer consider him my brother-in-law. He is my brother. And then there is my cousin Katherine, who has offered an endless resource of support and love. Our bond will never be broken. These personal encounters would be the first in a series of many which would change the perceptions that others held of me, and become my true introduction to a new life.

In December of 1990, Anita accompanied me to Pennsylvania Hospital for the first surgery that was scheduled. Going through the doors of the operating room was a true moment of isolation. I remember thinking that it would be easier for me to die on the table rather than to face more emotional abuse. Physical pain has limits. Psychological pain is limitless.

After surgery, I was returned to my room, coming out of the anesthesia when I heard my brother's voice in the room. I saw Anita standing over me and I heard my brother say, "I'm here to see my baby brother". That was the first day of the life I now call my own.

He had said the words that I had waited a lifetime to hear. My sister Dot, who has proven herself to be a loyal sister, was also there to see her brother Alan. Yes, I was their baby brother. I was their brother all of my life, and I was finally being recognized and accepted.

Six weeks after surgery, I was returning to work and feeling emotionally and physically stronger. Although I was nervous about going back to work, I was more comfortable walking through that lobby that day than I had ever been in the past.

My supervisor Maryanne and fellow coworkers were supportive and conscious of my personal struggle. These are very special people, reflecting a cross-section of society. Maryanne was and still is a friend, a smile, and a confidant.

I recall telling Linda, a coworker, how I wished that certain family members would accept me because family was always important to me. I remember Linda saying, "We could be your family". It was then that I understood that family is just another word for caring. Caring people are your family.

Since October of 1991, I have undergone several stages of phalloplasty surgery performed by Dr. Malloy. Each time, waking up from surgery, I promised myself that I would never again defend my life but now begin to live it.

It is truly a miracle that I am alive today. More than that, it is a miracle that I choose to be alive. I am here and I give validation to my life without restrictions. I will not be guided by the prejudice of others or conditional love.

This difficult journey has taught me something specific in regard to the sexes. The advantaged gender is the one in which the body coincides with the mind. A superior gender does not exist within my reality. Superiority is the kindness displayed by an individual, regardless of gender.

A transsexual is not what I want to be. It was either my birthright or birth defect, regardless; it is who I am. My brain, my heart, and my soul have not been changed through surgery. I am that small child who once played on the beach. That child, who struggled to adulthood, now walks through life content. My body and mind are finally in harmony.

Thank you, Dr. Malloy, for healing my body. Thank you, Pat, for healing my mind. Thank you, Anita, for your friendship.

Mom and Dad, thank you for my life.

CONNIE'S STORY: MALE TO FEMALE

The Psalmist in the Bible tells us in Psalm 90 that the days of our age are threescore years and ten; and though men be so strong that they come to fourscore years.... This is the story of my life and the beginning of my new life.

Seventy years ago, I was born to a well-educated and industrious couple; he was a mechanical engineer and she was a devoted wife and loving and caring mother. They already had two other children, both girls. The oldest daughter was four years and ten months older than me. The second girl was three years and three months older than me. The little family doted over the apparent first boy in the clan.

Four and a half years later, we were joined by a beautiful blonde baby boy. By this time, my play habits were fully developed.

We lived in a sparsely populated area and there were no other children living nearby, neither male nor female. I was used to playing with my sisters' toys and joining in their games. I was comfortable playing with dolls and playing house and being a mother to the dolls. When our brother arrived on the scene, I was already old enough to be accepted in kindergarten. This gave my mother a chance to spend more time raising her newborn.

It was the beginning of the depression. Men were losing their jobs. Business failures were prevalent. My father never lost his job but was transferred to a position a hundred and fifty miles from home and we only got to see him on weekends. There was no male influence in my life for the next three years.

Our family, for several generations, was involved in church music. My grandfather was a church organist and choir director. All of his children sang in his choirs. He was a talented teacher and musician. It was his desire that I be sent to an internationally known and respected choir school to receive my musical and secular training.

To further this plan, he taught me to read music at three years of age. He would teach me the words and I had to read the notes. He would stand me on the piano bench beside him, he would play, and I would sing the score.

At age eight, I passed the entrance examination and was enrolled in the school. Usually, it would take the boys two to three years before they were qualified to sing in the choir. I was singing as a regular member of the choir in one month. On November 1st of 1934, as the choir was singing the anthem in our All Saints' Day service, Dr. G_______ sent word to me from the organ that I was to sing the solo which would come in two more pages. I did so and my life as a choir soloist was launched. I was a soprano, alto, and tenor soloist in that choir for twenty-five years.

The choir school and the high school I attended were both boys' schools. I never sat in class with a girl until college. For education, this is a great plus for boys, having no distracting influences when trying to learn. I was never drawn to females during puberty. I was a "late bloomer". My voice didn't begin to change until I was sixteen.

This was an asset for me. Every year in the choir school, we would present an operetta as part of our commencement exercises. I was selected to play the female lead in all of these productions. I was very comfortable in these roles.

When I graduated from high school, the Second World War was in progress. I was inducted into the army and spent five years of active and reserve service.

In 1950, wanting to try to "fit in" to the conventional world, I met and married a wonderful and understanding girl. I say understanding because she knew that I was a cross-dresser. She accepted this at that time, provided that my habit remained within the walls of home and that I continued to provide for her future.

To prove to her that these were my intentions and to protect my financial holdings, I placed all of my possessions in her name. It was not until thirty-five years later that I found this arrangement to be a hindrance to my plans which developed.

In 1952, the story of George Jorgenson came to light in the press. George had become Christine at the hand of Dr. Christian Bernard (the father of the famous heart surgeon) in Denmark. It became clear to me that my life didn't have to be a dead end. There was one draw-back. I didn't have any contacts to those who could lead me to my hoped-for existence. In 1979, I heard about and made contact with the Pennsylvania Hospital team who would become responsible for my destiny.

I was accepted to pursue the course. I was assigned to a psychiatrist for analysis. After six months of analysis, I was approved for hor-mone therapy and the procedures to follow. After three years of treatment and living as a woman, I arranged for a conversation with the Judge of Family Court who would assign the judge to hear my suit for divorce. He advised me that, New Jersey being a community property state, my wife could demand a settlement in which all of our property would be awarded to her and I would not be able to afford my surgery.

In tears, I informed my endocrinologist of this. He told me to seek advice from my psychiatrist. My psychiatrist told me to remain faithful to my ambition and something might develop for me.

Everything was placed on hold. Then in 1990, my wife developed some abdominal pains. I took her to her gynecologist. He performed a Pap smear, found displaisic cells, and ordered further tests. The result was uterine surgery in which he found two polyps. The first was fully encapsulated; the second had a tentacle extending half-way through the wall of the uterus. We agreed to a total hysterectomy. The surgeon said that he had taken everything and some lymph nodes. There was no indication of metastasis. But, in order to be sure, he ordered internal radiation of her pelvis.

She recovered and all seemed well. In the spring of 1995, she had a recurrence of abdominal pain. Her oncologist ordered a CAT scan which showed three small tumors on her liver. We fought this with chemotherapy. She was very brave. She lost her hair. She was extremely nauseated. But six months later, two of the three tumors had been eradicated and the last one reduced to three centimeters. As soon as possible, he resumed her chemotherapy. After three sessions, my wife told the oncologist that she could no longer take it. In accordance with our living wills, she wanted only to be kept comfortable and let go.

We put her in home hospice care, and she passed away in six days. My psychiatrist was right, but I wish it could have been another way.

I turned seventy (threescore years and ten) the following month. I resumed my therapy, consulted my psychiatrist and social worker, took my MMPI, and was examined by the urologic surgeon. All was ready.

My rebirth into my second seventy years occurred on Friday, October 18th, 1996.

***

I would like to add a post script to my foregoing thoughts. I am not aware of any research which may have been done in the area, but this procedure has certainly worked for me, and it might work for others.

I have a high tolerance for pain, but I had no pain during or following my surgery. My counseors and others had warned me that this surgery was accompanied by extreme pain.

What worked for me was a theory I have practiced for most of my life. First, learn as much as possible about the procedures; the physical systems of the body to be involved and their interactions, their proper medical names and locations (Gray's Anatomy is a great source of this knowledge). Read all available literature covering techniques to be used. Discuss with the anesthesiologist the anesthesia to be used, how it is administered and any possible complications which might arise in its use. Keep yourself in as good physical condition as you can throughout life, but especially while preparing for your surgery. Eliminate stress from your life and try to become an optimist.

So the rules are to be fully informed, live a good healthy life, don't worry, be happy, expect the best, and follow all of your care-giver's rules. It works for me — it could work for you.

JOE'S STORY: FEMALE TO MALE

The gender trap: this is what I'll call it. Because it is truly a trap. You are either a male trapped in a woman's body or vice-versa, and what a hellish way to go through life! This is my story, because this is me. I went through it. I'm writing this hoping to help others understand and know there is help out there, hope and a world of happiness. You must be sure of what you want and pursue it.

I try to put my past behind me. Because of all those unhappy years I had, I find it difficult and painful to describe my life then. I was born and raised on a farm. There was always plenty of work; I can remember that at the age of 5 and 6 I was out milking a special cow at 5:00 in the morning. It wasn't something I was made to do, it was something I wanted to do. As I grew older I became more involved in all sorts of farmwork. I was a part of it and I loved being outside and working around the farm animals.

One thing I was always thankful for is that my parents were never under the influence of alcohol. They never drank it or had it in the house and I don't either. I'm sure they didn't surmise then what my life would be or what I would become in the future, but from the time I was old enough to know anything I only wanted and played with boys' toys.

When I reached puberty my sexual attractions were aimed at the girls. I often would have a school crush on one. But I played it cool. I really had no interest in school and dropped out at the age of 15. I was in my tenth year and did not want to graduate, because of the dressing up part.

I never talked to anybody about me. After all, what would they think? What would they say? What would they do? Something on this order you didn't hear about back then. I don't recall the excuse I made to drop out of school; however, whatever it was, it worked. My image of myself was different, far different than what other people could see. They didn't see me for what was within my body and soul, they only saw the cover, not the contents. Don't think I wasn't criticized, ridiculed, and put down, but I always had my one hope: that some day, maybe, by some miracle, I would awake and be the person I wanted to be. A worthwhile person, a good person, a Christian; and I would have a place in someone's life, along with health and happiness.

I was never the aggressive type but then I guess I had reason to hide my true feelings. But some girls I dated were very aggressive and sometimes quite bold. So what did I do to hide my true feelings? I lied, I did everything I could do to keep my secret even if it meant breaking off our friendship. I'm saying friendship here; I don't think relationship would be the word, as I could imagine what a disappointment I was. I started to work part-time at age 16. At 18 I was working a full-time job and pretty much on my own. I should mention now before continuing that I do have a sister; she is four years older than I. She is a wonderful person and has supported my decisions in the past. We are still very close even though she has spent the past eight years in a nursing facility. Regardless of how things were, I always managed to have work and had found steady work throughout. I'm thankful for that; I could retire now but prefer not to yet.

Most of my life was made up of lies. I lived my life that way as a cover, but I hated doing it. It made me feel terrible, but it was the only way I could get by. It haunted me constantly, but I just couldn't find a way to change things until one day, I just happened to pick up a Philadelphia Inquirer magazine and there it was, a way to change my life. There was an article about Pennsylvania Hospital, Dr. Malloy and reconstruction services for someone such as I. I immediately went to work on it, writing to the address given. In turn, I was sent forms to complete with all sorts of questions. Having answered the questionnaire and also having written a letter with it, I sent it back. After that I was given an appointment to attend a gender meeting.

The next step was to go to that gender meeting, at Pennsylvania Hospital in Philadelphia, Pennsylvania. It was at this meeting that I met Lynn Hubschman, Director of Social Services at this time. I was not alone, as I recall; there must have been at least six or more people besides me there. If I remember correctly, each one of us was given the opportunity to speak out. Some had cross-dressed, men wanting to become women and vice versa. We were evaluated to some extent to see if we were actually candidates for a sex change. To me, it was a journey, an adventure, a challenge, and a goal. I was so unhappy that I knew this was the only way I could change things. One thing was certain, you just cannot go there and say, I want to be this sex or that. You must be sure. Once you start there's no turning back. Some have to learn how to adjust; I did not. I lived my life until then being trapped in a woman's body, so I was already well-adjusted to the male role. No problem.

I was evaluated, both mentally and physically, and passed everything. So next came the surgery; rather, a number of surgeries. They all went well. I went through them mostly alone. No one but Lynn Hubschman provided support for me. She was always there when I needed someone. She was far more than a Social Services Director, she was a true and devoted friend. Of course, the Good Lord above was also with me all the way. I am ever thankful and thank God every day for what he has given me — a new life.

Before surgery, my self-esteem was very low. I was always angered by the ridicule I received and often felt left out. I could not socialize the way I wanted to. I lived in fear, and, worse, lived a life of lies which I hated. I wanted to become a member of a church organization but felt I couldn't. I could not truly love someone as I wanted to. I was frequently emotionally upset. I had no peace of mind.

After surgery I came out as the person I had always desired to be: one person, one body. It was as if I had been healed, both mentally and physically. Fortunately my insurance came through for me, because the procedures were quite costly. With the number of operations and hospital stays, it must have been $35,000, maybe more. Next in line was legal work. I'm a new person now. All documents had to be changed: driver's license, birth certificate, social security, etc. I engaged a lawyer to do most of the legal work. I also had to go to court before a judge with my attorney for a name change. Let me tell you, your given name had better be in the clear with no liens against you if you want a name change approved. Also, a letter has to be written from the doctor who did the reconstruction, stating that you are now male or female, in order for a birth certificate change. This is it. I am free now — a new life, a new beginning. What a wonderful feeling — finally, peace of mind!

There is also hormone therapy. This is a must and something you must take for the rest of your life. This can also be a little costly. It can be taken in pill form or by injection. For me, I prefer the injection, which I get every two weeks. I purchase my medication from a hospital pharmacy and go to my family doctor for the injection. It costs $15.00 just for them to give me the injection, so that alone is $30.00 a month. I furnish my own medication, which costs around $60.00 for a small vial that lasts approximately four months. I also have blood work done every three or four months.

I am pleased with the surgery physically. I really did not go through all this for the sex part alone, I did it for me. The feelings I had before surgery certainly did not correspond with my body, and now they do. I do like sex and enjoy it immensely, but with only one woman, my wife. Yes, I am married. My wife is truly a gem and I'm so very thankful to have found someone like her. We dated for about two months, then I gave her a diamond, and we were married six months later. We had a big wedding, dinner, and a live band for dancing at our large reception, the whole bit. This was also one of my fantasies fulfilled.

The wedding day was a beautiful day; everything fell right in place. It was just perfect then, and now, eight years later, it is still perfect. I must confess I did my wife a great injustice because I married this lovely lady, but kept my secret inside me and did not reveal myself to her. I was afraid of losing her and also that my secret would be threatened if someone else knew. This was truly a burden on me, and as time went on, it became even more depressing. Although I tried several times to give her some hints, she didn't pick up on it.

She is not one to probe so all this time she did not know about me, and all this time, I was feeling guilty. I felt a sense of betrayal. It just was not right. I finally got the courage to face it and told her my story. I had to take that chance and hope and pray that it would not change our lives and the love we shared together. I need not have worried, because my wife was so caring and understanding. She told me she loved me even more. I also told her why I had kept it from her for so long and I asked her to forgive me. We both were in tears. My wife is the only one that I've ever related my story to. She is the only one who really needs to know at this point. I wrote a little poem, which I think is appropriate to go with this story I'm writing.

MY WIFE

A lovely person
She is indeed
Loving, caring, she fulfills my needs

I can hold my head high
and look up at the sky
and thank God above
for my own true love.

For now she shares with me
My dreams, my happiness, my fantasies.

She knows now, what's in this heart of mine.
But, oh, it took so long for it to unwind
I did an injustice
I know I was wrong
for keeping a secret for so long.

My love for her is,
deeper still
I love you dear
and always will.

My wife and I have a very normal lifestyle. We love to talk, and do everything together. We are Christians, and I do believe. It took so many years for my life to change, but God must have heard my prayers sometime through those years for me to be the person I am today. I strongly urge any person out there, who may be in the same position I was once in, to get counseling, surgery, etc. Love yourself enough to pursue it. In order to love others you must love yourself first, and have respect for others as well as yourself. As I end my story, I truly hope I might have lifted someone's spirits and provided someone with a new outlook on life. God bless.

A NOTE FROM HIS WIFE

Once I said I wouldn't marry the best man walking, but I have been married now for eight years to the most wonderful and perfect gentleman. He is the kindest, most loving, caring, understanding, and very manly person.

I love him with all my heart and soul for what he is. He is not lazy, he is active in all ways of life. We talk, laugh, and cry together about his surgery and everything else. We have a very strong relationship. This is what I wanted to say for my husband's story.

INTERVIEW: DEIRDRE MCCLOSKEY WITH LIVIA POLANYI

The economist Deirdre McCloskey underwent a sex change in the autumn of 1995. Under the name Donald McCloskey, she had published the groundbreaking book The Rhetoric Of Economics, which claimed that economists' ideas were rooted in the very way they made their arguments. The sociolinguist Livia Polanyi interviewed McCloskey about the implications of her sex change and whether it influences her thinking about economics.

Q: Your life has changed dramatically in the course of the past year or so. Would you be willing to tell us something about your present circumstances and the process that you went through in order to arrive at the situation in which you now find yourself?

A: Yes, I've changed my gender. That's more exact than saying I've changed my sex. I've always wanted to do this, but for a long time I thought it was impractical. Last year I learned it was possible that I could succeed at it, so I started the process — hormonal and surgical and various other ways. I have completed what Churchill would have called the end of the beginning. Now I look forward to continuing my new life in the gender I prefer. I could elaborate if you wish. I'm very open about this. I realized early on that you cannot change your gender in private because in many ways it is a public performance.

Q: As far as I know you are the most well-known person in academia to have made this kind of a move. Is that correct?

A: Yes, although I'm not the only one. I have been in contact with other academics who have made this move. There is a professor at Swarthmore, a professor at the University of Washington, a female to male mathematician somewhere in the state university system in California, and a prominent sociologist at Berkeley. There are several of these folks.

Q: But is it fair to say you had the highest profile in your field?

A: Yes, I think so.

Q: As I have read stories, autobiographies, and memoirs of transgendered individuals, I've noticed that many people have allowed their stories to become public only very cautiously.

A: I made a decision about that last November. I was going to make the announcement in January, but I was "outed" by someone in Iowa. I was going to move to Holland and then come back after finishing the transition. After I was outed it became a story in the main newspaper in Iowa. I decided right then and there that it was much better to speak directly to my colleagues and to the general public about this because that appealed to their better nature. The alternative was to allow rumors to accumulate. To do this would have suggested that I was ashamed. Since a lot of people think I ought to be ashamed of it, but I'm not, it seemed an important political statement to make. The word "political" makes it sound more important than it is — it was an important statement to make. I'm not ashamed — it's not shameful to be a woman, it's not shameful to become one.

Q: Has your interest in how rhetoric, especially the rhetoric of economics, functions in society helped you manage this or aided you in thinking about the impact?

A: A little bit. I'm not quite so unaware as some economists are that everything we do is mediated through language, and so it did not come as a shock that how people talk about my transition is important or can be influenced by my own style of speaking about it. If I had a very simple British realist view of the world I might have handled it differently.

Q: I was thinking about your being a rhetorician and how that might have influenced the way you managed this or your interest in the way other people have reacted.

A: I am more sensitive than I would otherwise have been to how language itself is gendered. That may be perfectly obvious to anyone who knows anything about this, but a lot of people do not know anything about it. I grew up during the civil rights movement, and I was a college student and graduate student during the Vietnam War. I believe that I did not do enough in those two great political movements. I did not stand up to be counted the way I should have. Now, if I stand up to be counted, I can have some influence. I have been put in a position where I can have some small influence in normalizing this for other people. So I have made myself available to journalists instead of hiding it.

Q: I was actually thinking about the feminist adage of the personal being political . Many people argue that scientific interest or the particular paradigm that one embraces is also related in some critical way to one's personal circumstances. Could you comment on the relationship, if any, of your life to your work before and after this gender change?

A: There is a connection, but it was not my motivation for the change. The motivation for the change is very deep, personal, and of long standing — since I was eleven. But I have always been interdisciplinary, so to speak. I'm an economic historian, for example, which has to be done correctly: I have to be an economist and a historian at the same time.That's how my career and my intellectual interests have been. So there is a certain cross-quality to my thinking. I did not permit myself the slightest bit of anonymity before this, however. I was not a feminine man at all — not that I have anything against feminine men. In fact, I was suppressing it. I was very much a standard issue male academic, and I had learned how to do that, especially in graduate school. Rather contrary to my personality, I had learned how to be male in my style and in my choice of arguments and so forth. And now, on the other side, I am becoming more female in my interests in economics.

Q: What were some of the interests, approaches, or presentation styles that you might have otherwise explored, about which you might have said, "No, I'd better not do that because that's not male enough"?

A: For example, heavy emphasis on mathematics and quantification was characteristic of me, especially earlier in my career. I was more interested in writing than most economists are, and I viewed this as a masculine accomplishment. I tried to have a very masculine style, rhetorically speaking. Hard-hitting would be how one might characterize it, with a strongly masculine and assertive voice as opposed to a more modest, contemplative voice.

Q: Do you feel that you were pushed by this to embrace positions more strongly than you might otherwise have done if the world had been gendered differently?

A: Would I have behaved differently if I had been a woman all this time? Is that what you mean?

Q: What I was really asking is if you had not felt pressured to be so masculine, could you have taken a more even-handed style in certain ways? Did you feel as if you really needed to oversell your arguments?

A: Yes. Although I am very intellectually honest, that much I can claim without any false modesty. I am completely intellectually honest. I would not say that I playfully exaggerated, as I think some men do — as though saying, "Of course, I don't actually feel this way but I'll try it out." I am not that way constitutionally, so I did not quite go that far or in that exact direction. On the other hand, I think the sort of single-mindedness with which I approached some arguments would not have characterized someone who was not as anxious about his masculinity as I was.

Q: Could you give an example of a particular argument that you might have been less single-minded about?

A: My first substantial piece of scholarship was about English entrepreneurial failure in the late nineteenth century, and I took a very anti-sociological line on that. If I had not been so involved in proving my masculinity, I would have been more open to sociological approaches to the issue. My books would have been better because they would have had the quantitative arguments that I was interested in, but they would also have been more sympathetic to other points of view. I think my work would have been more persuasive.

Q: What about rhetoric itself, the work for which you are perhaps most widely known? Would that have been rhetorically or stylistically different.?

A: I'm currently engaged in an experiment on that very point. I am finishing a short book for the University of Michigan Press, which is an expansion of a speech I gave in Holland, an attack on modern economics. The problem is that this particular attack is one I have made before as Donald. Although I borrow a lot of arguments from an earlier time, it is interesting for me to try to approach this as a woman. Escaping the more macho style that I had for so long is not easy for me. I don't know if I should or can. This is my first attempt, and it has not worked very well. I think you would know this was written by a former man. I portray myself in the book as "Aunt Deirdre" scolding her nephews — other economists — who are playing sandbox games. It's a little heavy-handed, although I think one would be able to see that I'm struggling with this rhetorical problem.

Q: Do you think that other women economists are closer to "Aunt Deirdre" or closer to the boys in the sandbox?

A: Some of them are very close to the boys in the sandbox, but, on the whole, I think they are interested in the woman's perspective at the present time. There are distinctively female styles of arguments. There are women's ways of doing economic science, and, more to the present point, there are women's ways of expressing oneself in the sciences.

Q: Could you characterize a woman's way of doing economics? And is it independent of whether women identify themselves as feminists or are associated with various schools? Or is it an essentialist position?

A: It's a social-essentialist position, not biological — and I am bound to get into terrible trouble making any statement of this sort. I am in a very poor position for a man making such a statement: I haven't been a woman for very long. Let me give a single example, and then I'd prefer not to talk about it anymore because people will focus on that single thing. I think it's an indisputable fact that, disproportionately, women economists have been interested in the facts of the world. Not that there aren't any such things as female theorists.The best woman economist in the history of the discipline, Joan Robinson, was strictly a theorist. But, disproportionately, women have a different way of looking at the world. I think that is a glorious and important fact, and, therefore, economists would change a great deal if there were more women economists who were interested in the world.

Q: I was wondering why you say that Joan Robinson is the best woman economist. It seems as if that distinction is very clearly tied to one's view of economics and what economics could be or should be.

A: Although I do have a high opinion of her, she was strictly a purist, and I do not have a high opinion scientifically, in general, of the strict, exclusive focus on theory that so many economists indulge in. But she was a very original economist. She was very creative both before and after becoming a Marxist. I don't think anyone could seriously dispute that she ought to have received the Nobel Prize. It was scandalous that she did not.

Q: Do you envision any changes in your own thinking or approach to economics?

A: As a matter of fact, there has been an important change — an acceleration of the change that was going to happen anyway. I am now thinking that it's idiotic for economics to go on ignoring what you might call love — or you might call it solidarity, connection, socialization, or culture. I'm thinking about it quite a lot these days. I view it as a way of looking at the world that is obvious to women. Only a man could devise "Hobbes's problem", which has obsessed economists and other male social thinkers since the end of the seventeenth century. And that is: will a group of unsocialized individuals spontaneously form a civil society? It's an exceptionally silly question for any serious social scientist to ask, yet in every generation, great male social thinkers have spent lots of time thinking about it . It's a silly question because it ignores what Aristotle pointed out: that human beings are political animals, by which he meant that they desire to be members of a polis. It's simply a feature of humans. They are herd animals, pack animals. And to ignore the social character of economic actors is answering the wrong question. What we want to know is: will French people form civil societies? Will people who have grown up in families form civil societies? Will people who have been socialized in other ways form civil societies? Speaking as a Chicago economist who still thinks that markets are swell, my claim would be that many of the analyses of neo-classical and even Chicago school economics are wrong — not just partial explanations or somewhat incorrect, but wrong, because they have this very narrow view of what people are. And I think that view is highly gender specific.

Q: Are there any other women economists from whom you have learned or who have been useful to you in articulating this position or coming to this realization, or is it just because of your own feelings about being a woman?

A: The problem is that women in this profession must constantly show that they honor men, just as before my transition, I had to show that I was a proper macho man. There are some from whom I have learned a good deal, particularly Nancy Folbre of the University of Massachusetts, who has done important thinking about how we should account for the role of caring in an economy. When she was speaking in Holland, we became involved in a friendly way in a debate over Femecon [the feminist economics Internet service-Ed.] Because of my transition, I became a lot more open to her arguments.

Q: So it was a choice of making the transition or your new social positioning? What would have make you more open to those arguments?

A: It's a little hard to say. I have not had enough time to experience fully what it is to be a woman economist or, indeed, to be a woman. And I certainly had not had any time at all as a woman when this view started to become clear to me in January and February. Before all this, I was seen as a sympathizer with women economists and, in a funny way, a feminist economist. My opinions then were coming more from noblesse oblige than anything else. Since my transition began, I have become clearer on my own feminism.

Q: Do you think that had you been a woman all along you would have taken on this large social issue?

A: No, but I'm not taking on this large social issue. Hobbes's problem is a phony problem. In my present view, Hobbes is mistaken. Many economists, such as Kenneth Arrow and James Buchanan, have attempted to answer the question: "Would entirely selfish people form a society that was something other than the war of all against all?" That's a crazy question to ask.

Q: But we know that one of the strongest rhetorical moves in science is to reduce a serious but unsolved problem to a non-problem, that is to say, "Well, gee, you guys are all ridiculous. I don't see this as a problem." And that's a very, very strong rhetorical move within a field.

A: That's right, and that's exactly what I'm trying to do. I know women economists who would be as assertive as I am about this issue — for example, Barbara Bergmann or Joan Robinson. But having been socialized for fifty-three years as a male, I have a tremendous advantage, and I feel uncomfortable with this advantage. It seems unfair that now I get to be what I have always wanted to be, and yet I have this terrifically large amount of self-confidence that comes from being a man in our society. I'm bound to be a more assertive woman intellectually than the average female academic. I am sure you know more about this than I do. Hannah Arendt was not easygoing in that connection.

Q: One of the most interesting challenges to feminism and feminist thought is the question of what it means to be a woman if you were not, in fact, born as one. There are people, gendered female from birth, who feel resentment toward those, gendered male from birth, who declare themselves women and then operate as superwomen. Some argue that they can do this precisely because they were socialized as men. Your eminence within the field relative to others who are gendered female at the moment, and your own socialization, would seem to leave you in a position where this may be....

A: You're saying I may be attacked for this.

Q: Well, at least it's something that one wants to think about when one is thinking about love, solidarity, connection, and culture.

A: I'm certainly very sensitive to the advantage I have. I've been urged by my many women friends to use my self-confidence responsibly. So, I think that's probably correct. I do not believe in the extreme essentialism that makes it impossible for anyone ever to change gender. If I felt that was true I would not have done this at all.

Q: But isn't it also extreme essentialism to think that some people are lucky enough to be born into this gender while some people need to achieve it? Isn't that also in some sense an essentialism theme?

A: No, because I don't feel that I was born into the wrong body and so forth. I don't see why gender can't be chosen.

Q: It seems that for you gender is actually something rather abstract. It's in the body, but there's also something about it that is very abstract and conceptual. Obviously that's critical for you, otherwise you would not have undergone all these procedures.

A: I don't want to give the impression that anything I've done is because it's fashionable. I've actually had some problems with some of my English Department friends who seem to think: "He (they always say he) is doing the transgender thing." They continue to speak to me as Donald and think what I'm doing is fashionable. I was invited to a small conference in Holland by an American historian, and in her presentation she mentioned the American Indian traditions on the third sex, as though it applied to me. I did not find it offensive, but I found it, well, wrong for me. That's not what I'm in this for. I'm not in this to be fashionable. I'm not in this to explore the boundaries of gender. I admire such people, but that is not what I'm doing. I am trying to become a woman, period. Now, the question is, what is a woman? Is there something essentialist about my views on that? I don't think so. I would be prepared to defend essentialism if I thought it were true, but I don't think it is. I'm a social constructionist myself. My current view is that women are what women do. You might say it is a tribal thing. I am joining the other tribe, and to be a functioning member of the other tribe I must do the kinds of things they do. So I constantly observe women. I am very empirical about it.

Q: Are there things relating to your practices as an economist that make it more likely that you will achieve membership in that tribe, since membership is not something you decide on but is something that must be given?

A: I've been amazed, astounded, and gratified at the warmth, generosity, and sophistication of the reception by my female colleagues in economics and in other fields. Only one or two female colleagues have not been gracious about this. It turns out to be the men who have problems. If my experience of the past year had been that the tribe I was trying to join rejected me again and again and again, it would have been terrible. But that has not happened. Here's a small example: on Femecon the other day someone was thinking out loud about how we should get more women on the executive committee of the American Economics Association. She said we should to try to put forward well-known economists, such as Barbara Bergmann, myself, and some other people. You know, she mentioned me without saying "Oh yeah, maybe we should think about that transsexual." She just included me. See what I mean? And it was a very gracious thing to do. [McCloskey is a member of the executive committee of the American Economics Association — Ed.]

Q: Do you expect that you will have the same degree of influence and that your voice will be heard in the same way now that are a transgendered person?

A: I don't know, and I don't care as much. And I think women can understand that. I'm not as career-oriented as I was once. I don't think my career is going to be hurt. It may be helped. It may be that my notoriety on this score will collect an audience.

Q: Do you think that you are in line to be the first female recipient of a Nobel Prize in economics?

A: That's highly premature. The Nobel Memorial Prize in Economic Science is highly positivistic in its structure, and it would be extremely strange for the Nobel committee to give the prize to someone who has spent the second half of her career attacking the very idea of positive science. It doesn't make any sense. So, I don't think it's serious.

Reprinted with permission from Challenge—The Magazine of Economic Affairs, January-February 1997.

A DEFINITION AND SOME STANDARDS OF CARE

When you think of transsexuals, what comes to mind? Most of us know little or nothing about this unique group of people, or we have ideas that classify such individuals as crazy or weird. I am here to tell you that this unusual classification of people is probably one of the most conservative groups of individuals you will ever find. This is probably because they try so hard to conform to the perceived norm in society that they become the actual prototypes they read about or see on television or in the movies.

As a result of the long and careful screening process that any bona-fide pre-surgical program demands, transsexuals are both sane and functioning at a rather high emotional level. This would have to be the case for them to have continued living with such a dilemma for a long period of time, as most patients have done.

With that knowledge as a backdrop, let us define what a transsexual is. The short form is that these are people who believe that their bodies do not match the gender they believe they are. The long form is taken from the DSM IV (Diagnostic and Statistical Manual of Mental Disorders 1994) of the American Psychiatric Association, and states the following:

GENDER IDENTITY DISORDERS

Gender Identity Disorder

A. A strong and persistent cross-gender identification (not merely a desire for any perceived cultural advantages of being the other sex). In children, the disturbance is manifested by four (or more) of the following:

(1) repeatedly stated desire to be, or insistence that he or she is, the other sex

(2) in boys, preference for cross-dressing or simulating female attire; in girls, insistence on wearing only stereotypical masculine clothing.
(3) strong and persistent preferences for cross-sex roles in make-believe play or persistent fantasies of being the other sex.
(4) intense desire to participate in the stereotypical games and pastimes of the other sex.
(5) strong preference for playmates of the other sex.

In adolescents and adults, the disturbance is manifested by symptoms such as a stated desire to be the other sex, frequent passing as the other sex, desire to live or be treated as the other sex, or the conviction that he or she has the typical feelings and reactions of the other sex.

B. Persistent discomfort with his or her sex or sense of inappropriateness in the gender role of that sex. In children, the disturbance is manifested by any of the following:

(1) In boys, assertion that his penis or testes are disgusting or will disappear or assertion that it would be better not to have a penis.
(2) Aversion toward rough-and-tumble play and rejection of male stereotypical toys, games, and activities.
(3) In girls, rejection of urinating in a sitting position.
(4) Assertion that she has or will grow a penis, or assertion that she does not want to grow breasts or menstruate.
(5) Marked aversion toward normative feminine clothing.

In adolescents and adults, the disturbance is manifested by symptoms such as preoccupation with getting rid of primary and secondary sex characteristics (e.g., request for hormones, surgery, or other procedures to physically alter sexual characteristics to simulate the other sex) or belief that he or she was born the wrong sex.

C. The disturbance is not concurrent with a physical intersex condition.

D. The disturbance causes clinically significant distress or impairment in social, occupational, or other important areas of functioning.

Code based on current age:
302.6 Gender Identity Disorder in Children
302.85 Gender Identity Disorder in Adolescents or Adults

Specify if (for sexually mature individuals);

Sexually Attracted to Males
Sexually Attracted to Females
Sexually Attracted to Both
Sexually Attracted to Neither

Gender Identity Disorder Not Otherwise Specified

This category is included for coding disorders in gender identity that are not classifiable as a specific Gender Identity Disorder. Examples include:

(1) Intersex conditions (e.g., androgen insensitivity syndrome or congenital adrenal hyperplasia) and accompanying gender dysphoria.
(2) Transient, stress-related cross-dressing behavior.
(3) Persistent preoccupation with castration or penectomy without a desire to acquire the sex characteristics of the other sex.

So how does this phenomenon happen? Well, the fact is that, despite all the research that's out there, no one really knows. The closest I've come to any reason is that something happens while the mother is pregnant that affects the baby's central nervous system as it develops. If this is true, it is easy to understand the unending drive and motivation to change the body to match the mind. This desire, then, is not a choice or temporary wish. It becomes an imperative that no one can alter, short of surgery. Psychotherapy can't talk it away; giving the same-sex hormones to make a girl more feminine, for example, doesn't work; and trying to fight the mind, as it were, doesn't change the incessant longing for a surgical solution to achieve harmony.

It is not play-acting. This is the real thing. People with this problem believe they are the opposite sex, no matter what anyone else says or thinks, and no matter how they must present themselves to the outside world, including their families. The agonizing part is that more often than not, they try to conform to what society expects of them, based on the genitals they had at birth. Many try to force the issue; frequently they marry and have children, hoping that will change their secret desire. It never does.

What do we know about this issue historically? Gender dysphoria syndrome, another name for this category of problem, is not new. There are descriptions in classical Roman and Greek literature about sexual expression of this nature. The first mention in medical writing came from Germany in 1830, and later it was thought to be a form of paranoid psychosis. The French in 1877 thought that testicular atrophy came from excessive horseback riding, and that became an organic cause for gender reversal.

In 1910 a German sexologist, M. Hirschfeld, spoke of transvestism and cross-dressing. At the same time, Sigmund Freud was exploring homosexuality. It was Havelock Ellis in 1936 who wrote of living as the opposite sex and being accepted by society. D. Cauldwell from the United States first used the term "transsexual" in 1949. He thought it involved antisocial behavior. Not until the advent of Harry Benjamin, a research sexologist in New York in 1953, did the condition become more accepted and known.

Publicity surrounding the Christine Jorgenson case brought the subject to the attention of the general public. This involved an American ex-army sergeant changing from being a male to being a female. The operation was performed in Copenhagen, Denmark by a Danish plastic surgeon. The year was 1952. The first published report of transsexual surgery, however, came from Germany in 1931.

Professional curiosity was piqued, and in 1965 the Gender Identity Clinic of Johns Hopkins Hospital in Maryland was opened to perform sex reassignment surgery (SRS) following rigorous screening by many specialists and disciplines. The first operation conducted there was in 1966.

Since then, a number of centers and individual physicians have followed the guidelines of the Harry Benjamin International Gender Dysphoria Association, established in 1979, for identifying primary transsexuals as surgical candidates. These Standards of Care are given in the following chapter.

STANDARDS OF CARE: THE HORMONAL AND SURGICAL SEX REASSIGNMENT OF GENDER DYSPHORIC PERSONS

These Standards are the intellectual and legal property of the Harry Benjamin International Gender Dysphoria Association, Inc. They are reprinted by permission of the Association. These standards were being revised at the time of printing this book.

1. Introduction

As of the beginning of 1979, an undocumentable estimate of the number of adult Americans hormonally and surgically sex-reassigned ranged from 3,000 to 6,000. Also undocumentable is the estimate that between 30,000 and 60,000 U.S.A. citizens consider themselves to be valid candidates for sex reassignment. World estimates are not available. As of mid-1978, approximately 40 centers in the Western hemisphere offered surgical sex reassignment to persons having a multiplicity of behavioral diagnoses applied under a multiplicity of criteria.

In recent decades, the demand for sex reassignment has increased as have the number and variety of possible psychological, hormonal and surgical treatments. The rationale upon which such treatments are offered have become more and more complex. Varied philosophies of appropriate care have been suggested by various professionals identified as experts on the topic of gender identity. However, until the present, no statement of the standard of care to be offered to gender dysphoric patients (sex reassignment applicants) has received official sanction by any identifiable professional group. The present document is designed to fill that void.

2. Statement of Purpose

Harry Benjamin International Gender Dysphoria Association, Inc., presents the following as its explicit statement on the appropriate standards of care to be offered to applicants for hormonal and surgical sex reassignment.

3. Definitions

3.1 Standard of care. The standards of care, as listed below, are minimal requirements and are not to be construed as optimal standards of care. It is recommended that professionals involved in the management of sex reassignment cases use the following as minimal criteria for the evaluation of their work. It should be noted that some experts on gender identity recommend that the time parameters listed below should be doubled, or tripled. It is recommended that the reasons for any exceptions to these standards, in the management of any individual case, be very carefully documented. Professional opinions differ regarding the permissibility of, and the circumstances warranting, any such exception.

3.2 Hormonal sex reassignment. Hormonal sex reassignment refers to the administration of androgens to genotypic and phenotypic females, and the administration of estrogens and/or progesterones to genotypic and phenotypic males, for the purpose of effecting somatic changes in order for the patient to more closely approximate the physical appearance of the genotypically other sex. Hormonal sex-reassignment does not refer to the administration of hormones for the purpose of medical care and/or research conducted for the treatment or study of non-gender dysphoric medical conditions (e.g., aplastic anemia, impotence, cancer, etc.).

3.3 Surgical sex reassignment. Genital surgical sex reassignment refers to surgery of the genitalia and/or breasts performed for the purpose of altering the morphology in order to approximate the physical appearance of the genetically-other sex in persons diagnosed as gender dysphoric. Such surgical procedures as mastectomy, reduction mammoplasty, augmentation mammoplasty, castration, orchiectomy, penectomy, vaginoplasty, hysterectomy, salpingectomy, vaginectomy, oophorectomy and phalloplasty-in the absence of any diagnosable birth defect or other medically defined pathology, except gender dysphoria, are included in this category labeled surgical sex reassignment.

Non-genital surgical sex reassignment refers to any and all other surgical procedures of non-genital, or non-breast sites (nose, throat, chin, cheeks, hips, etc.) conducted for the purpose of effecting a more masculine appearance in a genetic female or for the purpose of effecting a more feminine appearance in a genetic male, in the absence of identifiable pathology which would warrant such surgery regardless of the patient's genetic sex (facial injuries, hermaphroditism, etc.).

3.4. Gender Dysphoria. Gender Dysphoria herein refers to that psychological state whereby a person demonstrates dissatisfaction with their sex of birth and the sex role, as socially defined, which applies to that sex, and who requests hormonal and surgical sex reassignment. Gender dysphoria, herein, does not refer to cases of infant sex reassignment or reannouncement. Gender dysphoria, therefore, is the primary working diagnosis applied to any and all persons requesting surgical and hormonal sex reassignment.

3.5 Clinical behavioral scientist. Possession of an academic degree in a behavioral science does not necessarily attest to the possession of sufficient training or competence to conduct psychotherapy, psychological counseling, nor diagnosis of gender identity problems. Persons recommending sex reassignment surgery or hormone therapy should have documented training and experience in the diagnosis and treatment of a broad range of psychologic conditions. Licensure or certification as a psychological therapist or counselor does not necessarily attest to competence in sex therapy. Persons recommending sex reassignment surgery or hormone therapy should have the documented training and experience to diagnose and treat a broad range of sexual conditions. Certification in sex therapy or counseling does not necessarily attest to competence in the diagnosis and treatment of gender identity conditions or disorders. Persons recommending sex reassignment surgery or hormone therapy should have proven competence in general psychotherapy, sex therapy, and gender counseling/therapy.

Any and all recommendations for sex reassignment surgery and hormone therapy should be made only by clinical behavioral scientists possessing the following minimal documentable credentials and expertise:

3.5.1. A minimum of a Masters Degree in a clinical behavioral science, granted by an institution of education accredited by a national or regional accrediting board.

3.5.2. One recommendation, of the two required for sex reassignment surgery, must be made by a person possessing a doctoral degree (e.g., Ph.D., Ed.D., D.Sc., D.S.W., Psy.D., or M.D.) in a clinical behavioral science, granted by an institution of education accredited by a national or regional accrediting board.

3.5.3. Demonstrated competence in psychotherapy as indicated by a license to practice medicine, psychology, clinical social work, marriage and family counseling, or social psychotherapy, etc., granted by the state of residence. In states where no such appropriate license board exists, persons recommending sex reassignment surgery or hormone therapy should have been certified by a nationally known and reputable association, based on education and experience criteria, and, preferably, some form of testing (and not simply on membership received for dues paid) as an accredited or certified therapist/counselor (e.g. American Board of Psychiatry and Neurology, Diplomate in Psychology from the American Board of Professional Psychologists, Certified Clinical Social Workers, American Association of Marriage and Family Therapists, American Professional Guidance Association, etc.).

3.5.4. Demonstrated specialized competence in sex therapy and theory as indicated by documentable training and supervised clinical experience in sex therapy (in some states professional licensure requires training in human sexuality; also, persons should have approximately the training and experience as required for certification as a Sex Therapist or Sex Counselor by the American Association of Sex Educators, Counselors and Therapists, or as required for membership in the Society for Sex Therapy and Research). Continuing education in human sexuality and sex therapy should also be demonstrable.

3.5.5. Demonstrated and specialized competence in therapy, counseling, and diagnosis of gender identity disorders as documentable by training and supervised clinical experience, along with continuing education.

The behavioral scientists recommending sex reassignment surgery and hormone therapy and the physician and surgeon(s) who accept those recommendations share responsibility for certifying that the recommendations are made based on competency indicators as described above.

Principles and Standards

Introduction

4.1.1 Principle 1. Hormonal and surgical sex reassignment is extensive in its effects, is invasive to the integrity of the human body, has effects and consequences which are not, or are not readily, reversible, and may be requested by persons experiencing short-termed delusions or beliefs which may later be changed and reversed.

4.1.2. Principle 2. Hormonal and surgical sex reassignment are procedures requiring justification and are not of such minor consequence as to be performed on an elective basis.

4.1.3. Principle 3. Published and unpublished case histories are known in which the decision to undergo hormonal and surgical sex reassignment was, after the fact, regretted and the final result of such procedures proved to be psychologically debilitating to the patients.

4.1.4. Standard 1. Hormonal and/or surgical sex reassignment on demand (i.e., justified simply because the patient has requested such procedures) is contraindicated. It is herein declared to be professionally improper to conduct, offer, administer or perform hormonal sex reassignment and/or surgical sex reassignment without careful evaluation of the patient's reasons for requesting such services and evaluation of the beliefs and attitudes upon which such reasons are based.

4.2.1. Principle 4. The analysis or evaluation of reasons, motives, attitudes, purposes, etc., requires skills not usually associated with the professional training of persons other than clinical behavioral scientists.

4.2.2. Principle 5. Hormonal and/or surgical sex reassignment is performed for the purpose of improving the quality of life as subsequently experienced and such experiences are most properly studied and evaluated by the clinical behavioral scientist.

4.2.3. Principle 6. Hormonal and surgical sex reassignment are usually offered to persons, in part, because a psychiatric/psychologic diagnosis of transsexualism (see DSM-UI, section 302.5X), or some related diagnosis, has been made. Such diagnoses are properly made only by clinical behavioral scientists.

4.2.4. Principle 7. Clinical behavioral scientists, in deciding to make the recommendation in favor of hormonal and/or surgical sex reassignment share the moral responsibility for that decision with the physician and/or surgeon who accepts that recommendation.

4.2.5. Standard 2. Hormonal and surgical (genital and breast) sex reassignment must be preceded by a firm written recommendation for such procedures made by a clinical behavioral scientist who can justify making such a recommendation by appeal to training or professional experience in dealing with sexual disorders, especially the disorders of gender identity and role.

4.3.1. Principle 8. The clinical behavioral scientist's recommendation for hormonal and/or surgical sex reassignment should, in part, be based upon an evaluation of how well the patient fits the diagnostic criteria for transsexualism as listed in the DSM-Ill-R category 302.50 to wit:

A. Persistent discomfort and sense of inappropriateness about one's assigned sex.

B. Persistent preoccupation for at least two years with getting rid of one's primary and secondary sex characteristics and acquiring the sex characteristics of the other sex.

C. The person has reached puberty.

This definition of transsexualism is herein interpreted not to exclude persons who meet the above criteria but who otherwise may, on the basis of their past behavioral histories, be conceptualized and classified as transvestites and/or effeminate male homosexuals or masculine female homosexuals.

4.3.2. Principle 9. The intersexed patient (with a documented hormonal or genetic abnormality) should first be treated by procedures commonly accepted as appropriate for such medical conditions.

4.3.3. Principle 10. The patient having a psychiatric diagnosis (i.e., schizophrenia) in addition to a diagnosis of transsexualism should first be treated by procedures commonly accepted as appropriate for such non-transsexual psychiatric diagnoses.

4.3.4 Standard 3. Hormonal and surgical sex reassignment may be made available to intersexed patients and to patients having non-transsexual psychiatric/psychologic diagnoses if the patient and therapist have fulfilled the requirements of the herein listed standards; if the patient can be reasonably expected to be habilitated or rehabilitated, in part, by such hormonal and surgical sex reassignment procedures; and if all other commonly accepted therapeutic approaches to such intersexed or non-transsexual psychiatrically/psychologically diagnosed patients have been either attempted, or considered for use prior to the decision not to use such alternative therapies. The diagnosis of schizophrenia, therefore, does not necessarily preclude surgical and hormonal sex reassignment.

Hormonal Sex Reassignment

4.4.1. Principle 11. Hormonal sex reassignment is both therapeutic and diagnostic in that the patient requesting such therapy either reports satisfaction or dissatisfaction regarding the results of such therapy.

4.4.2. Principle 12. Hormonal sex reassignment may have some irreversible effects (infertility, hair growth, voice deepening and clitoral enlargement in the female-to-male patient and infertility and breast growth in the male-to-female patient) and, therefore, such therapy must be offered only under the guidelines proposed in the present standards.

4.4.3. Principle 13. Hormonal sex reassignment should precede surgical sex reassignment as its effects (patient satisfaction or dissatisfaction) may indicate or contraindicate later surgical sex reassignment.

4.4.4. Standard 4. The initiation of hormonal sex reassignment shall be preceded by recommendation for such hormonal therapy, made by a clinical behavioral scientist.

4.5.1. Principle 14. The administration of androgens to females and of estrogens and/or progesterones to males may lead to mild or serious health-threatening complications.

4.5.2. Principle 15. Persons who are in poor physical health, or who have identifiable abnormalities in blood chemistry, may be at above average risk to develop complications should they receive hormonal medication.

4.5.3. Standard 5. The physician prescribing hormonal medication to a person for the purpose of effecting hormonal sex reassignment must warn the patient of possible negative complications which may arise and that physician should also make available to the patient (or refer the patient to a facility offering) monitoring of relevant blood chemistries and routine physical examinations including, but not limited to, the measurement of SGPT in persons receiving testosterone and the measurement of SGFr, bilirubin, triglycerides and fasting glucose in persons receiving estrogens.

4.6.1. Principle 16. The diagnostic evidence for transsexualism (see 4.3.1. above) requires that the clinical behavioral scientist have knowledge, independent of the patient's verbal claim, that the dysphoria, discomfort, sense of inappropriateness and wish to be rid of one's own genitals, have existed for at least two years. This evidence may be obtained by interview of the patient's appointed informant (friend or relative) or it may best be obtained by the fact that the clinical behavioral scientist has professionally known the patient for an extended period of time.

4.6.2. Standard 6. The clinical behavioral scientist making the recommendation in favor of hormonal sex reassignment shall have known the patient in a psychotherapeutic relationship for at least 3 months prior to making said recommendation.

Surgical (Genital and/or Breast) Sex Reassignment

4.7.1. Principle 17. Peer review is a commonly accepted procedure in most branches of science and is used primarily to ensure maximal efficiency and correctness of scientific decisions and procedures.

4.7.2. Principle 18. Clinical behavioral scientists must often rely on possibly unreliable or invalid sources of information (patients' verbal reports or the verbal reports of the patients' families and friends) in making clinical decisions and in judging whether or not a patient has fulilllled the requirements of the herein listed standards.

4.7.3. Principle 19. Clinical behavioral scientists given the burden of deciding who to recommend for hormonal and surgical sex reassignment and for whom to refuse such recommendations are subject to extreme social pressure and possible manipulation as to create an atmosphere in which charges of laxity, favoritism, sexism, financial gain, etc., may be made.

4.7.4. Principle 20. A plethora of theories exist regarding the etiology of gender dysphoria and the purposes or goals of hormonal and/or surgical sex reassignment such that the clinical behavioral scientist making the decision to recommend such reassignment for a patient does not enjoy the comfort or security of knowing that his or her decision would be supported by the majority of his or her peers.

4.7.5. Standard 7. The clinical behavioral scientist recommending that a patient applicant receive surgical (genital and breast) sex reassignment must obtain peer review, in the format of a clinical behavioral scientist peer who will personally examine the patient applicant, on at least one occasion, and who will, in writing, state that he or she concurs with the decision of the original clinical behavioral scientist. Peer review (a second opinion) is not required for hormonal sex reassignment. Non-genital/breast surgical sex reassignment does not require the recommendation of a behavioral scientist. At least one of the two behavioral scientists making the favorable recommendation for surgical (genital and breast) sex reassignment must be a doctoral level clinical behavioral scientist.

4.8.1. Standard 8. The clinical behavioral scientist making the primary recommendation in favor of genital (surgical) sex reassignment shall have known the patient in a psychotherapeutic relationship for at least 6 months prior to making said recommendation. That clinical behavioral scientist should have access to the results of psychometric testing (including IQ testing of the patient) when such testing is clinically indicated.

4.9.1. Standard 9. Genital sex reassignment shall be preceded by a period of at least 12 months during which time the patient lives full-time in the social role of the genetically other sex.

4.10.1. Principle 21. Genital surgical sex reassignment includes the invasion of, and the alteration of, the genitourinary tract. Undiagnosed pre-existing genitourinary disorders may complicate later genital surgical sex reassignment.

4.10.2. Standard 10. Prior to genital surgical sex reassignment a urological examination should be conducted for the purpose of identifying and perhaps treating abnormalities of the genitourinary tract.

4.11.1. Standard 11. The physician administering or performing surgical (genital) sex reassignment is guilty of professional misconduct if he or she does not receive written recommendations in favor of such procedures from at least two clinical behavioral scientists; at least one of which is a doctoral level clinical behavioral scientist and one of whom has known the patient in a professional relationship for at least 6 months.

Miscellaneous

4.12.1. Principle 22. The care and treatment of sex reassignment applicants or patients often causes special problems for the professionals offering such care and treatment. These special problems include, but are not limited to, the need for the professional to cooperate with education of the public to justify his or her work, the need to document the case history perhaps more completely than is customary in general patient care, the need to respond to multiple, non-paying, service applicants and the need to be receptive and responsive to the extra demands for services and assistance often made by sex reassignment applicants as compared to other patient groups.

4.12.2. Principle 23. Sex reassignment applicants often have need for post-therapy (psychological, hormonal and surgical) follow-up care for which they are unable or unwilling to pay.

4.12.3. Principle 24. Sex reassignment applicants often are in a financial status which does not permit them to pay excessive professional fees.

4.12.4. Standard 12. It is unethical for professionals to charge sex reassignment applicants "whatever the traffic will bear" or excessive fees far beyond the normal fees charged for similar services by the professional. It is permissible to charge sex reassignment applicants for services in advance of the tendering of such services even if such an advance fee arrangement is not typical of the professional's practice. It is permissible to charge patients, in advance, for expected services such as post-therapy follow-up care and/or counseling. It is unethical to charge patients for services which are essentially research and which services do not directly benefit the patient.

4.13.1. Principle 25. Sex reassignment applicants often experience social, legal and financial discrimination not known, at present, to be prohibited by federal or state law.

4.13.2. Principle 26. Sex reassignment applicants often must conduct formal or semiformal legal proceedings (i.e., in-court appearances against insurance companies or in pursuit of having legal documents changed to reflect their new sexual and genderal status, etc.).

4.13.3. Principle 27. Sex reassignment applicants, in pursuit of what are assumed to be their civil rights as citizens, are often in need of assistance (in the form of copies of records, letters of endorsement, court testimony, etc.) from the professionals involved in their case.

4.13.4. Standard 13. It is permissible for a professional to charge only the normal fee for services needed by a patient in pursuit of his or her civil rights. Fees should not be charged for services for which, for other patient groups, such fees are not normally charged.

4.14.1. Principle 28. Hormonal and surgical sex reassignment has been demonstrated to be a rehabilitative, or habilitative, experience for properly selected adult patients.

4.14.2. Principle 29. Hormonal and surgical sex reassignment are procedures which must be requested by, and performed only with the agreement of, the patient having informed consent. Sex reannouncement or sex reassignment procedures conducted on infantile or early childhood intersexed patients are common medical practices and are not included in or affected by the present discussion.

4.14.3. Principle 30. Sex reassignment applicants often, in their pursuit of sex reassignment, believe that hormonal and surgical sex reassignment have fewer risks than such procedures are known to have.

4.14.4 Standard 14. Hormonal and surgical sex reassignment may be conducted or administered only to persons obtaining their legal majority (as defined by state law) or to persons declared by the courts as legal adults (emancipated minors).

4.15.1. Standard 15. Hormonal and surgical sex reassignment may be conducted or administered only after the patient applicant has received full and complete explanations, preferably writing, in words understood by the patient applicant, of all risks inherent in the requested procedures.

4.16.1. Principle 31. Gender dysphoric sex reassignment applicants and patients enjoy the same rights to medical privacy as does any other patient group.

4.16.2. Standard 16. The privacy of the medical record of the sex reassignment patient shall be safeguarded according to procedures in use to safeguard the privacy of any other patient group.

5. Explication

5.1. Prior to the initiation of hormonal sex reassignment:

5.1.1. The patient must demonstrate that the sense of discomfort with the self and the urge to rid the self of the genitalia and the wish to live in the genetically other sex role have existed for at least 2 years.

5.1.2. The patient must be known to a clinical behavioral scientist for at least 3 months and that clinical behavioral scientist must endorse the patient's request for hormone therapy.

5.1.3. Prospective patients should receive a complete physical examination which includes, but is not limited to, the measurement of SGPT in persons to receive testosterone and the measurement of SGPT, bilirubin, triglycerides and fasting glucose in persons to receive estrogens.

5.2. Prior to the initiation of genital or breast sex reassignment (Penectomy, orchiectomy, castration, vaginoplasty, mastectomy, hysterectomy, oophorectomy, salpingectomy, vaginectomy, phalloplasty, reduction mammoplasty, breast amputation):

5.2.1. See 5.1.1., above.

5.2.2. The patient must be known to a clinical behavioral scientist for at least 6 months and that clinical behavioral scientist must endorse the patient's request for genital surgical sex reassignment.

5.2.3. The patient must be evaluated at least once by a clinical behavioral scientist other than the clinical behavioral scientist specified in 5.2.2. above and that second clinical behavioral scientist must endorse the patient's request for genital sex reassignment. At least one of the clinical behavioral scientists making the recommendation for genital sex reassignment must be a doctoral level clinical behavioral scientist.

5.2.4. The patient must have been successfully living in the genetically other sex role for at least one year.

5.3. During and after services are provided:

5.3.1. The patient's right to privacy should be honored.

5.3.2. The patient must be charged only appropriate fees and these fees may be levied in advance of services.

1DSM-1II-R Diagnostic and Statistical Manual of Mental Disorders ('Third Edition-Revised). Washington, D.C. The American Psychiatric Association, 1987.

Original draft dated February 13, 1979

Revised draft (1/90) dated January 20, 1980

Revised draft (3/81) dated March 9,1981.

Revised draft (1/90) dated January 25, 1990

THE THERAPEUTIC PROCESS: CHILDHOOD, ADOLESCENT, ADULT

The standards or criteria provided in the preceding chapter are not arbitrary or devised at someone's whim. They have been created by professionals who have worked in this field for many numbers of years and they have borne the test of time, having been used by every well-respected center for almost twenty years.

There is a caveat, however, and that is that no matter what the standards or lists of careful scrutiny, there is no substitute for a professional opinion, once that counselor has experience.

It takes a long time to acquire that experience, and I can recall any number of early experiences working with people who came requesting surgery when I was new to the field. At that point the rule of thumb was to beg for time and be super cautious. Even when the standards were met, as the coordinator for the program I would attempt to drag out the process just to be sure.

Now I can safely say that it's rare that I meet someone and don't form what turns out to be an accurate opinion fairly quickly. It's like experience in any other field; with time, you just know. The standards are there to assist in the decision and they are helpful, but the judgment of the clinician is invaluable.

What is difficult is the fact that people come for the required help at various points in their process. If a person comes in after having taken hormones, usually obtained without consent from a counselor, they look different from someone who is just beginning to question this idea.

Sometimes people will come requesting surgery after they have lived as the desired sex for years. By then they have learned how to dress, put on make-up if it's male-to-female, for example, and have varied mannerisms that the neophyte has to struggle to incorporate. When you stop and think about it, we all take so much for granted, learning in a slow, steady process what it means to be male or female. Just remember how long it took to be comfortable in high heel shoes or how it felt to lead when dancing.

It is mind-boggling to try to comprehend the process, and even after close to thirty years of working with transsexuals I still get amazed at the strength and courage it takes to walk this path.

That is why it is crucial to understand the premise that this is not a choice but a force that cannot be changed. That force drives transsexuals to do what must be done. One of the tragedies is when the individual cannot find the money to complete the process, that is, to proceed with surgery. This is often the case with female-to-male clients where the costs can exceed fifty thousand dollars and there is usually no insurance to cover it. Male-to-female, by contrast is one operation and runs about fifteen thousand dollars. Today female-to-male people represent about forty percent of the total transsexual population. Many stop after mastectomies and hysterectomy, and are considered legally male.

When we speak about the therapeutic process and what is involved in assisting someone who believes they are a transsexual in making a decision to have surgery, we are talking about a slow, agonizing back-and-forth procedure. While the patient may believe in their heart of hearts that this is what they are and what they want, the task of the therapist is to walk the road methodically. It is the role of the therapist to cover as many bases as possible. It is not just the client who is tortured about this drastic final phase, hoping that the guidelines currently at hand are correct. And these are only guidelines which can be adapted to fit the individual situation. The final decision has to work for the rest of the individual's life. No easy task. The therapist, along with the client, must challenge the request for surgery in order to sleep at night. Mistakes are not easily correctable, if at all.

The usual beginning of the relationship is the client presenting him or herself with a diagnosis of transsexual and wanting something specific, such as hormone therapy or plastic surgery, or sometimes the actual genital surgery. Many times they will tell the therapist that they have lived this way for many years and they are now ready or have the money to proceed. When the therapist puts the brakes on in one form or another, no matter how understanding or caring, the client usually gets angry and can't understand why someone else has any control or power over their decision or destiny, especially when they have struggled long and hard to get to this point. The fact that the therapist has just met them is of no consequence to their way of thinking. As recorded by some of the personal accounts in this book, most people will understand the dilemma and work with the therapist.

The therapist is also screening for the surgeons, who will not perform surgery unless they feel comfortable that two qualified mental health professionals agree that this is the best way to proceed. Any surgeon who will operate without this is questionable. Sometimes the clients themselves will be confused and not sure what they are or what to do, and then it is easier to begin, because the initial anger is not there. Since the total therapy is based on the relationship you have with your client, it is essential that there be mutual trust, respect and caring. However, the direction and process is the responsibility of the therapist, and it is important that the connection be professional so that it is not just like a pair of close friends. This is true for all types of therapy. It is difficult to describe, but the best definition of a good therapeutic relationship might be a good friend who does not allow their feelings to take over or get in the way, so that the focus is always on the client and all action is for their benefit. Of course, when the goal is achieved, whether it is to move to surgery or to decide against it, both participants should agree and still care about each other.

The checkpoints along the way are not so clear nor do they fall into any specific framework. The movement can be up and down and back and forth. The value of knowing and working with someone consistently over a year or two allows for this. There are some clients who come in dressed in their gender and it is difficult to imagine them as the opposite sex, and there are others who from the first meeting look the new part. None of this, however, makes the outcome sure. All of the people who wrote about their lives in this book had a process, and each one was unique and different. The most important sign that is tested is that of commitment. Whether it's going through costly painful electrolysis for the male-to-female or cutting hair short and wearing male clothing for the female-to-male, it takes perseverance and strength in spite of all odds. Family and friends may be hostile, self-doubt will come and go, the fear of recognition creeps in and out. Worries about legal issues and a host of other nightmares are all part of this package.

While the client goes through this uneasy period, so too does the therapist, guiding, assisting, offering encouragement and understanding and making suggestions. It is an uncharted course with hazards at every turn and no crystal ball to predict the outcome. It is exciting and scary. Often there are support groups that can be very helpful, and the therapist can offer that as a resource, or even another patient who would be willing to talk to the client. Just knowing they are accepted, not crazy, and not alone, is helpful.

Often other family members will be seen by the therapist, and while they have their questions answered, the more important gain is that they see someone who respects and cares about their family member. Since this interim period is so crucial and uneasy, there can be many misunderstandings and unclear communication. It is so important to hold onto the final goal and begin to do things like address the person as they wish, as he or she, and to comment on the attempts at cross-dressing and offer helpful hints. Sometimes during this stage the client can test out homosexual feelings, and some clients go back and forth with "Do I want to continue this?" At different points in this whole process the individual may be similar to homosexuals, or at times closer to what transvestites experience. More often than not, the transsexual rejects the role of anything but a transsexual in the end. Struggling with one's gender is so basic and frightening that it takes patience and a world of exploration. Trying to conform and please people who are important in our lives is a common experience, and this particular situation causes much displeasure.

The difficulty in trying to hide a penis or make a chest appear to have or not have breasts is no easy daily routine. Living a lie does not come easily to many people. Longing for love and romance and not being able to openly pursue these goals only adds to the overwhelming task. When families are religious, the tags of good or evil are superimposed on top of everything else. It is easy to see why if this were merely a quirk or a fetish, it might go away with time. These are not exhibitionists seeking admiration.

It is incumbent on the therapist to bring up crucial topics to discuss in detail, such as feelings, relationships, and sexuality, even though some clients have no experience in talking about such matters with a stranger. Again, the skill of the therapist and the therapist's understanding and accepting relationship with the client over time should allow both to be comfortable talking about intimate details. Inner fantasies are often about being the desired gender. The fact that information is confidential usually helps.

Once commitment to the surgical goal is assured, other aspects may prove easier to deal with. Some of these, such as family, friends, and job, take on special meaning and require careful handling. The reason commitment is so crucial is that without it there would be no way to survive all that follows. Testing commitment makes the person live in the real world, face difficulty and become strong emotionally, knowing that they can survive. It is a fulfilling process, and most clients recognize, along with the therapist, when this has occurred. It is not a light that goes off: it's more like being branded by fire and finally feeling reasonably comfortable in the new role, for a good part of the time. Being free to be oneself is most liberating for anyone, but especially in these cases. To be able to express oneself openly and not hide is like a re-birth.

It's standing up to the family and friends and saying that this is the way it will be. It's telling coworkers or a boss that this is the plan. In essence, it's announcing to the world, "What I am and what I always have been is now available for the world to see."

In my experience of over thirty years working with transsexuals, or, as they are now called, transgendered people, I have seen that most of them struggle on a conscious or unconscious level for years. The family, especially the parents, know something is wrong. Whether they discuss the problem or seek help varies with the family. When the child is quite young, parents notice the mannerisms, the preference of toys, or the wearing of opposite sex clothing, that their child chooses. Sisters and brothers learn of the secret life at some point, and they are often more ready than parents to talk about what they see.

When a client comes for counseling, the history is important, and it is not uncommon for people to report that their parents, especially their mothers, knew and allowed the behavior to continue. Some report that their mothers even bought girls' clothes for them, in the male-to-female cases. Most report extremely close relationships with their mothers. It is fathers and brothers who are problematic. This is true for the female-to-male as well.

If clients report not remembering or having no problem about gender in childhood, I view that as a red flag. There is usually some remembrance, no matter how insignificant it may seem, that should be there. Young children are aware of their sexual identity by the age of about three. They explore their own bodies and often others', those of siblings or friends. There is sex play, such as playing doctor, where the body differences are discovered. In counseling, it is easy to follow the life cycle beginning with early childhood.

The beginning of feeling different, perhaps confused or shameful, has its roots in early childhood. We are very hypocritical about sexuality in America, generally. We inundate the society with sexual material, while at the same time we give out the message that it is very private, dirty, or that only certain manners of behavior are appropriate. With that backdrop, the young transsexual is very likely to withdraw into him or herself and be frightened. No one wants to be weird, and for children this dilemma is indeed overwhelming. There is frequently nowhere to turn. These old feelings become locked in and the scar is difficult, if not impossible, to erase. The role of therapy here is to help resolve the conflict by accepting the patient and seeing them as "normal" with a long-standing problem. When they learn that and feel it, it offers relief. Putting a name on the problem gives it credibility. Learning that they are not alone helps enormously.

The age of the client and the hurt they have carried will vary. Some bit of feeling alien may linger forever and be aroused at different moments in time. The public is not kind, and when the past is brought to the surface, it is painful. If therapy has been successful, the client will have new tools with which to cope. Most of this will include building up the ego, stressing the individual's strengths and uniqueness, as well as learning how to handle or ignore uninformed, unsympathetic people. Compassion is not easy to encounter for transsexuals.

As children, many transsexuals believe they are gay. This is more acceptable for family and often for the individuals themselves. Many clients will report having dreams where they wake up in the desired gender. The fantasy life is rich, almost always filled with the thought of changing and living the role of the opposite sex.

Fear of being caught in mother's or sister's clothes is common. For the "tomboy," life is a bit easier and more acceptable in childhood. Wearing pants and playing ball or doing male things does not seem too unusual, and people believe it is just a phase. The male-to-female has a rougher course, as no one accepts boys acting as girls too readily.

If children could be brought into therapy at young ages, they might not suffer as long as most do. There is a caution, however: no qualified therapist should label a young child a transsexual. The usual format would be to try to make the child more comfortable in their gender and hope that it will indeed pass. The fact is that a true transsexual cannot be rid of their desire. At best it may be sublimated until later years. This is not a bad idea, as with time the individual can be educated about his or her condition and will have hope of possible change or at least time to develop to be able to cope more adequately. Telling a parent there is a problem but not being sure how it will resolve itself may also buy time. If parents become abusive or non-accepting of such a child, that needs to be addressed in therapy. There are countless families where such behavior does occur and no therapist is aware. The only hope here would be an enlightened person, for example at a school, who might offer help or a referral for help. When outsiders become involved, such as other family members or neighbors, the response, more often than not, is anger and resentment, with no follow-through for professional assistance. Denial becomes tighter. The recent movie, La Vie en Rose, deals with this.

The shame of being different in this significant way is not difficult to understand. Dealing with sexuality is still shrouded in secrecy.

It is always helpful to have family members involved in the therapeutic process, and at any point that is offered. The client's approval is necessary, and the mere arrival of the family member in therapy with them can be helpful. There is, however, usually a hard-core of family members who will not and cannot accept that their family member is a transsexual. While this is painful, the fact, usually, is that they feel guilty or threatened themselves, and cannot find it in their hearts to continue to accept or love the same person in a different body. Again, they feel their own hurt, not the patient's.

Today, unfortunately, we need to mention another part of childhood that is all too common, and that is sexual abuse. For transsexuals this occurs fairly regularly. Perhaps this can be explained by their unique condition and often passive behavior. Being unsure of themselves and feeling strange, they do not report these instances, and, like the general population, they wear this silent badge of fear and shame. I have even had clients in counseling tell me they thought they deserved this treatment for being what they are. Tragic!

Childhood, which we like to think of as carefree and protected, is not so for most transsexuals. An understanding therapist can lift many early burdens. A word of caution here: a number of well meaning professionals, not versed in this field, have offered advice or opinions that turned out to be quite damaging. It is important to check out the credentials of the therapist or physician and ask about their experience in this field.

Following early childhood and latency, the next crucial period is adolescence. The therapy must also center on this history because some crucial signposts need to be touched upon. This period offers many significant areas to explore from choice of career, ego strength, problem-solving, dealing with anger and rebellion, to the most important, testing one's sexuality. Whatever the early history offered, it is usually compounded by adolescence. Now behavior is acted out and the secret is harder to hide.

The issues in therapy continue to be self-acceptance and coping. Whatever the scars from childhood, they become tougher in adolescence. High school years are not often easy years, but for the transsexual they are excruciatingly difficult. Teasing and outright aggression is common.

Most transsexual teenagers attempt to date and some are fairly successful. It is almost as though they are trying to prove that they are wrong about how they really feel. Sublimation is rampant. Some try to be more female or male in order to prove that they can live as they were born. Trying to study is not easy, but some can lose themselves in this way and excel in school.

It is during these years that sexual conflict can be unbearable. While all teens test out their new found sexuality, the transsexual is in basic conflict. It's almost fighting oneself. The norm during this period is to emotionally rebel against the parental authority. For the transsexual this is scary, because they need their parents to love them, and to rebel would be too risky. As a result, many transsexuals do not complete this big step emotionally. Again, the patient, as well as the family, may believe the problem is one of homosexuality. Since a true diagnosis is frequently not made, let alone confirmed, until sometime in the twenties, this adolescent period is full of turmoil. Most teenagers do not like much about themselves and have a difficult time with the hormone changes in their bodies. The added conflict with parents, and the testing of one's attractiveness with the opposite sex, makes for a flood of emotion. What helps most of them endure and triumph is other teens who are going through the same process.

For the transsexual this peer group is non-existent. Therapy during this stage can offer a lifeline. Some teens do receive help at this point. It is not uncommon for a crisis to occur. Depression is even more pronounced with transsexuals. One of the most frightening situations is the threat of or attempt at suicide. Sexual issues are a primary cause for suicide among teenagers. A psychiatrist is necessary if this is the case, as drug therapy or hospitalization may be necessary.

Often teen transsexuals will tell someone they think they can trust, only to be disappointed and have the person reject them. This forces them further from people, and makes them even less trustful then they were before.

If in therapy the primary goal is to keep the adolescent stable with discussion about what daily steps need attention, delaying the diagnosis and treatment for the sexual diagnosis are also a factor. Obtaining any drug is a problem, but sometimes this group of patients find and take hormones from the street. This can be a dangerous step because there is no control or monitoring of what is being ingested and the result in the body. In our later review of hormone therapy, the list of problems will be explored.

Because the transsexual diagnosis should not be made so early in life, it needs to be noted that the changes brought about by hormones can be difficult to undo.

It is sometimes the case that teens hook up with other teens with problems or sexual identity issues, and as a small band they can get into trouble with the law or with prostitution, drugs, or pornography. If they decide to leave home and have no means of support, they can live on the streets or be prey to very unsavory characters. Being young, and needy, and alone, makes them exceptionally vulnerable to hardship and worse. More education is needed in schools, for example, about these issues. The television talk shows often present the topic but lately seem to be interested only in exploitation and making the topic sensational.

Trying to be the opposite sex doesn't happen by magic. It is a slow process. Attempting to wear make-up, walking in high heels, or being macho when you're born a girl is not easy, and there are no courses for training. Practicing all of these things as a teenager makes the person feel uncomfortable and awkward. A therapist can offer suggestions and comfort, and often another person struggling with a similar issue can be found for friendship. For example, I regularly introduce people with similar backgrounds to one another as support systems.

When the face and body don't look as though they will translate well into the opposite sex, it is very upsetting. This is especially true because the individual cannot change the ultimate goal and may in fact end up quite unattractive, especially the male-to-female. For the female-to-male, the main problem in this area is size, and being a petite man is not the easiest road for anyone to travel, on top of everything else.

A therapist can offer suggestions later about plastic surgery, for example, but not everyone cares to change. The adolescent agonizes about appearance.

There are a few cases where an adolescent will try to force the transition and go to school dressed in the opposite sex clothes, as well as attempt to use the other sex bathrooms. Schools will not allow this, and I know of no therapist who would recommend that this be done. Some people leave school and find work as the opposite sex, and sometimes they are successful for a while. There can be problems if they secured the job under false pretenses. There can also be problems with items such as health insurance. It is not a good idea. One of the sad concerns for therapists is that the fun that should also come with this period of life is frequently lost with young transsexuals. The hurt and suffering serve to make them introspective and compassionate to others.

Even if you as a therapist are positive that the individual is a transsexual, it is prudent to wait until adolescence has passed before moving ahead.

The sex drive is there as with other teens. What is done depends on the person and whatever experimentation they choose. Heterosexual sex, homosexual sex, and masturbation are all tried by this group, depending on their wishes. Some are celibate.

It is not uncommon to see radical changes in behavior from childhood to adolescence, and the docile obedient child can become the raging out-of-control teenager. With the transsexual, most report some changes but not the acting out that is more common in the general population. Their turmoil turns inward, it seems. It is not an easy task for a therapist to be trusted and for the client to share their innermost feelings with a stranger. It requires a great commitment and patience, coupled with a high degree of empathy to connect with a teen transsexual.

By the time people are out of adolescence and become young adults, the decision to proceed with surgery becomes stronger and more clearly identified. Most therapists meet clients who are in their twenties. The majority of surgery is performed on individuals who are in their late twenties or early thirties.

The Standards say that only people of majority or over twenty-one should be considered for surgery. There are some cases where surgery is performed on people over fifty.

By this stage, the person has explored whether they are gay or fit into another category. The first issue is always, "Is there any other way you can live?" The therapist is there to always present options and not just accept the diagnosis from the patient. This is very difficult, because the relationship between therapist and client is crucial and is established from the first meeting. Usually the client is presenting their strong desire to move ahead with the transsexual process, and the therapist is putting on the brakes and challenging this. It makes for a rough beginning.

There are, however, some clients who present themselves with uncertainty, and these cases are easier to work with, because both client and therapist have the same question about what the direction should be. The history is always important, and psychotic people must be referred elsewhere. The people who come to a therapist thinking that transsexual surgery will solve all their life problems need to hear that life and coping issues can be resolved with better means. Those people who have always had unsatisfying relationships need to learn that this surgery is not a magic wand to solve that type of concern.

One very bright client of mine said in a first interview, "Living as a male this way has been half-assed, and after surgery, I'll still be a half-assed woman, so which way do I want to live?" The slow step-by-step exploration of the questions and testing is the task of therapy.

How people deal with the anger and frustration needs to be looked at, and the reality of how therapy, electrolysis, and other costs will be paid for is a big concern. Relationships with family, and friends, and the workplace will be covered in detail later.

The major goal that is never lost sight of is, "Is this an appropriate candidate for surgery? Is this a transsexual?" Every question is looked at and all the road blocks are presented by the therapist. Most individuals have lived in a way that has caused them anguish, and much sacrifice, so the answer for them has already been reached. The therapist buys time by requesting that males have electrolysis, and females cut their hair and dress in a more masculine or unisex fashion.

By making small changes they begin to try the role on for size, and the aim is to eventually have them pass successfully in public and be comfortable in the chosen gender.

None of this is accomplished easily. There are a few people who refuse to move gradually and call family meetings. Then they transform themselves in one fell swoop. While it may seem to be shocking, I can tell you that I have participated in a few of these arrangements and they went exceedingly well, but it is rare. Most families are not as stunned as one might imagine, however, since they have known that the client seemed "different" for years. Once the truth is on the table, they are able to deal with it. Not everyone is accepting, and some take time to come around, but knowing what is happening, while a professional answers questions, is helpful.

The norm, however, is usually to start slowly, and gradually add to the process. It is a process with no time limit. Often the only problems are saving enough money for surgery and living in two worlds. For the male-to-female, we don't like the candidate to be on hormones for years because the penile skin will shrink and there might be less skin with which to construct the vagina. We prefer that they have a plan to pay for surgery within two to five years. Electrolysis should be well under way, so the new female doesn't have facial hair.

For the female-to-male, we don't want bearded ladies, so we hope they have money for bilateral mastectomies before growing facial hair from taking hormones. These are the initial procedures once the diagnosis has been confirmed. An MMPI and other tests, as mentioned earlier, are also used to assist in the assessment. The first procedures are all reversible and cosmetic, such as wearing different clothing, binding the breasts, taping or tucking in the penis, and working on electrolysis or voice therapy. Sometimes hormones can be given to help slow and soften the facial hair for the male-to-female. The usual rule of thumb is to delay hormones as long as possible, because they make irreversible changes which will be discussed later. Basically, they grow breasts in the male-to-female and grow facial hair in the female-to-male, and these are naturally visible to the outside world. The early stage of therapy is difficult because both you and the client are sort of in never-never land exploring step-by-step.

A light doesn't go off but the client decides when they are ready to make a commitment and take the next step, whether that is to tell family or friends, or to start growing nails and wearing pieces of jewelry, for the male-to-female, or to cut hair in a boy's cut for the female-to-male. There are any number of examples of movement, and often clients will move in gingerly, doing something that cannot be seen, such as wearing opposite sex underwear. Often female-to-male people will join a gym and start building up their muscles. The changes can be gradual or move more quickly, depending on the circumstances. Everyone is told that we are not in a rush, and the earliest anyone can have surgery is after living the role fulltime for one year. Most individuals take two to five years.

There are resources to help with mail-order items. These include clothing, shoes, underwear and breast or penis prosthesis equipment. Going into a mall or store to buy make-up or clothing is a big step, and the first trip is monumental. Frequently, transsexuals say they are buying things for other family members, and until they are comfortable and can try things on, clothing size is a guessing game.

One of the real problems is using the dressing rooms or bathrooms in the other gender. In our program, we provide a card stating that the person is part of a gender program and is required to dress in the opposite gender's clothes. Some people have their names and I.D. changed to conform to their desired role. Police and store guards can be understanding or punitive. The legal issues will be addressed in a later section.

For male-to-female clients, it is helpful to carry a woman's type wallet-purse as opposed to a masculine-looking wallet. The opposite is naturally true for the female-to-male clients. Once the initial challenge has been met and the person is having electrolysis, for example, or has cut their hair to a male look, the next step can be taken. This might include voice therapy and cross-dressing in private, or on weekends. It is helpful to have a friend to go out with, whether it's another transsexual, or just an understanding friend.

Dealing with work will be discussed at a later point. Hormone therapy can be considered after therapy has been in process for at least six months, but this should be handled conservatively and it is always an individual matter. The basic minimum might be seeing the therapist once a month, but again that depends on the case and needs.

For the female-to-male, the mastectomies should be done before hormones are begun. Hysterectomy can be done later, and this will be reviewed in the section on surgery. In the case of male-to-female, electrolysis should be completed.

One must bear in mind that while all of these things are happening, the individual must live and work and handle all the business of life that we all deal with on a daily basis. This only demonstrates the strength that transsexual people are required to have.

The clients who cannot deal with all of this may take a break from the transsexual issue and come back to it later. Some drop it forever.

What does the average two-year minimum wait for surgery in a conservative program provide? It forces the person to demonstrate that they can be convincing, and it shows their conviction. It also proves that not all of life's problems are located in or eventually solved by sex reassignment surgery. Basically, a therapist wants to make sure that the individual is not psychotic, or a dual personality (the MMPI helps by giving another perspective from the counseling), and to be sure that the person is not a homophobic homosexual (a homosexual who is afraid of admitting and behaving as a homosexual).

Therapists can be psychiatrists who are medical doctors licensed to write prescriptions, or psychologists or social workers. Psychologists are usually Ph.D. level and give psychological tests as well as counseling. Social workers are usually master's level and are trained in counseling and community resources. The fees can vary from about seventy-five dollars a session to over two hundred. The most important part of counseling is the emotional connection you as a prospective transsexual make with the therapist. If the chemistry is not right, you might consider changing therapists. How often you are seen for counseling depends on the individual case. It can vary most of the time from once a week to once a month to once every other month.

With time and counseling the correct diagnosis will become evident. Being sure that someone is a transgendered or transsexual person is not an easy or a rapid process. This is one arena where the wrong diagnosis is not acceptable for anyone. Therapy asks that the patient try every form of behavior to make sure this is the correct solution and that this drastic surgery is needed in order to live a full life.

Most people resent the fact that someone else is involved in their destiny and choice. By explaining the dramatic no-return nature of these procedures, the therapist makes most people less angry. Some resentment, however, may last a long time. There is what is labeled the "transsexual imperative," making the intensity for immediate hormonal or surgical resolution a problem in counseling. One of the main reasons for this is that many people have lived with this dilemma for years before coming into a program or counseling, so that once they make the move, they feel they are ready and no one should stand in the way of their decision. Often we hear statements like, "It's my body, and my money."

The first step is to help the individual realize that the therapist is there for them and that no major surgery is ever performed without some preliminary testing, whether physical or psychological. Once this hurdle is passed, the work of taking a complete history and understanding the person begins. The early history of identification with one parent and relationship to the other parent is always significant. There are some theories that suggest that there is a predisposition to gender dysphoria that is assisted by the early childhood experiences.

A primary tactic for the therapist at this stage is to look at the defense mechanisms and how this individual has coped and survived this basic problem, as well as other life situations. Support people are identified and work history is reviewed. The more mature and stable the person, the easier it will be to complete the process, as in most therapeutic situations. How compliant the client is will be important. Reinforcing the objective is the role of both client and therapist. Goals are to look at the daily life and to help the person move toward surgical resolution once the diagnosis of Gender Identity Disorder is made. The Diagnostic Statistical Manual (DMSIV) now lists this, rather than the former diagnosis of Transsexualism.

Most typical histories include feeling different as a young child. It is not uncommon to hear reports that a family member, often the parent, has fed into the gender conflict by supporting boys' toys or clothing for their daughter, and vice-versa for their son. If that does not happen, the child will play or dress secretly and no one may know, or more importantly, no one will talk about or acknowledge the problem.

In some families the daughter is seen as a tomboy, but it is harder for a boy to be seen as feminine in most cultures. The hope prior to puberty is that whatever is causing these feelings or behaviors will disappear in time. Frequently this period is seen as normal childhood development, and only if it is pronounced, or if the parents are very attuned and concerned, will the child be seen by a professional. Some pediatricians may counsel parents to wait and see what happens rather than suggest therapy. The rare case of hermaphroditism is not discussed here. Being born with "both sexes" is usually corrected surgically at birth, and usually the child is then considered female.

The next major developmental stage is puberty. It is during this period that the issue becomes more obvious. The fantasies and attractions to the same sex may raise doubt about what the person's sexual orientation is, and many transsexuals believe they are gay or homosexual during this phase. It usually is a time for some sexual acting-out, and this may be frightening when the person feels unsatisfied or tries to copy the opposite sex rather than relate to others of their own gender. Again, being different in this significant way may be hidden and not discussed. The recent movie, *Boys Don't Cry* shows what young transsexual males go through.

This is a most trying time of life for everyone, so that being a transsexual at this stage is one of the worst times imaginable. The normal rebellion and testing that takes place during this period can be pronounced and there may be severe depression, alcohol, or drug abuse. Becoming more independent is also harder.

Some people get into legal difficulty. For most, however, the history includes trying to conform and to be the sex they were born. This can include exaggerating behavior such as dating, sports activity and the like. Dress usually is unisex, and often there is mention of hating their genitals. Because most people learn who they are as they develop in families and then with people on the outside, the transsexual is at a distinct and painful disadvantage. They may be confused for years, then isolated and alone with their secret, or if they are brave and have attempted to share the secret, they may be ostracized or rejected completely. Looking for acceptance and love is a special situation for this group.

In short, every other way of life should be thought about, talked about, or considered, before deciding to have transsexual surgery. It is not just a major life change for an individual but it involves every other relationship in their life. While the numbers of transsexual operations are not huge, the number of people involved, including family, friends, and employers, is quite large. The dilemma is special, and always accompanied by emotional pain and suffering. Experimentation before any final decision is mandatory. The journey is a lonely one and the results are not perfect, but the goal cannot be denied. Difficult losses of family support, friends who cannot accept the problem, and struggles to survive and earn a living are always present. Big emotional prices are paid. Since it is not a choice, the motivation persists and is strong. The compromise when surgery is not affordable is truly awful. It is interesting to note that even with the blurring of sexual roles these days, the need to transform oneself in the case of transgendered people persists. Therapy is there to help.

MEDICAL PROCEDURES FOR MALE-TO-FEMALE PATIENTS

Hormone therapy should only be administered by an endocrinologist, or a physician with special training in treating transgendered people. The gender is determined by the Buccal test, from cells taken from inside the cheek, or other sophisticated tests. Most females are XX and males are XY. Hormone levels are usually normal for both of the sexes at the start of the process. Sometimes there can be abnormalities in the chromosomes. Dr. John Money at the Johns Hopkins School of Medicine has done extensive research in this area.

For males-to-females the procedure is as follows.

The normal levels of testosterone in males range from 350 to 1000 nanagrams per deciliter in the blood. The doctor will give Estradiol at .05 milligrams daily, in pill form, going from one a day to four a day, at three month intervals, until the testosterone level is suppressed to 50. This process can take six to nine months. The costs are about thirty dollars a month, not counting the original physical exam that can be higher in cost. The patient must be followed by a doctor regularly, as blood clots may occur in the legs. This risk is higher if there are varicose veins, or leg injuries such as fractures. Smoking should be stopped to avoid any risk of stroke. There are other rare instances of migraine headaches and liver tumors. All of the risks can be prevented by stopping hormones. If hormones are stopped before surgery, the old levels will return.

Transsexuals take hormones all their lives, but they are usually lowered to half dose after surgery. There are some changes that do not disappear if hormones are stopped, such as breast development. That is another reason for moving slowly to be sure about the choice, as mastectomies will have to be done if the decision was not correct to take hormones. Once hormones are started, the first noticeable change is in breast development. The size is based on genetic factors, so that if the women in the family are large-breasted, there is a good chance that the male-to-female transsexual will be too. It may take up to a year for the final result. While growing, there may be sensitivity and a tingly feeling in the nipples and breasts. Other changes include rounding of the hips, change in muscle mass, softer facial features, and softer hair. Pubic hair patterns will change. If a male is bald there may be hair growth, but it will take a long time. Even after time, a hairpiece or transplant may be needed. Erections will diminish and ejaculations will weaken and be different. Mood swings are often reported. After a fairly short time, most people report feeling happier.

Mannerisms that are second nature to most genetic females have to be practiced. These include walking in female shoes, sitting with legs crossed, and hand movements that appear graceful. Putting on makeup and dress are individual matters of taste, but the general rule of thumb is to look natural, and not stand out and draw attention to yourself. This takes time and practice. Makeup sales people in department stores can be helpful. Going to a hair stylist is also a good idea. Nail polish and jewelry will add a finished touch. A very few males have had their sperm stored for future use.

The primary surgery for a male to female is the creation of a vagina. An HIV test is required, and there should be some thought to donating one's own blood for the needs of the operation. The hospital stay can be five to ten days, and this can cost up to $1300 a day for the hospital bed. Anesthesia is about $1000, and the surgeon's fee can be $6000 for the penectomy. The total operation lasts about three to four hours. The testicles are removed and the penis is cut open, removing the tissue inside but preserving the outside skin. This skin is then tunneled inward to create the vagina. The scrotum is constructed into the labia, or vaginal lips. The prostate is kept. Questions about cancer have been asked; the answer is that the prostate gland is small due to the taking of hormones and therefore is not usually a problem.

COMMON PROCEDURES FOR MALE-TO-FEMALE SURGERY (VAGINOPLASTY)

(The following descriptions are based in part on a comprehensive review article by Drs. Karim, Hage, and Mulder, which appeared in the Annals of Plastic Surgery, v.37, pp. 669-675, in 1996. Thanks to Dr. Anne Lawrence for this summary.)

INVERTED PENILE SKIN FLAP, ABDOMINALLY ATTACHED

This is probably the most commonly used technique. The erectile tissue is removed from the penis through a scrotal incision, leaving the tube of penile skin attached abdominally. The vaginal cavity is created by dissecting a space between the rectum and the bladder, and the inverted penile skin is used to line this space. The penile skin must be pulled downward to reach the vaginal cavity; this usually requires undermining the skin of the pubic area and lower abdomen to allow sufficient stretch. If the amount of penile skin is limited, a free skin graft can be used to lengthen the skin tube, at what will become the apex of the vagina; this graft is typically abdominal skin, or scrotal skin from which the hair has been removed. Gauze packing is used to hold the penile skin in place for approximately one week. The scrotal skin is trimmed to create labia. The shortened urethra is sutured into the correct position, and a urinary catheter is left in place for about one week. A clitoris can be created from erectile tissue at the base of the penis, or from a portion of the glans with its nerves and blood supply intact.

PENILE-SCROTAL FLAP

This is similar to the above, but the abdominally-attached penile skin is split open to produce a rectangular flap. This is combined with a rectangular flap of scrotal skin to create a tube to line the vaginal cavity. This method has the advantage of creating more vaginal depth. The disadvantages are that it places hair-bearing scrotal skin in the vagina (unless the hair has been removed by electrolysis beforehand); and it creates long suture lines in the vagina, which can lead to constriction.

INVERTED PENILE SKIN FLAP, PERINEALLY ATTACHED

This technique was frequently used in the 1970s, but is much less common nowadays. It is also similar to the first-described technique, but the tube of penile skin is left attached on its scrotal side, rather than on the abdominal side. The advantages are that the penile skin tube is located closer to the vaginal cavity, and scrotal tissue can also be used to line the cavity. The disadvantages are: hair in the vagina (unless removed by electrolysis); usually the need for a second-stage procedure to construct the labia; and a less-acceptable cosmetic appearance of the anterior vulva.

RECTOSIGMOID TRANSPLANTATION

In this method, a section of large bowel is used to line the created vaginal cavity. It is most often used following a failed penile-inversion procedure, but some surgeons use it very successfully as a primary technique. After removal of the penile erectile tissue and creation of a vaginal cavity, a segment of bowel, with its blood supply intact, is isolated through an abdominal incision. The open end of this segment is delivered through the vaginal opening and sutured in place. The continuity of the remaining bowel is restored. The use of modern surgical stapling devices makes these tasks easier and faster, but this is still major abdominal surgery. The advantages of this technique, when done as a primary procedure, are: sufficient lining tissue to insure generous vaginal depth; availability of penile skin for construction of the vulva; and sometimes a self-lubricating vagina. The disadvantages include: greater expense; longer hospitalization; possible complications of abdominal surgery, both early and delayed; and sometimes excessive vaginal lubrication.

AFTER SURGERY

For about ten days there is considerable pain, which is controlled with medication. Urination is usually not a problem, as a catheter is placed in the bladder for several days. Bowel activity is more difficult, and hospital personnel can assist with medicine for this issue. Post-operatively there is a large bandage dressing which stays on for about four days. Dressing changes are sometimes done in the operating room. A stent, like a large fat tampon, is placed inside at the time of surgery to keep the vagina open, and this is cleaned each day with soap and water. After healing, it is recommended that the stent be worn at bedtime, perhaps forever. When the bandages are removed, the area looks like two puffy pieces of flesh; but as the swelling subsides and goes down, the genital area looks like any other genetic female's vaginal area. Occasionally there is a problem with the depth of the newly created vagina, and this sometimes can be corrected by using part of the large bowel, as mentioned above. This procedure, colon augmentation vaginoplasty, is the practice for some surgeons. It provides good depth to the new vagina.

A fistula can occur at any time, but if it happens it is usually early, following surgery. This is an opening between two organs, such as the rectum and the new vagina. Food particles would then come out of the vaginal opening. Just giving the bowel a rest by taking only liquids could heal it, or a temporary colostomy might need to be performed. A fistula can also be corrected surgically by having an operation to sew it together.

After discharge from the hospital, a follow-up schedule is recommended. The first visit back to the doctor is in two weeks, then one month, three months, and then as needed. Patients can return to work after four to six weeks and follow their former routine. After at least six to eight weeks, healing should be complete. Intercourse is then medically permitted. Orgasm is possible, because the prostate is left in, and even though it is atrophied, it produces pleasant sensations when rubbed, as in intercourse, and there may be some secretion.

There is some research about a procedure called a clitoroplasty. Basically it uses the glans to form the clitoris, utilizing the blood supply and nerves so that there is erotic sensation. Some problems with depth of the newly created vagina are reported with this method. The current work to improve this surgery should eventually produce a cosmetically good appearance and a functioning organ with sensitivity.

Feminine products sold in drug stores can be bought for more lubrication, if needed. Once all the swelling has disappeared, the new vagina looks and works like a genetic female's. There is no possibility of bearing children.

For the male-to-female, breast implants are available, but there has been much controversy lately over some of these. It is best to find a plastic surgeon who is associated with a teaching hospital to review the options. There should be, as with hormone therapy, an approval letter from a qualified therapist before any surgery is performed. Although the FDA still approves silicone gel, more physicians are recommending saline implants or some newer form of soy oil. The doctor's fee can run from $2500 to $4000, and this is performed as an outpatient procedure. Costs for the hospital will vary. The incision is made under the breasts, and the skin may become hard around the implant, causing scar tissue. As with any surgery, there may be bleeding. Since a foreign body is being put in, infection sometimes occurs. It is rare that infection will cause the implants to be removed.

Other plastic surgery can include re-contouring the face, as men usually have a more prominent bone under their eyebrows. Costs may be about $1500. Some people have their noses shaped using a procedure known as rhinoplasty, which usually requires a one night hospital stay, and the surgeon's fee may be $3000. A chin implant is not thought to be a good idea because the techniques are not perfected yet, but chin contouring can be performed as an outpatient and can cost about $2500. Cheek implants are fairly common and cost about $2500; they are also done as an outpatient procedure.

If a male wishes to become a female, the pre-surgical steps are as follows. A qualified therapist should know the patient for at least six months, and electrolysis should be under way. Cross-dressing should be done regularly, although this may not be able to be done at work. Most conservative programs require an MMPI (Minnesota Multiphasic Personality Inventory) and perhaps the Beck Depression

Scale. Electrolysis can take about two years for a moderate beard, and the cost can be about three thousand dollars. A new method called epilight is now also available. It uses light, and an average face can be done in about four sessions at an average cost of $700.00 a session. Epilight is usually performed in a plastic surgeon's office.

There are several standard methods available today, which include galvanic electrolysis, thermolysis, and the blend. A combination of computerized epilator machines that use thermolysis and the blend seem to do a good job. The outcome of the process can depend a great deal on the skill of the practitioner. The newer laser technique does not seem to be perfected as yet. It seems to be a temporary and painful method at this point in time. With the best process, ten percent of facial hair may grow back and have to be redone. Body hair may also need work. Only a licensed person should be used, as that will prevent scarring. There is some pain involved. I have heard of some patients taking medical shots such as dentists use to avoid the pain. In large cities, many beauty salons have people who do this work, and often they have had experience with transsexuals. I have little information about do-it-yourself techniques now being sold.

Some individuals may require voice therapy in order to be convincing. Sometimes one or two visits can offer help in learning how to modulate your voice. Practice is necessary. Large universities usually have students in their voice therapy programs who can help and are not so costly. Hormones, once begun, may help a bit but they will not change the voice significantly. Some people have large Adam's apples and they choose to have a surgical procedure called a laryngeal shave.

When a couple has been married prior to surgery, they usually must be divorced prior to surgery, but some states are changing this law. Some surgeons will accept a notarized letter from an attorney stating that the couple plans to continue to be married after surgery.

MEDICAL PROCEDURES FOR FEMALE-TO-MALE PATIENTS

For the female-to-male the same rule applies about going to an endocrinologist for hormone therapy. The average Estradiol level in females ranges from 20 to 60 picograms per milliliter in the blood in the early phase of the menstrual cycle. It can peak to 200 at the time of ovulation. Testosterone, 50 milligrams to start and going up to 200 milligrams, is given by injection every two weeks, until the menstrual period stops. This can take about four months. Injections continue every two weeks for life, and people can give them to themselves. A physician should be consulted regularly. The cost is about thirty dollars per month. Some common problems include facial acne, baldness, if this runs in the family, and, rarely, liver poisoning. Acne can be dealt with by a dermatologist. Other problems may be helped by lowering the dosage of hormones. Major changes include increased facial and body hair, changes in pubic hair patterns, coarser facial skin, and increased muscle mass. The voice may deepen. There may be mood swings and more aggressive feelings. Many people join a gym or try to build up their bodies. Other mannerisms of typical males can be practiced, such as walking and sitting, which take a different form from those of women. Style and dress are again individual, but the main thing is to blend in and not look unusual. Most people enjoy their new look and grow beards or mustaches.

Mastectomy and hysterectomy will be discussed next. These should be done after hormone therapy because surgery is permanent. Some people bind their breasts, but if they are too large, mastectomy should be considered around the same time as hormone therapy because no one wants to be a bearded lady. The patient will become sterile, but if hormones are stopped the patient will no longer be sterile after about six months.

Mastectomies are not covered by insurers unless you have an unusual private policy. The primary reason is that healthy tissue is removed, and until transsexualism is deemed a necessary reason for surgery, most medical insurers will not cover the costs involved. It is a difficult task for most physicians to remove healthy tissue under any circumstances. Some states have agreed to pay for transsexual surgery under Medicaid when the individual is in a program and two mental health professionals have stated in writing that surgery is necessary. One of the letters must be from a person at the doctoral level. Bilateral subcutaneous mastectomies are performed in hospitals and usually require a one night stay. The hospital costs will vary, as will the cost for anesthesia. In a large city hospital it may cost about $2000 for the hospital and anesthesia. The surgeon's fee may vary from $3500 to $4500, on average, depending on the size of the breasts and the complexity of the case. For small breasts the actual surgery may last up to one hour.

A small incision is made within the areola and tissue is removed, fat is contoured, and there are rarely any noticeable scars after healing takes place. In large-breasted women a reduction mammoplasty type incision is required. The nipple and areola are temporarily removed and then tissue is taken out. The skill of the plastic surgeon is important, as the nipple and areola must be grafted back and be even with one another. This operation can last two and a half hours. There is more scar tissue, and it may take a year or a year and a half for the breasts to look well. It is possible that problems can occur if the nipples become too flat or if the skin becomes lighter in color. Usually there is a quarter inch scar, slightly raised, when the area is fully healed. The surgery is not too painful and any pain is controlled with medication. Everyone has a drain from the breast area following the operation. This is a plastic-like tube with its own vacuum which remains in for three days, until the doctor removes it. After a week, the physician removes the stitches. There is a two to three week convalescence. During this time there should be no lifting or strenuous activity. There is rarely any major problem after surgery. During the first twenty-four hours, patients are watched for hematoma, wound separation, or bleeding. Most people are pleased with the results and happy not to have to hide their breasts any longer, or to stay away from the beach, for example.

A hysterectomy is usually performed on female-to-male patients any time after six weeks following the mastectomies. An abdominal hysterectomy is performed by making an incision three inches to the right or left of the navel. This is done so as not to destroy tissue that will later be used to construct the penis and contain the penile prosthesis, if one is used. The incision is a lateral one from the navel to the pubic area. The reason vaginal hysterectomies are not done is that it is harder to remove a non-dropped uterus and ovaries, which is often the case if the individual has never had children. The uterus, ovaries, and Fallopian tubes are removed, as well as the upper third of the vagina. The hospital stay is from four to six days. One day in a hospital can cost $1300, and anesthesia can cost $1000. The cost for the use of the operating room could be another $1500. The doctor's fee could be $2400. Some medical insurance policies may cover gender dysphoria, and if so, this operation may be covered. There is moderate pain for two days which is handled with medication, and mild pain for three to ten days. Patients are told not to walk stairs and not to lift more than ten pound items, for two weeks. They are asked not to drive or return to work for three weeks. Wound infections or skin separations are rare, but if they do occur, antibiotics are administered and the drain that is in the patient is made secure. The physician will see patients after four weeks to make sure that healing is taking place and to be sure there is no hernia. Since most patients have been taking testosterone for at least six months, the ovaries are small and inactive. The androgen in the male hormone will promote healing. There may be an increased risk for heart disease, as the cholesterol level is altered. This needs to be checked and can be regulated by diet, medication, and exercise. As might be surmised, there is decreased risk for breast, ovarian, cervical, or uterine cancer. Most patients are relieved after surgery and few experience depression.

For females-to-males, there are a number of operations. However, in some states you are legally declared male if you have had mastectomies and a hysterectomy, and live as and declare yourself a male. All prices will vary depending on the physician, program, and place chosen for surgery. Price should never be the only factor when making such an important decision. Surgery can be listed as SRS (Sex Reassignment Surgery) in any number of publications.

COMMON PROCEDURES IN FEMALE-TO-MALE SURGERY

PEDICLE FLAP

One primary procedure is the pedicle flap. The first surgery is the vaginectomy, where the vagina is removed. This is the first stage for the creation of the penis, or phalloplasty. Skin is taken from the abdomen and inner thighs and made into the form of a penis. It is attached on the abdomen with skin grafts around it for protection. At the same time, the testicular prosthesis is sewn on. Urination is performed as usual and a catheter is inserted for five days. The hospital stay is about five to ten days, which can be up to $1300 a day, plus operating-room costs of about $1500 and anesthesia for about $1000. The operation takes three or four hours and the surgeon's fee may be about $5000. A few patients require some blood transfusion, and in such cases it is recommended that your own blood be banked prior to surgery. This can be one or two units. This should be discussed when plans are initially made for any operation.

After at least six months, the second stage of the surgery can proceed. This is the urethroplasty. This operation allows urination to occur through the end of the new penis. At this point the new phallus is released from the abdomen and a catheter is inserted. The operation can last two to three hours and the hospital stay is about one week. The surgeon's fee is around $5000. There is less pain with this stage, and again, the risks include infection or a fistula. The catheter is removed prior to discharge, and there is close medical follow-up after the hospital stay. While there is discomfort for about two weeks, this surgery is not as difficult as the first stage. A return to work is possible after the two week check-up. Following that, a check-up is usually required at four, six and ten weeks after the surgery.

After at least six months, a penile prosthesis can be inserted with a hospital stay of about five days. The two most common types currently used include a semi-rigid one that is flexible and comfortable and can be used for intercourse for life. It is basically two semirigid cylinders inserted into the phallus. Once in place, the penis can be bent up for intercourse or bent down, close to the body, when not engaging in intercourse. It is always semi-rigid and comfortable for both functions, up or down. The other type is similar but includes an inflatable pump. This has four components, which include the placement of two cylinders in the phallus, a reservoir filled with cystoconray in the pelvis in the space of retsius, and a pump in the scrotum. These components are all connected so that when the pump is squeezed, the fluid in the reservoir is released and fills the cylinders, making the penis erect. When the individual wants the fluid to go back to the reservoir, he squeezes a release valve that causes the erection to go down. The inflatable type is often difficult to do in transsexuals; it is primarily used for men with impotency problems. The surgeon's fee for both of these operations described is about $5000, plus the cost for the hospital stay, operating room and anesthesia. All costs mentioned in this book are approximations that may or may not be accurate with any program or physician, so all fees must be checked.

Problems can occur, such as infection, which is treated with antibiotics; erosion; or perforation. The last two have to be treated surgically and may require removal of the prosthesis until the area heals in order to have it inserted again. There is not much pain with these procedures. The cosmetic affect is genuine-looking and most patients are pleased with the results. The ability to urinate through the penis is a positive factor.

Intercourse is described as pleasurable. In research that Dr. Harold Lief and I conducted, most of the males reported feeling orgasmic but said it was different from what they had experienced as females. The new penis had no feeling, so much of the response came from other parts of the body, even though the clitoris was saved. There is no ejaculation and no semen and therefore no ability to father children. This research did not include the radial forearm flap or procedures to free the clitoris.

RADIAL FOREARM FLAP

Another type of surgery is being performed for the construction of the penis. It is microsurgery and requires a high degree of technology. This is the radial forearm flap.

First there is a hysterectomy, oophorectomy, and vaginectomy, with urethral lengthening. This requires about a three-day hospital stay. After about three to six months, the next procedure is performed. This one takes skin and underlying tissue, including arteries and nerves, from inside the arm above the wrist to the elbow. This skin is then formed into a penis. This procedure can take up to twelve hours and usually requires a week in the hospital. A neoscrotum is formed from the vaginal lips. Patients with this type of surgery are able to urinate through the end of the new penis. This penis has sensation and looks genuine.

The risks are about five percent risk of loss of the flap, urinary fistula, and stricture. A scar will remain on the arm for life. Some surgeons have been able to decrease the scars by stretching the skin first. It can look like a bad burn, if skin grafts are used on the arm. Patients report sensitivity with their new penis after four to six months. This is due to the fact that sensation in the clitoris is transferred to the head of the penis with a nerve graft. Patients must have electrolysis in the vaginal area before surgery. This can be very painful.

Later there can be a permanent penile implant inserted as an option of phalloplasty, but many report mechanical failure with them. A pump method is also an option, for erection.

METAIDOIOPLASTY OR GENITOPLASTY

The third type of female-to-male surgery is the metaidoioplasty or genitoplasty. This is using the clitoris after it has hopefully been enlarged by the hormone therapy. The surrounding skin is freed and wrapped around the existing clitoris. At best, the new penis will be about two inches long. There is a secondary procedure to allow standing to urinate. The labia majora can be made to form a scrotum, and silicone testicles can be placed in the scrotum. If this procedure is done, any other type of phalloplasty will be more difficult. In this method the feelings and sensations are preserved with the nerves in place. The appearance is good but small.

Problems may occur, such as grafts not taking. There is a possibility that the testicular prosthesis may erode out from the neoscrotum and may need to be removed, to be redone at a later time. There is also the possibility of a fistula, as with the male-to-female surgery, occurring on the new phallus, which would require additional repair surgery. Infections are fairly common and they are treated with antibiotics and soaks. The bandage dressing put on in the operating room is changed after four days and there may be quite a bit of pain. This can be handled with medication. As the area heals, there can be skin tightening, which hurts and may cause difficulty in walking. There is some discomfort for about six weeks. Patients are told not to return to work for at least two weeks, which is after their check-up visit occurs. Photographs of completed surgery from a variety of surgeons can be seen in this text.

RELATIONSHIPS: PERSONAL AND IN THE WORKPLACE

To talk about relationships could take a lifetime. The nuances of human behavior in interaction with others are not static, and a variety of changes take place individually and in concert with other people. While all people share a common path, the road for the transsexual is unique, and this issue can be injected into the pattern at any point. Some families are aware very early that there is something wrong. Some people are aware as very young children that they are different. Some families deny or truly don't see the situation clearly for years, and so too for the individual.

The most significant relationships, and those that set the stage for all to come, begin when we are not even aware of their influence, in childhood, in our families. The maturity of parents, the quality of their marriage, the stability of income, and their capacity to nurture, all combine to lay the foundation. There is no perfect family, but some are indeed better for child-rearing than others. To put the needs of the child first is not easy, and we are not taught how to parent. Major problems such as alcohol or drug abuse, inability to deal constructively with anger, conflict resolution, and others cause distress and heartache for many family members. Young children are victims of the families into which they are born. Parents become the examples of what men and women are all about.

Two crucial questions are, "Did the parents want this child?" and "Is this the sex child they preferred?" If the child reminds them of themselves or of someone they love, that may be a favored child. Adopted children have a different history and are often spoiled; thus they frequently do not have limits.

How we get along with others goes back to our earliest childhood, and relationships with parents and siblings program the future, especially emotionally. A factor that also contributes to who we are and how we present ourselves to others is traced back to our place in the family. The special, experimental child, is the first-born. The hopes and dreams of the parents are projected onto this child and most have strong egos. Most first-born children are successful in life.

Sometimes they are selfish and demanding. An only child in a family is similar, only more so.

Middle children learn how to negotiate and get along with people. They are not the special first or the precious last, and often they struggle to be noticed and to get a spotlight on themselves. Some dress or behave in a way that draws attention. They are often quite contented with what life offers.

The baby of the family has a difficult time becoming mature. Parents like to keep baby as a baby. These people often want others to make decisions for them, and they do not take kindly to responsibility. Often they think they deserve everything just because they exist. They can play the adorable baby throughout their lives.

All of us learn how to react from what we experience in our families. These reactions are later called our defenses. They are the ways that we cope. One way is to avoid what we don't like. Some fight, while some find other releases for strong emotions. Whatever we have learned in those early years stays for life. What therapy can do is to put the person in touch with their history and how they got to be the way they are. The emotional responses usually are imprinted from the earliest years, but once we understand the background we can try to change the reactions and behavior we don't like. When therapists help clients to develop insight, it is a great feat and the joy is shared.

As I have said, an important facet of early development that affects our relationships later in life is the role we play in our families of origin. Some of this is based on the place we hold in the family, as I described above; another is a result of our personality. There is a theory that we come with a type of personality and the family responds to what we bring. We have all heard about what we were like as babies: loud, sickly, shy, and so on. As a direct result of what we bring, we are assigned a role. Some people are leaders, some are clowns to entertain the family, and some are peacemakers. There are an infinite number of roles, and they can change from time to time as we change or family circumstances are altered. The roles we learn in childhood are difficult to shed. The primary role is acted out again and again in other relationships outside the family.

The manner in which we deal with authority is transposed from what went on in the family. The ways in which we try to please or obtain acceptance and love are also a repetition of the emotional pattern we learned early.

Since there is no perfect family, we all have issues and areas that we would like to change. Some can do it on their own and others can benefit from therapy, but it is not a fast or easy program. With transsexuals there are a number of special considerations. First, they do not conform to the image of the "ideal" child that most parents have. They are not clear in their sense of self as a boy or girl, and that confusion translates into family relationship problems.

The female-to-male patients are often seen as "tomboys" and treated as young boys, especially by fathers. It is harder for the male-to-female children, because acting feminine as a boy is seen as shameful. Often this comes out around the issue of sports. The family does not welcome what they perceive to be a "gay" boy. Most families believe that the situation will turn around with time, and that it is just a passing phase. Other families try to secure professional help. It is important to mention here that finding a therapist skilled in these areas is of utmost importance. Some therapists can give wrong or hurtful messages if they do not have experience in the field of human sexuality coupled with family dynamics.

In some rare cases, infants are diagnosed as hermaphrodites, having some organs of both sexes. Usually this condition is corrected surgically at birth. It is common for pediatricians to be the first professionals to know that something is wrong, but in any number of cases, nothing is diagnosed or brought out into the open until puberty or later. Puberty makes a good bit of this more obvious. The person resents the development of secondary sexual characteristics, breast development, hair growth, and so on.

The fantasies and attractions may be to the same sex, and this leads to wondering if they are homosexual. It is usually a time for some sexual acting out, and this may be frightening. Individuals report being unsatisfied, feeling disgusting, and preferring to copy the opposite sex rather than being emotionally involved with them. Being so different from others during adolescence is a very lonely experience. It is then that most people cling to one another. It is a trying time of life for anyone, but for the transsexual it is horrendous.

Most report in their histories that they try to conform. They try to please parents. They try to date the opposite sex, and they try to be as they were born. Some even exaggerate in order to try to force the issue. But it just never feels right. If they come for therapy during this phase, the goal is to help the individual adjust and cope and try all other styles of life, not fixing on a diagnosis of transsexual yet. If family can be involved to understand and be supportive, it can be helpful.

Dress can be unisex during this period, and some try to hide their breasts or penis. Binding the breasts is common, and tucking in or taping the penis back is reported. There are mail-order houses for appliances to help with this. Many people report trying to trust someone with their secret during the teen years, often to be ridiculed or rejected. This only reinforces the image of being strange and causes people to retreat and bury the secret deeper. Being ostracized and misunderstood during adolescence is a hurtful wound that can remain forever. To remain with the choice to proceed takes special courage and strength. This is often accomplished alone.

Once past the teen years, people tend to concentrate on career, or job, and their love life. For the transsexual, both of these areas are fraught with concern and trepidation. Love relationships are a major part of everyone's life, but are scariest for those with gender confusion. All people look for a safe haven where they can love and be loved, but for the transsexual the question of who they are and how they can relate intimately with another carries an unusual weight.

For some, the beginning may appear to be homosexual. The true transsexual will tell you they feel and see themselves as the opposite sex. Whether they share that with their partner is an individual matter. Usually by the early twenties, the person knows they are transsexual and that the only solution to their painful existence is corrective surgery. To actually have the surgery, the youngest anyone can usually be is twenty-one, and that is rare. The cost makes it a problem, and it is not a good idea to start hormones and live in a halfway role for a long time.

Male-to-female people usually look for females to copy and talk with, and frequently after time they can open up and share their situation. While many do have intimate relationships with males, they feel they are female and will not allow the partner to touch their genitals. As a result they have an unfulfilled sex life, often for years. Many masturbate or have wet dreams. Once they start hormones, the erections become rubbery and the ejaculations diminish.

Some partners are told and do in fact understand. Some cases include the partner paying for the surgery and even living with the "new" female after surgery. It is not so easy for marriage in this group. When partners are not told the circumstances, they can become angry or violent upon discovering the truth. They thought they had a gay partner and that is what they want.

Some "female" individuals have prostituted themselves, and again, if honesty is not there, it can be a dangerous situation. Some say this is necessary to pay for surgery. The role of the therapist, again, is to guide the patient and help them look at the choices and their consequences. The background history will help provide insight, and the aim is to assist with self image and constructive goals.

The therapist should be able to provide information about the surgery, places for help, and means for dealing with stress. The need for patience is surely tested with this slow process. It must always be stated that this is a process and no quick decisions are made; the ultimate decision will be made by the client. To test that this is the right and therefore only way this person can continue to live a successful life is the justified end. In some cases, clients will remain celibate and lead a solitary, emotionally devoid life. The risk is too great for them to share. Work becomes their refuge or they find other activities to occupy themselves.

In a number of rare cases, people change their sex and still continue with same sex partners, being homosexual after surgery. Again, this is not a sexual problem but an identity change. It is not at all uncommon for males-to-females to want to test out their attractiveness, and they can spend a great deal of time learning how to dress, putting on makeup, jewelry and the like. In an effort to be sought after by males, they can go to extremes. The goal is to blend in with the crowd and not stand out. Sometimes in the beginning they like to be gawked at and they flirt. This can be dangerous if they are put into a compromising situation and a male thinks he has been duped by a male acting like a female.

Going out with a stranger alone, dancing closely, drinking, are all risky situations. It is better not to put oneself in a potentially harmful set of circumstances. Going to places like malls can be good for affirmation; however, before one is passing well, young teen boys especially can say nasty things when they think someone is cross-dressing.

The question of when to tell someone the circumstances is perhaps the most touchy of all. By and large, most people have handled this as they do other aspects of their lives. If they are very forthright, they tend to tell their story almost immediately. Others wait until they feel comfortable and trust the other person will understand. If a relationship has gotten to a point where the individuals believe they are becoming close, there is a risk of loss if the truth is not told. It is harder to lose someone at that point as opposed to before a relationship has progressed. For males-to-females this is a very painful issue. Males have a hard time being close to a "former" male.

In the female-to-male group the circumstances are also unique but in different ways. This group also wants to conform to the stereotypes that society has set up, and again they can exaggerate what they believe to be their maleness. With time and practice they need to blend in with mannerisms, some as simple as how men sit as well as dress. While some of the roles have changed in America, the traditional ones seem to remain. Men can be sensitive and cry, for example, but it is still more common for men to hold back and not talk about or share their feelings as easily as women.

Even with all the talk and literature about roles and work, men still seem to dominate in their families and in society. Men hold more positions of leadership and are the primary decision-makers. Males still see themselves as the main wage earners and the physically and emotionally strong ones.

Transsexuals are frequently surprised to learn the societal differences after they move about in their new world. "Females" report being afraid to go out alone at night, and "males" report new freedoms. Females-to-males like to grow facial hair and work out in gyms building muscle mass.

It is often the case that new "males" become aggressive in behavior and words. Most have girlfriends, and often these relationships last after surgery and many go on to marry. It is easier for the "male" to go out alone and meet women. Again, telling the truth is important and not as risky or dangerous for this group. It seems to also be easier for this group to continue to move up or change jobs. There appears to be less discrimination.

Intimate relationships are another story and one that is intricately involved. Most, if not all, people want to find love and find a safe haven to give love. This becomes a major dilemma for the transsexual. First of all there is the question of who am I, followed by who will accept me as I am? Usually by the early twenties the person believes they have an answer, and that answer is corrective surgery. Sometimes people take longer to really define themselves as transsexual. Others are not even aware that such surgery exists.

Male-to-female people look for female friends to talk with and copy. They may be attracted to males but do not want to be in homosexual relationships. Some do become involved with males but never feel their behavior is homosexual. The partner may or may not accept this. Other people report that they will have sex with their male partner but do not want their own genitals touched. As a result, their own sex drive and fulfillment is rarely achieved. Some masturbate or have wet dreams, but the hormones cause the erections and ejaculations to diminish.

Partners may be understanding, and a number of cases are recorded where the partner paid for the transsexual surgery and later married the new female. More often than not, however, the male partner is gay and wants the transgendered partner to remain male. If the partner is not told, there may be a relationship that endures for a long time without honesty. In some instances, patients have prostituted themselves, and they usually say they do this for money to pay for surgery.

The role of the therapist is always to guide the patient in looking at the available choices and their consequences. Insight into why certain behavior is going on can be helpful in many cases. While any qualified therapist can offer counseling services, there are some areas of special need that this population presents. Background in human sexual development and behavior is extremely important, as well as specific knowledge about transsexualism and the Benjamin Standards. The details of surgical procedures are necessary pieces of information, and the special emotional stress that patients and their families undergo must be understood. Since this is a slow process, the need for patience and step by step movement is critical. Acceptance of the individual and their struggle cannot be emphasized enough. Therapists who are certified by AASECT, (American Association of Sex Educators, Counselors, and Therapists) and AAMFT (American Association of Marriage and Family Therapy), are usually well trained.

A large number of people remain celibate, are not able to engage in close relationships with the opposite sex, and therefore avoid social contact. There is an interesting theory that states that if the individual prefers the same sex as themselves before surgery, they will do well after surgery. This however does not hold true for those people, mainly male-to-female, who prefer to be lesbian after surgery. Being celibate is quite frustrating for people, especially if their sex drive is pushing them forward and they are unable to express this important part of themselves. Being a contented human being usually includes being sexually content. This is a powerful life force, especially in the late teens and through middle age. It may diminish in later years.

While SRS surgery is not primarily for the sexual life of the individuals seeking it, sex is an important part of life. The little research that has been done and my own anecdotal experience confirm that a reasonably good sex life is possible after people have this surgery.

Frequently, male-to-female people want to test out their sexuality and attractiveness, and they spend much time in order to look good. They are attractive and sought after. There is always the insecurity about comparing how they look with both genetic females and other transsexuals. Again, some people are sensitive about different parts of themselves. The hands, feet, height, voice, face, and hair are all special points of concern.

When men are encountered in social situations, the atmosphere can become strained because the question becomes how far to go and what to say. Usually it is best to go out socially with at least one other person so that there is no chance for a dangerous situation to get out of hand. There have been cases where the male looking for a date has pressed until the transsexual had to excuse herself and get away from the person. Other situations need to be maneuvered, such as close dancing and being alone or going home with a stranger. If the male believes he has a female date and then discovers that this is not the case, there is a risk of anger and even violence. It is best not to put oneself in potentially harmful or dangerous situations, especially prior to surgery.

An interesting question often occurs as to why anyone would choose to be female in a predominantly male-controlled society. Again, this is not a choice.

As with the female group of transsexuals, being intimately social before surgery is risky. When dating, it is about the same difficulty level for the male to meet and decide how far to go with someone as for the female, but there is usually less physical risk of danger if the female finds out this is not a genuine male.

As with any relationship, the factors of self-esteem, ability to trust and communicate openly, and resolving differences constructively are what makes couples compatible. There are, to be sure, many relationships that are immature and destructive, that people cannot change. However, many of these relationships can last and be satisfying to those who live them. Only the people involved know what life is like for them and only they can decide how they choose to live. Outsiders always pass judgment, and this is especially sensitive for transsexuals in relationships. Again, it takes great strength and perhaps professional help to withstand this aspect of living. Sometimes ethnic or racial differences may play a role, and any therapist dealing with couples or individuals must be aware of the messages and standards that the particular group values.

One of the delicate issues facing a partner of a transsexual is the issue of authenticity. Since the role is not one the transsexual was born into, there is always some concern about being genuine, and as "good" as a genetic male or female. A great deal of time and emotional energy is spent on this, and reinforcing "passability." Along with this, there is the concern about being loved and appreciated as the desired sex. This may be exaggerated on the part of the patient as well as the partner. As a result, this may cause major problems, as the relationship may then become one-sided, artificial, and forced. With time and discussion, many of these areas can be openly shared. It is helpful if the partner can learn to devote more time to everyday issues, as opposed to spending the majority of the time discussing issues relating to transsexuality.

One of the topics that is common for couples to argue about is former relationships or current flirtations. This often seems more pronounced with this group than with general marriage counseling couples. Being jealous and threatened is more pronounced in these couples. Perhaps it relates to the basic insecurity of the transsexual role, which takes time and experience to work out well. A partner who understands this does not have to be caught up in the dilemma or threatened. As with most situations, being empathetic will help. This does not mean that the partner must do all the work to make the relationship satisfying. The transsexual should be held accountable for their part of the team. Teasing out the other issues rather than only using the transsexual concern is most important here, otherwise it can become a copout and the real issues can be avoided. To be sure, the transsexual has a particular sore spot, but it is not an excuse for everything that goes wrong in a relationship that is supposed to be loving.

It is interesting to note that partners are especially wary of the past relationships that their transsexual lovers have had. Often these past lovers remain friends, and it is a cause of dissension for many couples. The friendships remain because they have usually shared a basic secret and they are bound together in significant ways. If the current partner can be made to feel that they are the primary person and the past is past, the situation should not become dangerous emotionally. There is also the added burden of those people who have had both same sex and opposite sex lovers. Here the partner is doubly worried about what the preferred sex partner will be. Again, it is incumbent upon the transsexual to reassure their partner about their feelings.

Only a brief note here about AIDS and safe sex, as the media has done an excellent job of education. Any direct sexual behavior should include the protection of a condom and all persons should be tested for the virus. There are also other sexually transmitted diseases, and a physician should discuss and test for these.

Anyone who saw the film *The Crying Game* saw the potential for a caring relationship between a straight man and a transsexual female.

It was an example of the triumph of the human connection beyond the problem of gender. There are many other such examples, both public and private.

After over thirty years as a counselor, I have seen that in any long term relationship, it takes hard work to have it remain satisfying. There are no magic or quick, easy solutions to problems and changes. In many relationships the sexual life serves as a release of tension and binds couples to one another. This can be the case here too, but the more important aspect is the closeness that the two people share beyond the sexual bond. Touching and holding are also physical acts.

When it comes to issues such as marriage, each state's laws must be examined. I believe that a partner who is not honest about their history will have a difficult time in any marriage, as the basis of such a relationship should be trust. If the transgendered partner has not disclosed this fact before marriage, and it is discovered later, I believe this might be grounds for annulment or unequal property settlement.

Raising children as a transsexual, as well as custody issues, can be a legal as well as an emotional roller-coaster. Again, no one rule applies and each case is judged differently, based on the particular facts of the family. In my practice, transsexual parents have been both given and denied rights. The only research that has been done on children of transsexuals seems to imply that these children are no better or worse off than children without a transsexual parent. The many other factors that go into child-rearing must be considered. The two most important factors affecting this issue seem to be the age of the child and the strength of the child to withstand what the outside world may say about their transsexual parent. The child who is not able to comprehend the change may be confused and this may cause problems in their own sexual identification. It might be better to protect and shield the child who is under ten, depending on their maturity, from dealing with the issue at all. Once the child is old enough to understand what is happening and the parent does not want to hide their new identity, then a counselor might talk with both parents, followed by an opportunity for professional counseling for the child.

Teen-aged boys seem to have great difficulty with this issue. Again, many factors will determine the outcome, but more often than not a parent who is perceived as loving will eventually be accepted by their child. If the spouse is angry and bitter, sometimes the children become the foil and their way of getting back at the hurt they believe the transsexual partner has inflicted on them. This is always a sorry state of affairs and much emotional pain is felt by all involved. The transsexual parent who is denied rights to see or be involved in the regular life of their children should try to keep in touch through the phone or by writing. In some extreme cases a break in the relationship does occur, and again, sometimes this is reversed with time.

Transsexuals often pay a heavy emotional price to be who they are. Some families stay together "for the sake of the children" for a while. Other families stay together until the partner can earn a living and move out on their own. In some cases, children tell lies about the missing parent to avoid the shame or derision that other children may display. Other children are able to deal with it up front.

SOME LEGAL ISSUES

Once past adolescence, people tend to concentrate on their jobs and love life. For the transsexual, both of these areas are fraught with concern and trepidation.

Finding work — no matter how skilled — may not be the problem, but camaraderie and friendship in the workplace is. Most transsexuals report the shame of coworkers talking behind their backs, and in many cases being quite obvious in wanting to observe them. Using the bathroom is an especially tricky situation. If the individual passes, it is easier. While most laws now prevent people from being fired because of gender dysphoria, some instances have been reported where the employer made the atmosphere so distasteful that it was impossible for the person to work. For a time the disabilities program protected this group, but that may be modified now. Therapists can be supportive and helpful with this issue, but the daily strength it takes to compete under these conditions becomes super-human. The best results seem to occur when the patient is able to talk to their boss or supervisor and appeal to their understanding for support. If that can happen, the road is much easier. Just having one person at work to talk to will also be the thing that gets people through this aspect of their life.

As with many other situations, the people who know the least about a topic are the most curious and afraid. When patients have been able to educate a few people at their jobs, they have gained unusual acceptance and support. Sometimes this is best done after work hours by inviting a coworker for a drink or dinner and then explaining the situation. By trusting instincts, most people can probably pick out someone who might want to be a friend. If the cross-over has not occurred, there may be a good reason to change jobs after the change of dress and name, when passing is no problem.

The decision to come out is done differently for each individual. For the male-to-female, usually it is a gradual process, starting with an earring, a bit of make-up or unisex manner of dressing. How and when in a person's life this occurs is unique. Some people just get tired of the charade. Others bite the bullet and let the chips fall where they may. Others are shy and move very slowly and painfully each step of the way. There is no right or wrong way. A therapist can be supportive, giving encouragement and helpful suggestions, and this will give the client strength to proceed.

People have made the change every possible way, from living and working in the same place to moving where no one knows them. Again, it is always a good idea to know someone who is going through the same process, or someone who has walked the same road. Support groups or therapists can supply names or people to be there for you. Some resources will be listed later in this book.

The basic rule is that if the individuals conduct themselves well, they will be treated well or they will deal with whatever problems arise. If the job is being performed, that should be the bottom line. There are frequently transsexuals who are professionals, and others who own their own businesses. The thought to bear in mind here is that people pay for skills and service, not for gender. Often during early phases of transition, the changing from one gender to the other, from work to home, becomes too difficult. It should be gradual, but some have chosen to just change all at once. If you look the part it's usually fine, but if you look exaggerated, then there can be problems. Drawing unnecessary attention to oneself is not a good idea.

By talking to key people in any organization and bringing a picture of yourself dressed as the sex into which you are changing, you can often break the ice and explain the situation. Those people who wish to ask questions should be given the opportunity. Explanations should be done with all levels of personnel, and those who cannot accept the change can be ignored.

The main issue will be how you face the world; if it is with dignity and fairness, others will take their cue from you. The old image from bad television programs which only wanted to sensationalize the issue made people believe that all transgendered people were freaks. Dispelling this negative image is the goal.

The International Conference on Transgender Law and Employment Policy Inc. is an agency dealing with legal issues pertaining to the transsexual community. They present an annual conference in August in Houston. The proceedings are published and widely distributed. The following policies are from recent meetings.

International Conference On Transgender Law And Employment Policy, Inc.
P.O. Drawer 1010
Cooperstown, New York 13326
(607) 547-4118
A Non-Profit 501CX
Pursuing Justice And Equality For Transgendered People The World Over

ICTLEP's Mission:

1. To undertake educational activities relating to laws affecting the transgender community.
2. To study existing laws and provide strategies for progressive changes that provide relief from discriminatory legislation affecting the transgender community.
3. To provide information to educate the general public, and the legal profession, about legal issues unique to the transgender community.

Please Note:

ICTLEP does not provide direct legal assistance, counsel or representation to individuals or organizations.

ICTLEP does provide a lawyer referral service for those seeking legal services. See Services and Project Activities below.

ICTLEP's Tax Exempt Status

The International Conference On Transgender Law and Employment Policy, Inc. (ICTLEP) is a non-profit Texas corporation. ICTLEP is funded entirely by donations and income from publications and services. Please help ICTLEP help transgendered people, their families and their friends, in the pursuit of justice and equality.

ICTLEP is exempt from federal income tax under Internal Revenue Code section 501 C (3). Donations to ICTLEP are tax deductible.

Contributions should be made payable to "ICTLEP" and forwarded to the address above. ICTLEP financial reports are available on request to the Corresponding Secretary.

Donors are invited to inquire about monthly pledge contributions automatically debited to the contributor's credit card.

ICTLEP Services and Project Activities

Health Law Project:

ICTLEP monitors health law and health care issues affecting transgendered people, including transsexuals and intersexed people. ICTLEP has promulgated Health Law Standards Of Care For Transsexualism. E-Mail inquiries regarding the Health Law Project should be forwarded directly to: Shannon Minter, Health Law Director, at: shanminter@aol.com. Mail or telephone inquiries regarding ICTLEP's Health Law Project can be directed to ICTLEP, Health Law Project, P.O. Drawer 1010, Coopcrstown, NY 13326. Tel: (607) 547-4118.

Miltary Law Project:

ICTLEP monitors developments in U.S. Armed forces and military organizations worldwide that affect transgendered service members, transgendered civilian employees of the military and defense contractors, and the families of military personnel. Key issues are discharge and retirement of transgendered military service members, security clearances, and dependent entitlements. ICTLEP collects data regarding transgendered military service members. Inquiries should be directed to ICTLEP, Military Law Project, P.O. Drawer 1010, Cooperstown, NY 13326. Tel: (607) 547-4118 E-Mail: ictlephdq@aol.com.

Attorney Referral Service:

ICTLEP maintains a database of lawyers in the U.S.A and other countries who are known to have represented transgendered clients or who have expressed an interest in representing transgendered clients. Those transgendered clients seeking legal services and needing a referral should contact ICTLEP, Lawyer Referral P.O. Drawer 1010, Cooperstown, NY 13326. Tel: (607) 547-4118. E-Mail: ictlephdq@aol.com.

This is a new service and ICTLEP is working to build a more comprehensive database. Interested attorneys should contact ICTLEP at the above address to request a Referral Listing Questionaire.

Warning: ICTLEP does not expressly warrant, or otherwise guarantee or warrant, the services or competency of any attorney on the ICTLEP Referral List.

Prison Law Project:

ICTLEP tracks the treatment and disposition of transgendered people who are incarcerated in correctional institutions. ICTLEP promulgates Correctional Standards for Transgendered Inmates. E-Mail inquiries for the Prison Law Project should be forwarded directly to: Ray Hill, Imprisonment Law Moderator at rayhill@iah.com. Mail or telephone inquiries for the Prison Law Project should be directed to ICTLEP, Prison Law Project, P.O. Drawer 1010, Cooperstown, NY 13326 Tel: (607) 547-4118. E-Mail: ictlephdq@aol.com. With regard to Ray Hill, readers are invited to consult 107 SCt 2502.

Employer Education Project:

ICTLEP promulgates the International Bill of Gender Rights (IBGR), a statement of ten fundamental human and civil rights for transgendered people. Inquiries should be directed to ICTLEP, Gender Rights Project, P.O. Drawer 1010, Cooperstown, NY 13326. Tel: (607) 547-4118. E-Mail: ictlephdq@aol.com.

ICTLEP
THE INTERNATIONAL CONFERENCE ON
TRANSGENDER LAW AND EMPLOYMENT POLICY, INC.
a.k.a. The Transgender Law Conference
a.k.a. Transgender (year of conference)

September 11, 1996

ICTLEP Considers DOMA impact on same-sex TG Marriages

For over four years ICTLEP has announced and pronounced to the lesbigatr community that same sex marriages already exist in the United States and that the lesbian, gay, bisexual portion of the inclusive lesbigatr community should use the transgender same-sex marriages as both an equal protection argument to obtain same-sex marriage and as an argument against the passage yesterday of the misnamed Defense of Marriage Act (DOMA) by the United States Congress.

During those four years, ICTLEP's above notices have fallen on deaf lesbian, gay, and bisexual ears. Now, ICTLEP makes the following suggestions to those transgender same-sex marriage partners who may feel the brunt of this unconstitutional law. YOU WILL HAVE TO FIGHT FOR YOUR RIGHTS TO KEEP YOUR MARRIAGE, AND YOU WILL HAVE TO FIGHT IN THE OPEN IN THE COURT SYSTEM. YOU MAY LOSE AT THE TRIAL LEVEL, BUT ICTLEP FEELS THAT YOU WILL WIN AT THE APPELLATE LEVEL.

Unfortunately, ICTLEP retains the incorrect perception of being a strong and well financed legal organization. We are not well financed at all, and unfortunately cannot fight your legal battles. But there are four things that we can do and hope that you will avail yourself of these four things.

First is the acknowledgement that you have a valid marriage: If you are in a legal marriage, where the two of you had different genitals at marriage, and if you do not fall into the usual void categories of bigamy or incest or being legally insane, and if you also do not fall into such voidable categories as underage, then you have a valid, legal marriage in all 50 states. And if one of you is transgendered and has either completed the transsexual transition via genital surgery or via long-term irreversible hormonal alteration without genital surgery as recognized by a court in your Jurisdiction, then you STILL HAVE a valid, legal marriage in all 5O states. And if neither of you wishes to file for divorce, then NO ONE, not even the state or federal government or your parents or kids or neighbors, absolutely no one has legal standing to force you to divorce. Therefore, as ICTIEP has announced and pronounced to the lesbigatr (rhymes with alligator) for over four years, you have a valid and legal same-sex marriage in all 50 states.

Second is the strategy for the lawsuit to protect your marriage. The marriage partner that files the lawsuit to protect the marriage and to declare the application of DOMA on your marriage as being both void and unconstitutional must be, MUST BE, must be, the non-transgendered spouse. The logic is this: if the transgendered spouse files, a court could rule (just as they have in many other bad decisions in our past) that the transgendered person gave up their rights when they chose the transsexual alteration via genital surgery or via long-term irreversible hormonal alteration without genital surgery as recognized by a court in your jurisdiction. But when the non-transgendered spouse files and says to the court, “All I did was remain true to my marriage vow — for rich or poor in sickness or in health until death do us part,” only a judicial hernia could rule the marriage invalid. The general public, quite possibly even the so-called religious public, would not stand for the marriage of the non-transgendered spouse to be attacked under such a strategy.

Third is your legal advocate (or how to pick a lawyer). ICTLEP has a small but growing directory of transgender friendly attorneys and law professors. If we have one in your area, we will provide you with that name. ICTLEP also has a guide about how to find an attorney who will not only be understanding of who you are, but who will learn the nuances (such as those above) necessary to win in a fight over subtle transgender marriage issues. Ask for the "Non-Lawyer Checklist for Transgenders Who Consume Legal Services", which is found in the ICTLEP Proceedings, volume III, pp102-06, or may be ordered separately. (We suggest that you lean on your university library and your county law library to put a full set of the Proceedings on its shelves.)

Fourth is to teach yourself so that you can demand of your lawyer. ICTLEP suggests the following articles on transgender marriage which are in the Proceedings volumes and may also be ordered separately.

"Cramming Their Laws Down Their Throats", from the Family Law Project Report 1992, 1, pp. 506.308, 314.

Family Law Project Report 1992, I, pp. 295.323; 1993, II, pp.142-150, A10-2; 1994, III, pp. 86-87.

"Legal Aspects Of Transgendered Behavior", 1995, IV, pp. l-5.

"Insurance, The DSM a New Tort, Oathkeepers, No Divorce,

Apartheid of Sex, Violence, and the Non-Op Option", 1994, III, pp. 107-417.

"Respecting Choice: Genital Surgery as an Option", 1995, IV, pp. 8-17.

"Taped Speech from March on Washington", 1993, II, pp.169-171.

Voir Dire for Transgender Client or by Transgender Attorney, 1994, III, pp. lO3-104; 1995, IV, pp. ll7-119.

ICTLEP isa 5OI(c)(5) non-profit organization that needs and actively seeks your donation of whatever amount, small or large, or monthly debit of your bank, Visa or Mastercard account.

THE INTERNATIONAL BILL OF GENDER RIGHTS was drafted in committee and adopted by The International Conference on Transgender Law and Employment Policy, Inc. (ICTLEP) at that organization's second annual meeting, held in Houston, Texas, August 26-29, 1993.

Please note that this document is subject to review and revision at each annual meeting of ICTLEP. This document, though copyrighted, may be reproduced by any means and freely distributed by anyone supporting the principles and statements contained herein.

International Conference On Transgender Law And Employment Policy, Inc.
P.O. Drawer 1010, Cooperstown, New York 13326
Tel: (607) 547-4118 E-Mail: ictlephdq@aol.com
A Non-Profit 501C (3) Organization
Pursuing Justice and Equality For Transgendered People The World Over

International Bill of Gender Rights (IBGR)
(As adopted July 4th, 1996, Houston, Texas, U.S.A.)
History of the International Bill of Gender Rights

The restatement of the International Bill of Gender Rights (IBGR) was first drafted in committee and adopted by the International Conference on Transgender Law and Employment Policy, Inc. (ICTLEP) at that organization's second annual meeting held in Houston, Texas, August 26-29, 1993. The IBGR has been reviewed and amended at subsequent annual meetings of ICTLEP in 1994, 1995, and 1996.

The IBGR is derived from two earlier documents, both of which sought to articulate basic human rights for transgendered people. JoAnn Roberts of King of Prussia, Pennsylvania drafted and disseminated a "Bill of Gender Rights"" in 1991. Working independently and without knowledge of Roberts' efforts, Sharon Stuart of Cooperstown, New York, published a proposal for a "Gender Bill of Rights" in the 1991 annual meeting newsletter of the International Foundation for Gender Education (IFGE). Basic concepts in the two documents were similar although each author took a different approach.

Following the first annual meeting of ICTLEP in August 1992, Ms. Stuart began the work of drafting an expanded Bill of Gender Rights that incorporated the concepts embodied in Ms. Roberts' work as well the substance of her own proposal. This project, which was undertaken at the request of Phyllis Randolph Frye, Executive Director of ICTLEP, sought both to unify and expand the two documents into a more comprehensive view of human rights from the transgender perspective. The work proceeded with the knowledge of JoAnn Roberts, but circumstances prevented her direct participation in the redrafting process.

The first draft of the IBGR, presented in August 1993 at ICTLEP's second annual meeting, was extensively revised and refined in commitee. Principal contributors to the 1993 committee's efforts included Dr. Susan Stryker of Berkeley, California, Jan Eaton of Virginia, Martine Rothblatt of Silver Spring, Maryland and Phyllis Randolph Frye of Houston, Texas.

In recent years, major contributions to the IBGR's language and punctuation have been made by Alice of Houston, a consummate grammarian.

Although she has not participated directly in the drafting of the IBGR, the contributions of JoAnn Roberts remain substantial, particularly in the first two sections of the IBGR that form the foundation for what follows. It should be noted that Ms. Roberts continues to promulgate and distribute her own "Bill of Gender Rights" as amended.

Additional amendments and new sections were added to IBGR in 1994 and 1995. Minor changes followed in 1996. Although many minds and hands have contributed to ICTLEP's document, Sharon Stuart as Principal Drafter for the IBGR and her capacity as Gender Rights Director, bears ultimate responsibility for both the document's virtues and flaws. Ms. Stuart continues to act as Principal Drafter and Compiler for the IBGR.

The Purpose and Effect of the International Bill of Gender Rights

The IBGR strives to express fundamental human and civil rights from a gender perspective. However, the ten rights enunciated below should not be viewed as special rights applicable only to transgendered people. Nor should these rights be limited in application to persons for whom gender identity and gender role issues are of paramount concern. All ten sections of the IBGR are universal rights that can be claimed and exercised by every human being regardless of their sex or gender.

The IBGR is a theoretical expression that has no force of law absent its adoption by legislative bodies or recognition of its principles by courts of law, or by administrative agencies and international structures such as the United Nations.

In recent years, the IBGR's principles have been embodied in various legislative acts and constitutional provisions designed to protect the rights of transgendered people. Several such laws have been adopted by municipalities, and in the state of Minnesota. Meanwhile, the rights of transgendered people are gaining increased recognition and protection in such countries as Canada, South Africa, Australia, Great Britain and countries of western Europe and Scandinavia.

Apart from legislative and constitutional reform, individuals in many countries are free to adopt the universal truths expressed in the IBGR, and to lead their lives accordingly. In this fashion, the truths recited in the IBGR will liberate and empower humankind in ways that transcend the powers of legislators, judges, government officials and diplomats.

As the principles of the IBGR are understood, embraced, and given expression by humankind, the acts of legislatures and the pronouncements of courts and administrative bureaucracies will necessarily follow. Thus, the path of free expression trodden by millions of human beings seeking to define and express their own identities and give meaning to their lives will ultimately determine the course of the culture and civilization.

The IBGR is a transformative and revolutionary document. It is grounded, however, in the bedrock of individual liberty and free expression. As our lives unfold, these kernels of truth are here for all who would claim and exercise them.

The "Bill of Gender Rights" as produced by JoAnn Roberts of King of Prussia, Pennsylvania, remains a separate, distinct document, independently produced and distributed.

Comments & Contact Information

The IBGR is subject to review and further revision by ICTLEP. Proposed revisions to the IBGR, questions or comments, should be forwarded to Sharon Stuart, P.O. Drawer 930, Cooperstown, New York 13326, U.S.A. E-Mail: ictlephdq@aol.com Tel: (607) 547-118.

International Conference On Transgender Law
And Employment Policy, Inc.
P.O. Drawer 1010, Cooperstown, New York 13326
Tel: (607) 547-4118 E-Mail: ictlephdq@aol.com
A Non-Profit 501C (3) Organization
Pursuing Justice And Equality For Transgendered People The World Over

THE INDIVIDUAL'S RIGHT TO DEFINE GENDER IDENTITY:

All human beings carry within themselves an ever-unfolding idea of who they are and what they are capable of achieving. The individual's sense of self is not determined by chromosomal sex, genitalia, assigned birth sex, or initial gender role. Thus, the individual's identity and capabilities cannot be circumscribed by what society deems to be masculine or feminine behavior. It is fundamental that individuals have the right to define, and to redefine as their lives unfold, their own gender identity, without regard to chromosomal sex, genitalia, assigned birth sex, or initial gender role.

Therefore, each individual shall have the right to define their own gender identity, regardless of chromosomal sex, genitalia, assigned birth sex or initial gender role; and further, no individual shall be denied Human or Civil Rights on the basis that their self-defined gender identity is not in accord with chromosomal sex, genitalia, assigned birth sex or initial gender role.

THE RIGHT TO FREE EXPRESSION OF GENDER IDENTITY:

Given the right to define one's own gender identity, all human beings have the corresponding right to free expression of their self-defined gender identity.

Therefore, all human beings have the right to free expression of their self-defined gender identity; and further, no individual shall be denied Human or Clvil Rights by virtue of the expression of a self-defined gender identIty.

THE RIGHT TO CONTROL AND CHANGE ONE'S OWN BODY:

All human beings have the right to control their bodies, which includes the right to change their bodies cosmetically, chemically, or surgically, so as to express a self-defined gender identity.

Therefore, individuals shall not be denied the right to change their body as a means of expressing a self-defined gender identity; and further, individuals shall not be denied Human or Clvii Rights on the basis that they have changed their bodies cosmetically, chemically or surgically, or desire to do so as a means of expressing a self-defined gender identity.

THE RIGHT TO COMPETENT MEDICAL AND PROFESSIONAL CARE:

Given the individual's right to define their own gender identity, and the right to change one's own body as a means of expressing a self-defined gender identity, no individual should be denied access to competent medical or other professional care on the basis of the individual's chromosomal sex, genitalia, assigned birth sex, or initial gender role.

Therefore, individuals shall not be denied the right to competent medical or other professional care, when changing their body cosmetically, chemically or surgically, on the basis of chromosomal sex, genitalia, assigned birth sex or initial gender role.

THE RIGHT TO FREEDOM FROM PSYCHIATRIC DIAGNOSIS OR TREATMENT:

Given the right to define one's own gender identity, individuals should not be subject to psychiatric diagnosis or treatment solely on the basis of their gender identity or role.

Therefore, individuals shall not be subject to psychiatric diagnosis or treatment as mentally disordered or diseased, solely on the basis of their expression of a self-defined gender identity.

THE RIGHT TO SEXUAL EXPRESSION:

Given the right to a self-defined gender identity, every consenting adult has a corresponding right to free sexual expression.

Therefore, no individual's Human or Civil Rights shall be denied on the basis of sexual orientation; and further, no individual shall be denied Human or Civil Rights for expression of a self-defined gender identity through sexual acts between consenting adults.

THE RIGHT TO FORM COMMITTED, LOVING RELATIONSHIPS AND ENTER INTO MARITAL CONTRACTS:

Given that all human beings have the right to free expression of a self-defined gender identity, and the right to sexual expression as a form of gender expression, all human beings have a corresponding right to form committed, loving relationships with one another, and to enter into marital contracts, regardless of their own or their partner's chromosomal sex, genitalia, assigned birth sex, or initial gender role.

Therefore, individuals shall not be denied the right to form a committed, loving relationship with another, and to enter into marital contracts, regardless of their own or their partner's chromosomal sex, genitalia, assigned birth sex or initial gender role.

THE RIGHT TO CONCEIVE OR ADOPT CHILDREN; THE RIGHT TO NURTURE AND HAVE CUSTODY OF CHILDREN AND EXERCISE PARENTAL RIGHTS:

Given the right to form a committted, loving relationship with another, and to enter into marital contracts with another, together with the right to sexual expression of one's gender identity, individuals have a corresponding right to conceive or adopt children, to nurture children and have custody of children, and to exercise parental rights with respect to children, natural or adopted, without regard to chromosomal sex, genitalia, assigned birth sex, or initial gender role.

Therefore, no individual shall be denied the right to conceive or adopt children, or to nurture and have custody of children, or to exercise parental rights with respect to natural or adopted children, on the basis of their own, their partners or their children's chromosomal sex, genitalia, assigned birth sex or initial gender role.

NOTES

The International Bill of Gender Rights is based on two similar documents drafted independently in 1991 by JoAnn Roberts and Sharon Ann Stuart. Copies of these documents can be obtained by request to the address below. Please enclose $3.00 to for copy cost and postage.

The International Bill of Gender Rights is distributed by The International Bill of Gender Rights Project, an activity of the International Conference on Transgender Law and Employment Policy, Inc.

Individuals and organizations are invited to consider and adopt this statement as their own expression of principles and truths with respect to the gender rights of all human beings.

Comments and proposed revisions are invited and should be addressed to: International Bill of Gender Rights Project, P.O. Box 930, Cooperstown, NY 13326. Telephone: (607) 547-4118. Voice messages and telefacsimile transmissions can be accommodated by the same telephone number.

ICTLEP HEALTH LAW STANDARDS OF CARE FOR TRANSSEXUALISM

International Conference On Transgender Law
And Employment Policy, Inc.
P.O. Drawer 1010, Cooperstown, New York 13326
Tel: (607) 547-4118 E-Mail: ictlephdq@aol.com
A Non-Profit 501C (3) Organization
Pursuing Justice And Equality For Transgendered People The World Over

HEALTH LAW STANDARDS OF CARE FOR TRANSSEXUALISM

INTRODUCTION

These Standards Of Care were developed and adopted by consensus on September 15, 1993, after a two year period by the Health Law Project of the International Conference on Transgender Law and Employment Policy, Inc. (ICTLEP), a non-profit 501C (3) Texas corporation.

Those taking part in the Health Law Project included professionals in the fields of law, health care policy and gender science. Most of those working on the Health Law Project are transgendered. The Health Law Project also included interested lay transgendered people in attendance at the first and second ICTLEP conferences in 1992 and 1993.

The International Conference On Transgender Law and Employment Policy, Inc. makes an effort to disseminate these Standards of Care to all persons involved in the medical treatment of transsexualism. We suggest that you give these revised Standards of Care to gender services providers in your area. The Standards of Care also include standard legal forms for consent and waiver of liability.

The Health Law Project and the Standards Of Care were developed in the wake of widespread dissatisfaction with the Harry Benjamin Standards of Care. Four years later, that dissatisfaction remains. Also relevant is the pending de-listing of transsexualism per se as a mental disorder from the DSM-IV. Four years later, that de-listing is still pending.

As a result, many, if not most, of the transgendered patients seen for gender services may not require psychological services, a finding established in 1994 after the three year Boulton and Park survey (n=934) of non-clinical transgenders. And, with the growth of the female-to-male (FTM) transgendered community, it became obvious that the Standards of Care did not address FTM issues fully. Thus, Standard 3 was recently revised.

For a full transcript of the Second ICTLEP Conference that led to the adoption of the initial Standards of Care, please send $65.00 plus $5.00 s/h to the address shown above. Please specify whether you prefer text or audio. A video version is also available for $95.00 plus $5.00 s/h. If ordering to ship to a New York state address, please add the applicable county sales tax. Please add $30.00 for shipment outside the U.S.A.

The Standards of Care For Transsexualism have been reviewed and amended in 1994, 1995, 1996 and 1997. Further review and amendments may be initiated at future ICTLEP annual conferences. ICTLEP welcomes comments and constructive opposing points of view. Unfortunately, to date, most detractors of possible amendments to the Standards of Care have not attended ICTLEP conferences. To participate in future reviews and possible amendments to the Standards of Care, you are invited to attend future ICTLEP conferences, or to address your comments to ICTLEP at the above address.

Signed: Phyllis Randolph Frye, Executive Director and Founder
Martine Aliana Rothblatt, former ICTLEP Director and Initial & Primary Author Spencer Bergstedt, Director, Revision Committee Chair

Principle 1. Transsexualism is an ancient and persistent part of human experience and is not in itself a medical illness or mental disorder.

Transsexualism is a desire to change the expression of one's gender identity.

Principle 2. Persons have the right to express their gender identity through changes to their physical appearance, including the use of hormones and reconstructive surgery.

Principle 3. Persons denied the ability to exercise control over their own bodies in terms of gender expression, through informed access to medical services, may experience significant distress and suffer a diminished capacity to function socially, economically and sexually.

Principle 4. Providers of health care (including surgical) services to transsexuals have a right to charge reasonable fees for their services, to be paid in advance, and to require a waiver of all tort liability except negligence.

Principle 5. It is unethical to discriminate in the provision of sex reassignment services based on the sexual orientation, marital status, or physical appearance of a patient.

Standard 1. Physicians participating in transsexual health care shall provide hormonal sex reassignment therapy to patients requesting a change in their sexual appearance subject only to (1) the physician's reasonable belief that the therapy will not aggravate a patient's health conditions, (2) the patient's compliance with periodic blood chemistry checks to ensure a continued healthy condition, and (3) the patient's signature of an informed consent and waiver of liability form. If the patient is married, the physician may not require divorce but may also require the spouse to sign a waiver of liability form.

Standard 2. Physicians providing hormonal sex reassignment therapy shall collect and publish on an annual basis the number of hormone prescriptions they have issued and the number and general nature of any complications and complaints involved. The publication requirement of this Standard shall be satisfied by providing the collected statistics in writing, together with other current information on the potential risks and complications of sex hormone therapy, to all prospective patients inquiring into the physician's hormone therapy services.

Standard 3. Surgeons participating in transsexual health care shall provide sex reassignment surgery to patients requesting a change in their sexual appearance subject only to (1) the surgeon's reasonable belief that the surgery will not aggravate pre-existing health conditions, (2) the surgeon's reasonable determination that the patient has been under hormonal sex reassignment therapy for at least one year, and (3) the patient's signature of an informed consent and waiver of liability form. If the patient is married, the surgeon may not require divorce but may also require the spouse to sign a waiver of liability form.

Standard 4. Surgeons providing sex reassignment surgery shall collect and publish on an annual basis the number of sex reassignment surgeries they performed and the number and general nature of any complications and complaints involved. The publication requirement of this Standard shall be satisfied by providing the collected statistics in writing, together with other cuurent information on the potential risks and complications of sex reassignment surgery, to all prospective patients inquiring into the surgeon's sex reassignment services.

Standard 5. Physicians and surgeons shall not divulge the nature or identity of any patient requesting or receiving sex reassignment services except as explicitly directed in a notarized written request by the patient.

These Standards of Care were developed and adopted by consensus over a two-year period by the Health Law Project of the International Conference on Transgender Law and Employment Policy, Inc., and will be revised as necessary, at subsequent conferences. The Health Law Project's membership includes professionals in the fields of law, health care policy and gender science — most of whom are transgendered themselves. We suggest you distribute these freely and widely. The Health Law Standards of Care were developed in the wake of widespread dissatisfaction by many in the transgendered community with the Harry Benjamin Standards of Care. Also relevant is the pending de-listing of transsexualism per se as a mental disorder from the DSM-IV. Many, if not most, of the patients doctors see for gender medical services (hormones; surgery) do not require any psychological services.

Form 1
Informed Consent And Waiver Of Liability

I, ______________________________, having been fully informed in writing of the potential risks and complications of hormonal or surgical sex reassignment, do hereby choose of my own free will and consent to undertake this treatment because I want to alter my physical appearance to more closely reflect my gender identity.

I hereby release Dr.______________________________ of any and all liability for my decision to undertake a change of my sexual appearance and, for long-term use of hormones or for sex reassignment surgery, to affect on a permanent, irreversible basis my current sexual functioning.

I promise not to sue Dr.____________________________ for any of the consequences of my hormonal or surgical sex reassignment unless those consequences are the result of negligence in the conduct of my hormone therapy or in the carrying out of my surgery.

Dated at______________________________, this____________ day of________________________

Patient Signature:____

Witness:____

Form 2

Spousal Informed Consent and Waiver of Liability

I, ____________________________________ am presently married to:

(Spouse)

____

(Patient)

I understand that Patient wishes to alter his or her physical appearance to more clearly reflect his or her gender identity, and has been trying to do so for at least________ year(s). I have been actively involved in and fully support Patient's sex change process.

I have been fully informed of that nature of transsexualism and sex reassignment surgery or hormonal therapy. I fully understand that the surgery and the effects of long-term use of hormones is not reversible and that Patient will never be able to sire or bear children after the surgery or long-term hormonal therapy.

I also understand that the sex reassignment process involves dangers and risks including, but not limited to, post-operative infection, depression, emotional changes, and other physical and psychological changes. It is with my full knowledge and consent that my spouse, the Patient, undergoes sex reassignment surgery and hormonal therapy to cause a change of his/her sex to occur.

I hereby release and hold harmless Dr. __________________________ from any and all claims arising out of performance of sex reassignment surgery or hormonal therapy, actual negligence excepted. I fully understand that I will not be able to seek monetary damages for any loss of sexual companionship between Patient and myself, the loss of Patient's ability to sire or bear children, or any similar problems that may arise from the performance of the sex reassignment surgery or hormonal therapy.

Dated at___________________________, this ________________ day of___________________________

Spouse Signature:____

Witness:____

ICTLEP Policy for the Imprisoned, Transgendered

Adopted at the 2nd International Conference on Transgender Law and Employment Policy, 28 August, 1993.

NOTE: Although this is copyrighted, ICTLEP invites all empathetic persons to photocopy and broadly distribute, either in-person or anonymously, to jailers and sheriffs, and prison officials in every locale.

1. Segregation in the interest of an inmate's safety and dignity shall not deprive any inmate from the rights, privileges and facilities afforded to other general population inmates.

2. Access to counseling shall be afforded all transgendered inmates and shall include peer support group participation by those from inside the institution and those from the outside where possible. Counseling professionals should be qualified with respect to the current standard in gender science.

3. Transgendered inmates shall be allowed to initiate or to continue hormone therapy, electrolysis and other transgendered treatment modalities as prescribed by the involved professionals.

4. The transgendered inmate shall have access to clothing, personal items and cosmetics that are appropriate to the gender presentation of that inmate and appropriate within the institutional setting.

5. Special care shall be taken not to make a spectacle of transgendered inmates to the amusement of others, or to deny or to deprive transgendered inmates of their dignity.

6. A process shall be established to afford the hearing of grievances to the above policy items and appropriate resolution shall be made.

The 3rd International Conference on Transgender Law and Employment Policy is in Houston, Texas, 17-21 August, 1994. The entire Criminal Law Report and the entire Imprisonment Law Report are in Proceedings from the first and second conferences, respectively. Each copy of the written Proceedings is $65, obtained from ICTLEP.

ICTLEP MILITARY LAW PROJECT AND SURVEY

The Military Law Project is an activity of the International Conference on Transgender Law and Employment Policy, Inc. (ICTLEP), founded by Phyllis Randolph Frye, a Houston, Texas attorney, and a member of the gender community. To contact ICTLEP write to: 5705 Firenza Street, Houston, TX 77035-5515 U.S.A. Telephone: (713) 723-8368. FAX: (713) 723-1800.

Note: While ICTLEP's primary locus is on the legal issues affecting transgendered individuals in the area of military law, the concerns of our gay and lesbian personnel brothers and sisters are also examined. This broadening of the Military Law Project mission recognizes recent policy developments with respect to gay and lesbian military individuals. While homosexuality and transgenderism spring from distinct origins, there is considerable overlap between the two phenomena and a resulting mutual interest among those who find themselves in this human condition. Accordingly, the homosexual community and the gender community are natural allies in the struggle to educate against bigotry.

1. To assemble a resource file of primary and secondary military law resources which affect transgendered, lesbian, and gay military personnel.

2. To assess the status of military laws and regulations, and related federal laws and regulations, with respect to transgendered, lesbian, and gay military personnel; to evaluate the impact of military law, regulations and policies upon the legal rights of transgendered, lesbian, and gay military personnel.

3. To draft model laws, regulations and policy standards with respect to transgendered, lesbian, and gay military personnel, to be implemented by the Department of Defense and all service branches.

4. To develop and implement strategies to educate and to effect progressive change and reform of military law, regulations and policies with respect to transgendered, lesbian, and gay military personnel.

5. To conduct a descriptive survey of transgendered military personnel, including active duty, reserves, discharged, and retired personnel in all service branches and the National Guard; to assemble a resource file of case histories and data regarding the circumstances of their service, their performance of duty, their gender-related concerns, their treatment by command authorities, and their contacts with the military, legal, and medical branches.

6. To provide consultation and information to transgendered military personnel confronted with disciplinary and administrative actions by the military, and to inform their military and civilian counsel regarding gender-related issues.

7. To draft and distribute 'Legal Do's and Don'ts" for transgendered, lesbian, and gay military personnel to inform them of their legal rights and obligations as service members.

In implementation of paragraph 5 above, the Military Law Project is working with Dr. George R. Brown, M.D., a civilian research psychiatrist with twelve years of service in the U.S. Air Force. Following a pilot study of over 100 service members conducted between September, 1992 and August, 1993, the Military Law Project and Dr. Brown have joined together to carry out a greatly expanded descriptive survey of transgendered military personnel. Dr. Brown is the author of 'Transsexuals in the Military: Flight into Hypermasculinity," Archives of Sexual Behavior (1988), Volume 17, pp 527-537.

The expanded survey will encompass at least 250 respondents, and it is hoped that over 500 responses will be obtained by the end of 1995. The expanded survey of transgendered military personnel will commence in November, 1993.

There are some general guidelines that have been issued, such as avoiding high risk areas like public washrooms and certain bars, and not drawing unnecessary attention to yourself. Always use your birth name and gender on legal documents, as not doing so could be a misdemeanor. If you are in a program, contact authorities for the procedure to be followed. If you are pulled over on a highway, stay in the car, roll down the windows, keep your hands visible, and produce documents asked for by the officer. Never lie to a police officer. Do not use a phony name or address, and do not act arrogant or try to bribe or resist arrest. If the officer is not in uniform, ask to see ID. If ever arrested, go peacefully, contact family and lawyer, and ask for a postponement of court appearance. Carry your birth-gender-appropriate clothes to wear in front of a judge or magistrate. Always carry sufficient bond money with you, usually fifty dollars for a misdemeanor. Do not sign any confession or written statement and do not admit or deny any charge or allegation. Also, do not discuss your case with any other prisoner.

One of the problems currently is that prisons place people according to their gender, and if surgery has not been completed, a person may be incarcerated and their life put in danger by being placed with other prisoners. There have been very few cases, a very small percent, of transgendered people who have committed serious crimes. Many crimes occur when people are in crisis and attempt to relieve themselves of their psychological pain; there are some cases of self-mutilation, trying to cut off testicles or a penis or attempted suicide.

Some patients, prior to surgery, have reported being able to get a U.S. passport in their desired gender to use when they are travelling outside the U.S. for the purpose of gender surgery. They need a date and physician's letter stating the reason for the trip. The passport in these cases is usually issued for a year.

To legally change a name is not difficult and may not even require an attorney. Some people have requested the Bureau of Vital Statistics in the place where they were born to change their name to the name they are currently using. Others have used lawyers to do this, but the fees have not been high. After surgery, the doctor will give the patient a letter documenting the procedures. This can then be sent to the Bureau of Vital Statistics where the birth is registered and they will, in most cases, amend the birth certificate to reflect the new gender.

A GENERAL SUMMARY

When the subject of sexuality in America is discussed, it must be remembered that this society was founded on Puritanical principles. Even though we look differently today and behave in new ways, the underlying guilt and lack of freedom to think and act sexually is still present. It seems to me, having been a sex educator and family counselor for almost thirty years, that this topic is still not openly talked about and our children are not liberated from our past values. What is even more difficult today is the fact that every group with a point of view is heard from, and there is no national consensus or standard, making the entire issue very confusing to young people trying to form a basis for their own lives. Adults can also become confused.

People will tell you all sorts of private information, including what they earn, but try bringing up the subject of personal sexual behavior and it is still difficult to talk about. It bares the individual to the core of the self.

Schools have been in a constant curriculum struggle over what and how to teach children about sex and everything surrounding it. Parents are embarrassed and often so ill-equipped by lack of information or biases that they cannot convey anything but negative attitudes about what their children should do. It is rare in any audience I have ever approached that anyone received positive messages about what a wonder and joy human sexuality can be. On the other hand, the media, especially film and television, have strong sexual images that are rarely enveloped in relationships that teach people how to include love, or how to work through differences in relationships.

Americans believe in Cinderella, but no one ever wrote a follow-up book on how to hold a relationship together over time. A mix of experts now tells people how to think, feel and behave. Another point that needs to be mentioned is that Americans, probably with the help of psychiatry, believe that happiness is a right, and a right for the individual at any cost, all the time. We should teach instead that happiness is an accomplishment, and give assistance about how to achieve it.

With all of this as a backdrop, it is easy to see how society is changing and becoming more frayed. In March 1993 The Wall Street Journal reported statistics from the Index of Leading Cultural Indicators that indicated certain changes in our society since 1960. Despite government effort to improve life here, the quality has dramatically declined. The population has increased 41%, the domestic product has tripled, social spending has increased five times, welfare spending has increased by 630%, and spending on education has increased 225%. During this same 30-year period there has been a 560% increase in violent crime, a 419% increase in illegitimate births, a quadrupling in divorce rates, a tripling of children living with a single parent, a 200% increase in teenage suicide rates, and an 80 point drop in SAT scores. When instant pleasure, sex for sex's sake, lack of respect, low morals, and greed take over, we are all the losers. There is nowhere to turn and no one leading the way. Family, school, church, law and order, and other institutions have been rendered impotent. As a result, people become bored and cynical and give up, turn off, or turn to alcohol and drugs.

While there are no fast and painless solutions, education can assist in changing the current state of affairs. Understanding differences does not have to include acceptance. Having a collective peer standard may help, and caring about one's neighbor and treating him as one would hope to be treated may still be the best hope for the future. Television could help, but there soon will be so many choices for viewing that again, each person will run the risk of merely reinforcing their own values and ideas. Standardized school curriculums may offer some assistance, but forming any consensus on what to teach is almost impossible to achieve.

How gender is defined within a culture is part of this fabric and discussion, because a society can only continue if it prepares the next generation. When rules were universally standardized and stereotyped, such as women producing and caring for children and tending the home while men worked and supported the family, there was little accepted deviation. This was not so very long ago, and in a large part of the world it remains the case.

Some believe that biology is destiny and that because women have changed their role, societies are crumbling. Others argue that the use of the mind and talent, as well as the need for two incomes, forces this change and benefits the individual, family, and society. Of course, the need for two incomes may only be for a new car or larger house, not to put food on the table. So far the record is not great. It is difficult, if not impossible, to change the basic drives of nature and evolution over millions of years. This is another reason the study of transsexuals is so fascinating.

When I began my work with this group, the jokes and parade of exaggerated examples, such as portraying transsexuals as freaks, was common. Today, I am pleased to say that much of that picture has changed. By educating people, by appearing on television with patients, we have made a difference. While this is not to say there is not more to do, the public has come to learn that this surgery is not an active choice that people make; it is necessary for survival.

The public hears that parents feel guilty and suffer over what their part may have been, and they see the suffering and struggle for selfhood that each transsexual endures. Each case history and each individual is unique, but there are some common elements. Family members are seen as having the same everyday problems of all humans.

The fact that homosexuals do not want surgery to change their bodies and prefer to share intimacy with a same-sex person has been learned by the public. That transvestites are heterosexuals who receive sexual stimulation from wearing the clothes of the opposite sex has also been learned. What is difficult for some people to understand is how an individual can be a transsexual and go through surgery and still choose to be with someone of the same sex. This sometimes occurs with males-to-females but I have no knowledge of this happening with females-to-males.

Another fascinating part of all this for me has been the common themes that have come from both my heterosexual marriage counseling practice and my transsexual group. When I subtitled this book, "Life From Both Sides," I was aware that it was not really true, because most transsexuals have only felt that they were on one side — the desired side.

It is easier for those people who were born at a time when surgery and other information were available than for those people who were born in earlier years and had to wait for surgery because technology was not yet advanced enough. Lack of money is still an issue for many people requesting surgery. The abiding questions are always, "Is this surgery necessary?" and "What if surgery is not possible?" Therapists need to explore these answers with every client, because the natural depression that accompanies anyone who is not free to live as they are takes untold strength to overcome. Transsexuals are strong, brave people. They are caring and sensitive because they all, one way or another, have suffered. Imagine dealing with ridicule, rejection, shame and fear all of your young life. They are probably more conformist than the general population, and they achieve according to their talents and skills the same as the general population, once they are whole. While they try to fit the usual stereotypes, they usually look good and care about their appearance. Acceptance is always an issue, and those who are open usually find little problem. As with any group, they pick and choose whom they trust and like.

My own ideas have been expanded and my values have been regularly challenged so much that I believe my clients have made me a humbler person. There are times when I think about and help others think about daily problems in a new light based on what my gender patients go through.

Some of my biases based on my experience include gender specific behavior. While these are generalizations, most seem to be true more often than not. Stereotypes are there for a reason. What is important for all transsexuals is to be genuine and not try to play a role as seen in the media, or elsewhere. Trying to prove anything never works, especially where sexuality is involved. It is an advantage to have walked in another role or to have attempted to conform, but once that gender is "replaced," the brain has to work a little harder to have all the parts come together and be comfortable. It is easier for some than for others. If you have not liked or identified with the parent of your birth gender, it is a struggle from very early ages.

Males seem to view sexual performance as proof of love, and sometimes they use love to obtain sex. They need respect and time to be free, alone, and without conversation. They do not like long psychological inquiry, and are frequently just pragmatic. They prefer to take action as opposed to talking about issues. Males try to please females and become angry and frustrated when females do not appreciate them. If controlled, they become sneaky and defensive. Almost all the male transsexuals I have worked with have girlfriends or wives, and most of the males did not want their pictures included in this book. Males fear criticism, and anything that sounds like they are not in control makes them feel incompetent. Their reaction is often anger. Interestingly, those men who are involved with women following surgery seem to follow a stereotypical male behavior pattern. They like to fix cars, work out, and watch TV in silence! Many like being dominant. However, having been "on the other side," they are often more sensitive and loving in relationships than those born male.

Females fear loss of love, and often use sex to get love. Females long to be cherished and like talking about and engaging in relationships.

Being "pretty" is a high priority and many have plastic surgery. They try to be "nice". Some male-to-female transsexuals express surprise at the fact that females are discriminated against in the workplace, receiving less income for the same job as men. While women are stereotypically "touchy-feely," these transsexuals also have problems with sexual harassment and, for example, fear walking alone at night. Some are quite assertive and others enjoy being more docile.

Both groups exhibit jealous and competitive natures. Commitment seems to be easier for the females, although both want a haven in which to love and be loved. It seems to be a quality of the human condition to long for the mother's earlier unconditional acceptance and love. Most of the females agreed to have their pictures in the book. Few had lovers or husbands, and of those who did, I found that only one of these males was ready to write anything for the sections on family reactions. Interestingly, several had boyfriends who were French. Almost all of the partners, both for males and females, considered themselves to be heterosexual and had lived primarily heterosexual lives. As mentioned earlier, and as some of the histories show, there are a fair number of females who choose to be lesbian after surgery. Some of these people are very active in women's groups and issues. I have not found or read of any males after surgery choosing a homosexual life style. Cultural differences show up from time to time and they represent small percentages of the transsexual population, as they do the general population. None of the African-American, Hispanic, or Asian patients wanted to be included. Diffferent cultural backgrounds give different messages about how to be male or female, and they must be understood by anyone working with these groups. Living as a minority of any sort is hard.

Statistics are varied and hard to assess. It is believed that there are about 30,000 postoperative transsexuals in America, and there is no idea about the numbers pre-op; I have seen figures ranging up to 100,000. Currently the percentages seem almost equal in requests for male-to-female as female-to-male surgery. Years ago it was very skewed, as there were many more males requesting the surgery to become female. With the improved surgery for the female-to-male transformation, we see the numbers evening out. The numbers of transsexuals who marry vary, but it appears that more post-op males marry than post-op females. We have few statistics on the numbers of children in transgender familes, or the numbers of adoptions after surgery.

Some statistics suggest that the orgasm rate for transsexuals post-op is higher than for the general population. Just as they seem to care about and work more on their appearances than the general population, perhaps they also work and care more about sexual satisfaction. Recent research is included in this book but we need much more about people after surgery. It is hard to keep in contact after surgery, as many people just want to go on with their lives at that point. So, in summary, what makes someone a male or female is not so clearly defined as one might think, and when forced to come up with criteria, the transsexual experience offers new insight for the general population. The total society can benefit from understanding this phenomenon. Just looking at it without the labels of "bizarre" and "freak" is a forward step in and of itself.

RECENT RESEARCH

Title: "New Women: Sexological and Psychological Outcomes of Male-to-Female Gender Reassignment Surgery"
Paper presented at the Harry Benjamin International Gender Dysphoria Association Bi-Annual Meeting, Vancouver, British Columbis, Canada, September 1997.
Author & Affiliations: Maryann Schroder, Ph.D., University of Chicago; 5841 S. Maryland Ave. MC 3051; Chicago, IL 60637; Phone: (773)702-3914; E-mail: mschrode@uhs.bsd.uchicago.edu; Carroll, Ph.D., Northwestern University Medical School; 303 E. Ohio Suite 550; Chicago, IL 60611; Phone: (312)908-1854; E-mail: rcarroll@nmff.nwu.edu

This descriptive research study investigated sexological and psychological outcomes of gender reassignment surgery in 17 postoperative male-to-female transsexuals (new women). A median of 11.17 years (range = 1 to 25 years) transpired between the gender reassignment surgery and the date of the research session. The research was conducted at a major midwestern academic medical center. Surgeons from the U.S.A., Canada and Europe had performed the gender reassignment surgeries. Study procedures included: 1) a structured interview and self-report questionnaires (Gender Dysphoria Assessment: Postoperative Questionnaire and Interview; SCL-90-R; MMPI-2; MCMI-2; and Stress Inventory) about the sexological and psychological outcomes; 2) a medical history and physical examination; 3) a detailed gynecological exam using the first author's unique clinical instrument, the New Woman's Gynecological Index; 4) medical photographs of the subjects, including the genitalia, taken to visually document the gynecological findings; and 5) baseline neovaginal blood flow assessment by photophlethysmography.

The results of descriptive analysis, correlational analysis between medical, psychological and sexological variables, discriminant analysis and multiple regression analysis identifying predictors of good sexual functioning are presented. Over 90% of the new women rated the gender reassignment process as successful. Only one individual viewed the gender reassignment surgery as very unsuccessful and was considering a return to her original male gender role. Genital sensitivity and congruence between gender identity and body were shown to be the best predictors of orgasmic potential. The Stress Inventory total score and the genital neurosensory evaluation on the New Woman's Gynecological Index were shown to be the best predictors of sexual satisfaction. Vaginal depth and vulvular cosmesis were revealed as the best predictors of overall success of gender reassignment.

The New Woman's Gynecological Index provided a standardized assessment tool to evaluate gynecological outcomes in postoperative male-to-female transsexuals. The study found that photophlethysmography monitoring yielded a baseline physiological measure of the new women's neovaginal blood flow. To be normal or complete women was the major reason reported for the respondents to have gender reassignment surgery. About half were sexually attracted to males; about one-third were bisexual; and nearly one-fifth were sexually attracted to females. About two-thirds of the new women reported masturbation and being orgasmic from self-pleasuring. About two-thirds engaged in vaginal intercourse. Slightly over half were orgasmic during partnered sex. About half expressed sexual satisfaction, and about one-quarter of the subjects were completely dissatisfied with their sexual lives.

High levels of satisfaction with genital appearance, sensitivity and function as well as vaginal depth appeared to correspond with greater sexual satisfaction, more frequent reports of being orgasmic, and overall success of gender reassignment. Subjects reported elevations on several subscales of the SCL-90-R and other scales of psychological functioning. However, the pattern of results from the SCL-90-R and the MMPI-2 suggests that this group of new women is currently experiencing mild to moderate elevations in psychological distress, especially related to social interactions, but at a level below that of people who seek treatment for mental health problems.

PROGRAMS AND PHYSICIANS

The following is a list of physicians who are known to perform transsexual surgery . A letter was sent to each one asking a number of questions about their experiences and background. Those who responded have their information included. Every surgeon follows the Benjamin Standards of Care. Some programs are more conservative than others and require more psychological testing or time before writing letters for approval for surgery.

Some programs have individual screening and others have a group screening for the initial visit. This follows filling out a lengthy questionnaire. A depression inventory may be included as well as a sexual identity profile. Again, each program or physician will decide how they choose to use the Standards. One of the major problems is that there are some doctors who will give hormones to anyone without any psychological approval. Sometimes patients will get hormones on the street or from friends. This may give them an edge, so to speak, because they will look the part by the time any counselor sees them. The counselor will still take the time and history to make sure the person is appropriate for surgery.

The usual procedure is for the counselor to use their professional skills to assist in the process of decision making. The counselor must have experience in order to imagine the final appearance when someone comes in and has not taken hormones or begun the process. It is also true that there are many varieties of people, large and small, fat and thin, beautiful and not so attractive. There is no one mold.

In this case, gender is a manner of being, not how someone looks. Gender is psychological and social. Sex is biological. In some rare cases, people have been living the role of the other gender for many years, and this may speed up the process a bit.

Hospitals in large cities that have teaching capacity are usually more expensive. It may also be true that they are better equipped with a variety of medical disciplines at hand in case of a medical emergency. It is also true that larger institutions are not as well educated about this topic, so personnel may not be understanding. In smaller hospitals where this is the primary surgey performed, the entire hospital population and staff are senstive to the issues involved. Again, it depends on the training and empathy of the people involved. What is uniquely true is that surgery is usually anti-climactic. So much work has been done, dealing with the life of each patient, that the surgery is viewed as a dream come true. It is as though the person is newly born and relieved at the time of recovery, even though there is pain. What had been desired for a long time is completed. The individuals after surgery are usually happier and more productive. Society benefits as a result. It might be noted here that the new health plans being discussed by the government still do not include payment for transsexual surgery. Taking out or changing non-diseased organs is seen as cosmetic.

Each program will have forms and consent procedures. Some surgeons are better than others but all doctors can have a problem from time to time. Just because there is a law suit or talk about someone who had a problem with a particular physician does not mean that that doctor might not do a superb job for you. It is important to research what you need to know. Experience and training are important, but there are wonderful young surgeons doing marvelous work as well. Personality is a factor, but the physician's skill should be the bottom line.

I might add that every doctor in the world whom I knew that did this surgery was sent my questionaire. Only a very small percent did not want to be included in this list of surgeons. Again, the commitment to do this form of work is not for everyone, but those people who share their skills with the transgendered community are for the most part empathetic.

This book is not recommending any doctor over any other. The physicians who sent photographs or were asked for permission to use photographs of their work were most gracious. Those who did not may have been too busy to respond or perhaps had personal reasons. Photographs were taken at different points in time following surgery. The details about any procedure need to be reviewed with any physicians you choose. The individuals who gave permission for their faces to be included did so in order for others to see how well they blend in with society and to give hope and provide information for those who might benefit from their kindness.

Physician List

Gary Alter M.D.
435 Bedford Drive, Suite 300
Beverly Hills, CA 90210
310-275-5566
Medical degree from UCLA, 1973. Board certified in Urology and board eligible in Plastic Surgery. Has performed about 10 male-to-female operations. Uses Century City Hospital.

Stanley H. Biber M.D.
406 First National Bank Bldg
Trinidad, C0 81082
719-846-3301
Medical degree from U. of Iowa, 1948. Board eligible in general surgery. In practice 46 years. Male-to-female operations number over 3000, and female-to-male about 150. Uses Mt. San Rafael Hospital. Other plastic surgery is available. Dr. Biber also speaks Spanish.

Dr. James Dalrymple FRCS FRCSC
36 Weymouth Street
London WIN3LR England
071-224-3646
Two London hospitals are used and the cost for the doctor and hospital stay of 10 days is 6,950 English pounds. He emphasizes that he takes full care of the patients himself. He only does male-to-female and has done about 900 operations.

Ira Dushoff M.D.
6144 Gazebo Park Pl So 102
Jacksonville, FL 32257
904-260-3400
M.D. degree from U. of Pennsylvania School Of Medicine, 1956. Board certified by American Board of Surgery as well as Plastic Surgery. In practice since 1964. Male-to-female operations number about 250 and female-to-male about 300. Reports high satisfaction rates with both groups. Uses Methodist Medical College in Jacksonville, Fla. Contact Judy O. Jennings.

Milton Edgerton M.D.
U of Virginia Medical Center
Gender Identity Clinic
P.O. Box 376
Charlottesville, VA 22908
Medical Degree from Johns Hopkins University School of Medicine, 1944.
Board certified in General and Plastic Surgery. Performed about 300 male-to-female operations, and 120 female-to-male. Uses University of Virginia Hospital. Not taking new patients due to retirement plans.

Prof. Dr. Wolf Eicher
Diakonissen Krankenhaus
Speyerer Strasse 91
68163 Mannheim, Germany

J. Eldh M.D.
Department of Plastic Surgery
Karolinska Hospital
Stockholm, Sweden
46 8 729 2000

Edward Falces M.D.
1150 Bush Street
San Francisco, CA 94109
415-673-3940

R.H. Fang M.D. and C.F. Chen M.D.
Department of Surgery
Veterans General Hospital
No. 201, Sec, 2 Shih-pai Rd.
Shih-pai Taipei
Taiwan 11217, Republic of China

J. William Futrell M.D.
668 Scaife Hall
U of Pittsburgh Medical Center
Pittsburgh, PA 15261
412-648-9675
Medical Degree from Duke U in 1967. In practice over twenty years. Board certified in General and Plastic Surgery. Performed about 30 male-to-female, and about 70 female-to-male operations. Uses U of Pittsburgh Hospital.

David A Gilbert M.D.
400 West Brambleton Ave #300
Norfolk, VA 23510
757-622-7500

Lawrence Gottlieb M..D.
5841 S. Maryland Ave
M.C. 6035
Chicago, IL 60637
773-702-6302
Medical Degree from Pennsylvania State University in 1977. Board certified in Plastic and Reconstructive Surgery. Only female-to-male. Primarily radial flap. Contact Aileen Jellema RN.

Daniel Greenwald M.D.
505 South Boulevard
Tampa, FL 33606
813-258-2425
Degree from Yale University Medical School, 1985. Board Certified in Plastic Surgery and Hand Microsurgery. Male-to-female operations number 20, and female-to-male about 12, using a wide variety of methods. In practice for four years after a number of years training in this field. Has a team approach and also works with a team in Miami for female-to-male patients.

John Gregory M.D.
6125 Clayton Avenue #141
St. Louis, MO 63139
314-768-3073
Medical degree from Columbia U College of Physicians and Surgeons, 1965. Board certified in Urology. Has performed about 60 male-to-female operations. Uses Deaconess Hospital.

Peter Haaertsc M.D.
209/2 Pembroke ST
EPPING
New South Wales
Australia 2121
61 2 868-5155

J.J. Hage M.D.
Free University Hospital
Department of Endocrinology
P.O. Box 7057
1007 MB Amsterdam
Netherlands
Physician with a Ph.D. Medical degree in 1986 in Amsterdam. Board certified in Plastic Reconstructive and Hand Surgery. Male-to-female operations number about 100, and female-to-male about 50. Uses the Academic Hospital of the Free University in Amsterdam. Only operates on Dutch citizens.

Charles E. Horton Jr. M.D.
902 Medical Tower
Norfolk VA 23507
757-626-3911
Degree from Eastern Virginia Medical School, 1983. Board certified in Urology. Has performed about 40 male-to-female procedures, and the same number of female to male. Uses Sentara Norfolk General Hospital.

Ted Huang M.D.
Rosenberg Clinic
1103 Rosenberg
Galveston, TX 77550
409-762-8757
Medical degree from U of Texas, 1965. Board certified in both Surgery and Plastic Surgery. Male-to-female operations number about 130, and female-to-male about 48. Use a variety of female-to-male procedures. Uses University of Texas medical branch hospitals in Galveston and Mainland Regional Medical Center in Texas City.

Donald Laub M.D.
1515 El Camino Real
Palo Alto, CA 94306
415-327-7163
Medical College of Wisconsin, 1960. Board certified in Surgery and Plasitc Surgery. Male-to-female about 450, and female-to-male about 250. A variety of procedures for the female-to-male are used. Uses Plastic Surgery Center of Palo Alto and Recovery Inn of Menlo Park. Also uses Stanford University Hospital . Some procedures done as outpatient lower the costs. Long-standing comprehensive program. Contact: Judy Van Maasdam 415-326-4645

Laurence Levine M.D.
1725 West Harrison St #917
Chicago, IL 60612
312-829-1820
Medical degree from U of Colorado, 1980. Board certified in Urology. Mainly female-to-male, about 20 operations. Works with Dr. Gottlieb doing procedures following phalloplasty for urethral strictures and fistula problems and placing of penile prostheses.

Larry Lipshultz M.D.
6560 Fannin St #1002
Houston, TX 77030
713-798-3473
University of Pennsylvania Medical School 1968. Board certified in Urology. In practice 20 years. About 90 male-to-female operations. Uses St. Luke's Episcopal or Methodist Hospitals.

J. William McRoberts M.D.
Department of Surgery
University of Kentucky
Lexington, KY 40506
606-257-3533

Terrence Malloy M.D.
299 South 8th Street
Philadelphia, PA 19107
215-829-3409
University of Pennsylvania Medical School 1963. Board certified in Urology. In practice over 25 years; male-to-female abut 65, and female-to-male about 35. Uses Pennsylvania Hospital.

Arnold Melman M.D
Montefiore Medical Center
1049 Fifth Ave Suite 2d
New York, NY 10028
212-629-1561
Medical degree U of Rochester in 1966. Board certified in Urology. In practice about 22 years and has performed about 250 male-to-female operations. Uses Montifiore Medical Center.

Toby R. Meltzer M.D.
3181 S.W. Sam Jackson Park Road L352A
Portland, OR 97201-3098
503-525-9323
Louisiana State University Medical School 1983. Board certified in Surgery and Plastic Surgery. Performs both female-to-male and male-to-female surgery. Reports operating on two to three per week with about an even split of male-to-female and female-to-male. Uses Oregon Health Sciences University Hospital. A variety of other plastic surgery is also offered, some at the time of SRS.

Yvon Menard M.D.
1003 Boul St Joseph EST
Montreal, Quebec H2J1L2514-288-2097
M.D. Laval University Quebec, 1964. Fellow of Royal College of Surgeons and Certificate of specialist of plastic surgeon of Quebec and College Royal du Canada. In practice 22 years. Has performed about 100 male-to-female cases a year since 1971, and is beginning to do female-to-male surgery. Uses Centre Metropolitan de Chirurgie Plastique Inc. Patients stay in Montreal up to 10 days after surgery.

Luis G. Morales M.D.
Perex Guerrero Y 10 de Agosto Esquinia
Edificio Hospital De Mexico
Quito, Eecador
527-400
Trained in Mexico in Plastic Surgery and speaks Spanish. Has English-speaking staff to assist with language problems.

Sava Perovic M.D. Ph. D.
University Children's Hospital
Department of Urology
Tirsova str 10
11000 Belgrade, Yugoslavia
381-11-685200

Veronica Pimenoff, M.D. Ph.D.
Nekkilanahontie 15
FIN 80850
Paihola, Finland
358-73-1713240

S.S. Ratnam M.D.
Dept. Of OB/GYN
National University Hospital
Lower Kent Ridge Road
Singapore 119074
65 772-4262

Michael Royle, Physician
32 Westbourne Villas
Hove, Sussex
BN3 4GF England
0273-747778
London University St Mary's Hospital Medical School, 1959. Fellow of The Royal College of Surgeons of England and Fellow of the American College of Surgeons. Accredited in Urology. Has been performing SRS for over 15 years. Male-to-female about 500, and six female-to-male.

Dr. Jurgen Schaff, M.D.
Kreisklinik Dachau
Krankenausstr, 15
85221 Dachau, Germany
49-8131/76210

Eugene A. Schrang M.D.
240 First Street
Neenah, WI 54946
414-725-6661
Medical degree from Loyola University of Chicago, 1957. Board certified in Plastic and Reconstructive Surgery. Doing male-to-female since 1986, about two to three a week. Also does female-to-male. Uses the Clark Regional Medical Center. Other plastic surgery also available.

Michel Seghers M.D.
B 1200 Bruxelles
Avenue de Broqueville 60
Belgium
011322-770-01-08
Medical degree from Catholic University of Luvain in Belgium, 1957. Does plastic and reconstructive surgery. Performing male-to-female surgery since 1966, about 650 operations. Uses Foundation Lambert Hospital in Brussels.

Michael P. Small M.D
7100 West 20th Avenue #602
Miami, FL 33016
305-558-1440
Medical degree from University of Louisville, 1962. Diplomatic American Board of Urology. Palmetto General Hospital is used. Has performed about 25 female-to-male and about 50 male-to-female operations. Patients use local hotel across from hospital for aftercare. Recently opened nonprofit Gender Institute for total comprehensive care for male-to-female patients. Female-to-male patients are sent to Dr. Daniel Greenwald in Tampa, FL. Contact: Lynn Hubschman. Dr. Small is not doing surgery as of the year 2000 due to a medical problem with his hands.

Michael Sohn M.D.
Dept. Of Urology
University Clinics of RWTH Aachen
Pauwisstrasse 30
52057 Aachen, Germany
49-241-808/9758

Preecha Tiewtranon M.D.
Chollada Clinic
70/4 Sukumvit Soi 1 Sukumvit Rd
Bangkok, 10110, Thailand
66 2 252 5560

L. Von Szalay M.D.
Frankfurt Clinic for Plastic and Reconstructive Surgery
Finkenhofstrasse 15
D-60322 Frankenfurt/Main, FRG Germany

Jan Wallinder M.D.
University of Linkoping
Department of Psychiatry
University Hospital
S-581 85 Linkoping, Sweden

Neal Wilson M.D.
3011 West Grand Blvd #571
Detroit, MI 48202
313-874-5735
Medical degree University of London, 1963. Board equivalency in Surgery and Plastic Surgery. In practice 20 years, performing about 100 male-to-female operations, and about 50 female-to-male. Hutzel or Harper Hospitals are used.

ORGANIZATIONS, RESOURCES, AND WEB SITES

Printed with permission from Transgender Tapestry, division of The International Foundation for Gender Education, Waltham MA 02254-0229

INTERNATIONAL AND NATIONAL

Abled Queer
(L,TG,BI,G,G-friendly)
1517 B. Missouri
Houston TX 77006.
E-mail: james_e@iah.com

American Boyz (FTM)
Gary (410)392-3640
E-mail:
f2m-admin@tantalus.clark.net

American Educational Gender Information Service, Inc
PO Box 33724
Decatur GA 30033-0724
(770)939-0244 helpline
FAX (770)939-1770
E-mail: aegis@mindspring.com
Educational, mental health services and support group

Female-to-Male International
5337 College Avenue, #142
Oakland CA 94618
Educational outreach

International Conference On Transgender Law And Employment Policy
PO Box 35477
Houston TX 77235-5477
Annual conference on transgender legal and policy issues

International Foundation For Gender Education
Box 229
Waltham MA 02254-0229
(617)899-2212
FAX (617)899-5703
E-mail: ifge@world.std.com
Educational, outreach, peer counseling

JESS (Deaf/Hard of Hearing/SI)
(202)547-9524 (tdd only)
E-mail:
11mtanzar@gallua.gallaudet.edu

National Gay And Lesbian Task Force
2320 17th Street NW
Washington DC 20009-2702
(303)332-6483 extension 3301
FAX (202)332-0207
TTY (202)332-6219
Numerous gay and lesbian support groups. Write NGLTF for a referral to someone near you

Outreach Institute Of Gender Studies
126 Western Ave, Ste 246
Augusta ME 04330
Ariadne Kane, MEd, Director
(207)621-0858
Programs for professionals

INTERNATIONAL AND NATIONAL (continued)

Renaissance Education Association
987 Old Eagle School Rd, #719
Wayne PA 19087
(610)975-9119 (24 hrs)
E-mail: angela@ren.org
Educational outreach and support group

Society For The Second Self (Tri-Ess)
PO BOX 194
Tulare CA 93275
E-mail: TRISINFO@aol.com
Educational outreach and support group for heterosexual crossdressers. Write for referral to local chapter

Transsexuals In Prison
c/o Roni Lynne Soubrette
104 Quineveree Ct.
Castle Rock WA 09611
Support group

AMERICA

ALABAMA

Sigma Rho Gamma (TRI-S)
SERGA
PO Box 16174
Huntsville AL 35802
Michelle Steadman
(205)880-9660
Support group

Sigma Rho Gamma South (TRI-S)
SERGA
PO Box 66286
Mobile AL 36660
Lisa Jackson
Support group

Montgomery Medical & Psychological Institute, Inc
PO Box 3361
Montgomery AL 35109
Jerry or Lynn Montgomery
(205)272-2726
Mental health services/support group

ALASKA

Alaskan T-People
c/o Bobbie Wendy Tucey
PO Box 670349
Chugiak AK 99567-0349
Support group

ARIZONA

Gender Outlaws (CD/TS/TG)
PO Box 55863
Phoenix AZ 85078
(602)274-9599
Hotline, professional referrals

A Rose (CD/TS)
PO Box 1738
Tempe AZ 85280-1738
(602)488-0959
Support group

Alpha Zeta Chapter (TRI-S)
PO Box 1738
Tempe AZ 85280-1738
(602)488-0959
E-mail: sss@tri-ess.org
Support group

Evolver (CD/TS/TG)
416 E 22nd St, Tucson AZ 85713
(520)884-0541
Support group

Tau Upsilon (TRI-S)
8802 E Broadway Blvd
#145, Tucson AZ 85710
(520)296-3472

ARIZONA (continued)

Wingspan
422 N 4th Ave
Tucson AZ 85705
Support group

Soronity
(602)293-3456
Support group for family, friends

ARKANSAS

Danielle's Getaway (CD/TS/TG/SO)
c/o Danielle Storm
PO Box 61
Jonesboro AR 72403-0061
Support group

Metro'on Of Catalina
E-mail gallae@azstarnet.com
Focuses on study of the spiritual heritage of the Gallae, the transgendered priestesses of Cybele and Attis

CALIFORNIA, SOUTHERN

Pathfinders (SO)
PO Box 2973
Corona CA 91718-2973
Support group for genetic women involved with gender community

Loved Ones Of Transsexuals (SO)
(714)786-6891
Support group

People Expressing Alternative Lifestyles (CD/TS)
Gay and Lesbian Center
12832 Garden Grove Blvd, #A
Garden Grove CA 92832
(714)534-0862
live Wed. 8:00-9:30
Monthly support group

Gender Expressions (CD/TS)
PO Box 816
Lakewood CA 90714
(310)869-4241
Outreach coordination

Crossdresser Heterosexual Intersocial Club (CD/SO)
PO Box 8487
Long Beach CA 90808
(818)243-2442
Web site:
http://www.transgender.or.tg/chic
Support group

On The Scene Night (CD/TS)
Marlayna Lacie
1856 Cherry, #608
Long Beach CA 90806
Parties and socials

Alpha (TRI-S)
PO Box 411352
c/o Kathy Helms
Eagle Rock Station
Los Angeles CA 90041
(818)352-9448
Support group

CD Social Group (CD)
PO Box 224
Montrose CA 91021

PSGV Transgendered Support (CD/TS/SO)
401 S Main St, Suite 104
Pomona CA 91765
(909)620-8987
Support group

Born Free (CD/TS/SO)
PO Box 3822
Riverside CA 92519-3822
Support group

CALIFORNIA, SOUTHERN (continued)

AIS Support Group (IS)
c/o Sherri Groveman
4203 Genessee Ave, #103-436
San Diego CA 92117-4950
E-mail: aissg@aol.com

Neutral Corner (CD/TS/SO)
PO Box 12581
San Diego CA 92112
(619)685-3696
E-mail: neutrlcrnr@aol.com
Support group

Trans Action (TG)
PO Box 632954
San Diego CA 92163-2954
Support/advocacy group

Club Cherchez La Femme (CD/TS)
PO Box 10873
Santa Ana CA 92711-0873
Send SASE for details. Private membership club

Society For The Second Self (TRI-S)
c/o Carol Beecroft, Box 194
Tulare CA 93275
(209)688-9246
Support group

Tri-Chi - Tri-Ess (TRI-S)
PO Box 194
Tulare CA 93275
(209)688-9246
Support group

CALIFORNIA, NORTHERN

Pacific Center For Human Growth (CD/TS/SO)
2712 Telegraph Ave
Berkeley CA 94705
(510)548-8283
I&R (510)841-6224
E-mail: paccent@pacbell.net
Web site: www.pacificenter.org
Support group

Diablo Valley Girls (CD/TS/SO): PO Box 272885, Concord CA 94527-2885. (510)937-8432
Support group

Transmale Taskforce (FTM/TS/TG)
1259 El Camino Real, #151
Menlo Park CA 94025
(415)780-9349
FTM support

FTM International (FTM)
5337 College Ave, #142
Oakland CA 94618
Support group for FTM TSs

San Francisco Gender Information (CD/TS/SO)
3637 Grand Ave, Ste C
Oakland CA 94610-2029
Maintains database of TG resources for SF Bay Area

Sacramento Gender Association (CD/TS/SO)
PO Box 215456
Sacramento CA 95821
(916)482-7742
Support group

CALIFORNIA, NORTHERN (continued)

Barbara F. Anderson, MSW, PhD
1537 Franklin St, Ste 104
San Francisco CA 94109
(415)776-0139
FAX: (415)441-0936
Certified Sex Therapist
Clinical Sexologist

Educational TV Channel (CD/TS/SO)
PO Box 426486
San Francisco CA 94142-6486
Hotline: (415)564-3246
BBS: (415)564-4903
Telzey (510)849-4112
Support group

FPSG (FTM TS)
584 Castro, PO Box 410-990
San Francisco CA 94141-0990
Support group for FTM TSs of COLOR ONLY

Transgender Nation San Francisco (CD/TS)
584 Castro, PO Box 288
San Francisco CA 94114-2588
(415)863-6717
Political action group

Significant Others Support (SO)
attn: Ginny Knuth
2478 28th Ave
San Francisco CA 94116-2305
(415)644-1499
E-mail ginny@sirius.com
Support group

The Billy Defrank Center (Gay/Les/TG)
175 Stockton Ave
San Jose CA 95126
Support group

Rainbow Gender Association (CD/TS/SO)
PO Box 700730
San Jose CA 95170
Warmline: (408)984-4044
Support group

Swan's Inner Sorority (CD/TS)
PO Box 1423
San Jose CA 95109
(800)610-SWAN
(408)297-1423
FAX: (408)993-8173
E-mail sisht02@aol.com
Support group

Thursday Irregulars (CD)
c/o Joan Sheldon
PO Box 6541
San Jose CA 95150-6541
Support group

Redwood Empire Social Group (CD/TS)
PO Box 1531
Sonoma CA 95476
(707)938-8029
Support group

Sigma Sigma Beta - Tri-Ess Sierra Silver Bells (TRI-S)
PO Box 19933
S Lake Tahoe CA 96151
Support group

Pacific Center For Human Growth (CD/TS/SO)
1250 Pine St, Ste 301
Walnut Creek CA 94533
(510)939-7711
Support group

COLORADO

Teenage Kids Of TS (SO)
c/o Laurie Ciccotello
1740 S Buckley Road, #6-178
Aurora CO 80017
Support group

Delta Denver (TRI-S)
PO Box 11504
Denver CO 80211
E-mail: ladyblovly@aol.com
Support group

Gender Identity Center Of Colorado, Inc (CD/TS)
1455 Ammons St, Ste 100
Lakewood CO 80215
(303)202-6466
Educational outreach

FTM Support Group (FTM)
Meets third Wednesdays at 7:00 p.m.
John, (303)698-2385

Support Group Of Pueblo (CD/TS)
PO Box 1918
Pueblo CO 81002
(719)543-6460
Support group

CONNECTICUT

connecticuTView (CD)
c/o Denise Mason
PO Box 2281
Devon CT 06460
E-mail: MasonD@aol.com
Newsletter and directory

Connecticut Outreach Society (CD/TS/SO)
COS
PO Box 162
Haddam CT 06438
(860)657-4344
E-mail: ctsupport@geocities.com
Support group

P I Group (CD/TS/SO)
PO Box 245
Haddam CT 06438-0245
Discreet photo, video, scanning, and desktop publishing services

XX (Twenty) Club (TS/SO)
PO Box 387
Hartford CT 06141-0387
Support group

DELAWARE

Transsociety Sisters Of Delaware (CD/TS)
c/o Linda Marie
Ivy Hall, #6
Newark DE 19711
Support group

Renaissance - Delaware Chapter (CD/TS/SO)
PO Box 5656
Wilmington DE 19808
(302)376-1990
Support group

FLORIDA

Gender Congruity Center
9960 Center Park Blvd South, #404
Boca Raton FL 33428
(800)328-2633

Enchante (TS)
ACP
1180 Cleveland St
Clearwater FL 34615
Jackie, (813)845-0284
Support group

Starburst (CD/TS/SO)
PO Box 17411
Clearwater FL 34622-0411
(813)523-8760
Support group

Gamma Chi Beta (TRI-S)
12587 New Brittany Blvd
Ft Myers FL 33907

Florida Chapter Montgomery Institute, Inc
PO Box 141133
Gainesville FL 32607
(904)332-6638
Referrals

Gender Inform Network Of Gainesville (CD/TS/SO)
Gail Driaper, (904)332-8178
Referrals

Serenity (CD/TS/SO)
PO Box 307
Hollywood FL 33022
(954)436-9477
E-mail: susan@aol.com
Support group

The Consultancy For Change:
Roger N. Millen, PhD
304 16th Ave
Indian Rocks Beach FL 33785-2824
(813)595-8457
E-mail: TforChange@aol.com
Counselling and psychotherapy for individuals and couples

Animas (CD/TS/SO)
PO Box 420309
Miami FL 33242
Support group

Butterflies Of The World (CD/TS)
For information contact
April-Lynne Fowler
PO Box 2782
Orlando FL 32802-2782
(407)841-3125
Support group

Fantasia (CD/TS)
714 E Colonial Dr
Orlando FL 32803-4639
(407)425-4527
E-mail: GLCS@flamingopark.com
Support group

Pantra (CD/TS/SO)
PO Box 3426
Tallahassee FL 32315-3426

Tau Lambda (TRI-S)
PO Box 3426
Tallahassee FL 32315-3426

Tampa Sisters (CD/TS)
PO Box 272819
Tampa FL 33688-2819
(813)935-6848
Kimberly Westwood
Please leave contact information
Support group

FLORIDA (continued)

Phi Epsilon Mu/Central Florida Sisters (TRI-S)
PO Box 3261
Winter Park FL 32790-3261
(407)382-8389
E-mail: DeniseSFL@aol.com
Web site: http://www.horizon-usa.com/misc/fem.htm
Support group

GEORGIA

AGE (CD/TS/SO)
PO Box 77562
Atlanta GA 30357
(404)223-5351
E-mail: ageinfo@aol.com
Web site:
http://www.transgender.org/tg/age
Support group

Sigma Epsilon (TRI-S)
PO Box 272
Rosewell GA 30077-0272
(770)552-4415
Web site:
http://pages.prodigy.com/kerrico/sigep.htm
Support group

HAWAII

Hawaii Transgendered Outreach
PO Box 4530
Honolulu HI 96812-4530
(808)923-4270
E-mail: tghawaii@poi.net
Support group

ILLINOIS

Outpost Transgender Group (TG)
123 W Church
Champaign IL 61825
Elizabeth, (217)359-5113
E-mail: bridgett@prairienet.org
Support group

Transgender Significant Others (SO)
Star, (217)328-4469
Support group

Chicago Gender Society (CD/TS/SO)
PO Box 578005
Chicago IL 60657
(708)863-7714
Support group

The Sunday Society (TS)
PO Box 478850
Chicago IL 60647
Sampognaro & Louise L. Raeder
(312)486-3125
Sheila L.
(312)252-7024
Support group

Parents and Friends of Transgender Community
c/o Ellie Altman
Northbrook IL 60062
(847)564-9496
E-mail: EllieAlt@aol.com
Support group

Central Illinois Gender Association (CD/TS/SO)
PO Box 182
Washington IL 61571
JoAnn
(309)444-9918
Support group

ILLINOIS (continued)

Chi Chapter (Tri-S)
PO Box 40
Wood Dale IL 60191-0040
(630)262-8707
E-mail: chitriess@aol.com
Web site:
http://users.aol.com/chitriess/trisss/chim ain.htm
Support group

INDIANA

IGS (CD/TS/FTM/MTF/SO)
Attn: Linda BB
PO Box 425
Carmel IN 46032
Angela, (317)781-0834
E-mail: kaylin@iquest.net
Support group

Transgender Outreach of Northern Indiana (TG)
Attn: Linda BB
PO Box 425
Carmel IN 46032
Angela, (317)781-0834
E-mail: kaylin@iquest.net
Support group

Indiana Cross-Dressers Society (CD/TS/FTM/MTF/SO)
(219)929-8533
E-mail: claudiakl@aol.com
Support group

IOWA

Iowa Artistry (TRI-S)
Box 75
Cedar Rapids IA 52406
E-mail: wander5980@aol.com
Support group

River City Gender Alliance (CD/TS/SO)
PO Box 680
Council Bluffs IA 51502-0680
(402)398-1255
E-mail: sgibbons@synergy.net
Support group

Phoenix (TS)
E-mail: ASuper@aol.com
Support group

KANSAS

Crossdressers and Friends (CD/TS/SO)
Box 4092
Overland Park KS 66204
(913)791-3847
E-mail: jbfts@aol.com
Support group

Wichita Transgender Alliance (CD/TS)
PO Box 16831
Wichita KS 67216-0831
Support group

KENTUCKY

Louisville Gender Society (CD/TS/SO)
PO Box 5458
Louisville KY 40255-0458
Lori, (502)368-9918
Patricia, (502)589-9556
Support group

LOUISIANA

Gulf Gender Alliance (CD/TS/SO)
PO Box 56836
New Orleans LA 70156-6836
(504)833-3046
E-mail: alycm@concentric.net or TIAC@juno.net
Support group

MAINE

Maine Gender Resource And
Support Service
c/o Jean Vermette
PO Box 1894
Bangor ME 04402-1894
(207)945-3092
Education, referrals, outreach

Outreach Institute Of
Gender Studies
126 Wester Ave, #246
Portland ME 04330
(207)621-0858
E-mail: ajaxamk@aol.com
Web site:
http://www.cowart.com/outreach
Education, referrals, outreach

Transupport (CD/TS/SO)
Box 17622
Portland ME 04112
(207)945-3092
Support group

MARYLAND

Baltimore Boyz
Mary, (410)837-8888
Gary, (410)392-3649

Tranquility (Renaissance affiliate)
(CD/TS/SO)
c/o GLCC
241 W Chase St
Baltimore MD 21201
Support group

The Club Victoria (CD/TS/SO)
Box 682, Bowie MD 20718
(301)805-2255
Support group

Couples' Group
Maureen Carlson or Tambrey Zang
(301)977-2403

Washington-Baltimore Alliance
(CD/TS)
PO Box 4064
Rockville MD 20849-4064
Support group meets in Bethesda MD

MASSACHUSETTS

Gender Support Services For TSs
(GISST) (TS/TG)
(617)227-6216
Support group for TS/TGs with
addiction issues. Meets in Boston.

AXA (CD/TS/SO)
PO Box 38-0547
Cambridge MA 02238
Support group

Reflections (CD/TS)
PO Box 4002
East Dedham MA 02026
(617)323-6528
Support group and other services

Sunshine Club (CD/TS/SO)
PO Box 564
Hadley MA 01035-0564
(413)586-5004
E-mail: sunshineclb@aol.com
Support group

Enterprise (FTM)
PO Box 629
Jamaica Plain MA 02130
(617)441-5165

FTM Support group
East Coast Female-to-Male Group
(TS/FTM/SO)
PO Box 60585
Florence Station
Northampton MA 01060
(413)584-7616

MASSACHUSETTS (continued)

Innvestments (CD/TS/SO)
PO Box 2194
Orleans MA 02653
Support group

Partners, Family, & Friends of FTMs (SO/FTM)
385 Essex St
Salem MA 01970
(508)744-7213
Support group

Salem Support Group (FTM/TS)
385 Essex St, Salem MA 01970
(508)744-7213

American Boyz (CD/TS/FTM)
PO Box 229
Waltham MA 02254-0229
(617)899-2212
Support group

The Officers' Club (FTM)
123 Moody St
Waltham MA 02154
(617)683-1095
Support group

The Myriad Network (CD/TS)
PO Box 288
Williamstown MA 01267
Support group

Tiffany Club of New England, Inc (CD/TS/SO)
PO Box 2283
Woburn MA 01888-0483
(617)891-9325
Tues 7-10pm ET
Support group

Tiffany Club Wives' Support Group (SO)
PO Box 2283
Woburn MA 01888-0483
(617)891-9325
Tues 7-10pm ET
Support group

MICHIGAN

National Gender Dysphoria Organization And Support Group (CD/TS)
PO Box 02732
Detroit MI 48202
Justina Williams, president
(313)842-5258
Education and support

Theta Omega Gamma Detroit (TRI-S)
c/o Tri-Ess
8880 Bellaire B2, Ste 104
Houston TX 77036 (temporary)
Support group

IME of Western Michigan (CD/TS/SO)
PO Box 1153
Grand Rapids MI 49501
Web site: http://www.iserv.net/~ime
Support group

Crossroads
PO Box 1245
Royal Oak MI 48068-1245
Messages: (313)537-3267
Support group

MINNESOTA

Beta Gamma (TRI-S)
Box 8591
Minneapolis MN 55408
(612)870-8536
E-mail: triessbg@tri-ess.com
Web site: http://www.tri-ess.com
Support group

MINNESOTA (continued)

City Of Lakes Crossgender Community (CD)
PO Box 16265
Minneapolis MN 55414
(612)229-3613
Support group

Gender Education Center
PO Box 1861
Minneapolis MN 55311
Debbie Davis, director
(612)424-5445
FAX: (612)424-8595
Educational outreach

Transgender HIV/AIDS Prevention Program
Human Sexuality, Dept of Family Practice and Community Health
U Minnesota Medical School
1300 S 2nd St, Ste 180
Minneapolis MN 55454
(612)625-1500
FAX: (612)626-8311
Educational outreach

District 202
2524 Nicollet Ave
S Minneapolis MN 55408
Safe place for youth

Minnesota Freedom of Gender Expression (CD/TS/SO)
Box 17945
St Paul MN 55117
Voice mail: (612)220-9072
Support group

MISSISSIPPI

Aurora (CD/TS)
c/o Kim Brown
PO Box 1306
Florence MS 39073
(601)845-1328
Support group

Beta Chi Mississippi (TRI-S)
PO Box 31253
Jackson MS 39206-1253
Lee Frances, secretary
(601)982-7678 (24 hrs)
Support group

MISSOURI

Gender Dysphoria Support (TS)
Stacey K. Connors
1101 S Liberty Dr
Liberty MO 64068
(816)792-0304
Support group

Mid-America Gender Group Information Exchange (CD/TS)
c/o StLGF
PO Box 9433
St Louis MO 63117
Coalition

St Louis Gender Foundation (CD/TS/SO)
PO Box 9433
St Louis MO 63117
(314)367-4128
E-mail: StLGF@aol.com
Support group

Sigma Mu (TRI-S)
PO Box 2502#298
Springfield MO 65801
(417)831-3433
E-mail: LSolomon@mail.orion.org

NEBRASKA

River City Gender Alliance (CD/TS/SO)
PO Box 3112
Omaha NE 68103
(402)398-1255
E-mail: sgibbons@synergy.net
Support group

NEVADA

Tau Upsilon (TRI-S)
8802 E Broadway Blvd, #145
Tucson AZ 85710
(502)296-3472
Support group

Silver Rose Gender Association (CD/TS/SO)
c/o Lynda Cheney
PO Box 1334
Carson City NV 89702
E-mail: lyndach@aol.com
Support group

Theta Upsilon Gamma (TRI-S)
PO Box 42401
Las Vegas NV 89116
(702)387-3891
E-mail: sage@intermind.net
Web site:
http://www.intermind.net/theta/theta.html
Support group

Transsexuals Support Group (CD/TS/SO)
Leave a message for Marty
(702)594-7884
Support group

Turnabouts of Las Vegas (CD/TS/SO)
PO Box 927
Las Vegas NV 89125
(702)222-7814
Support group

NEW HAMPSHIRE

Gender Talk North (CD/TS/SO)
PO Box 421
Peterborough NH 03458
(603)924-8828
E-mail: gtnorth@top.monad.net
Web site:
http://monad.net/~gtnorth/index.htm
Support group

Seacoast Outright (G/L/Bi/T/Q Youth)
PO Box 842
Portsmouth NH 03802
(603)431-1013
Resource referral, support for those 21 and younger; referral only for those over 21

Writers, Etc
c/o Abby M Greene
PO Box 6211
West Franklin NH 03235
(603)934-3379
Support group

NEW JERSEY

NJSupport (CD/TS)
c/o T Risley
301 F Saunders Ave
Bellmawr NJ 08031
(609)933-2233
Meetings 1st Saturday of the month, Unitarian Universalist Church of Washington Crossing
Renaissance affiliate

Northern New Jersey (CD/TS)
c/o Ms Lynda Frank
PO Box 9192
Morristown NJ 07960
(201)663-0772
Support group

NEW JERSEY (continued)

Jumpstart Cable (CD/TS)
PO Box 622, Paramus NJ 07653
Support group

Sigma Nu Rho (TRI-S)
1092 St. Georges Ave, Ste 234
Rahway NJ 07065-2664
(908)826-5287
24-hour hot line:
(800)480-3152, in near states
E-mail: carolannsnr@juno.com
Support group

East Coast Couples Network (CD/SO)
c/o MOTG
PO Box 8243
Red Bank NJ 07701
Support group

Monmouth/Ocean Trans Gender (CD/TS/SO)
PO Box 8243
Red Bank NJ 07701
(732)219-9094
E-mail: vikkimmotg@aol.com
Support group

Chi Delta Mu (TRI-S)
PO Box 1
River Edge NJ 07661-0001
(800)484-7593 (code 4985)
E-mail: cdm@carroll.com
Support group

Transit (CD/TS/SO)
(908)526-2369
Support group

NEW MEXICO

Phi Fiesta! (TRI-S)
8200 Montgomery NE, #241
Albuquerque NM 87109
(505)299-2533
Support group

Support Group (CD/TS/SO)
c/o Stephanie
2449 Algodones NE
Albuquerque NM 87712
Support group

NEW YORK

Transgenderists' Independence Club (CD/TS/SO)
PO Box 13604
Albany NY 12212-3604
(518)436-4513, live Thurs 7-9 pm
(or leave a message and instructions for calling back)
Support group

Nu Phil Chi-Buffalo Belles (TRI-S)
PO Box 1701
Amherst NY 14226-1701
(716)643-2626
Support group

Girls' Night Out (CD/TS/SO)
c/o Barbara Fortune
PO Box 350369
Brooklyn NY 11235-0007
(201)794-1665 (ext 2021)
Support group

MGN/STAR (TS/FTM/MTF)
214 16th St
Brooklyn NY 11215
(718)965-2911
E-mail: directlink@mindspring.com
Support group

NEW YORK (continued)

New York Girl & Partners (CD/TS/SO)
PO Box 456
Centereach NY 11720
(516)732-5115
Support group

TG Society of Northern New York (CD/TS/SO)
26646 Smith Rd
Dexter NY 13634
(315)649-5534
Support group

Lambda Chi Lambda (TRI-S)
PO Box 97
Ilion NY 13357
Support group

Bi-Gender Rap Group
c/o Lynda Frank
330 W 45th St, Apt 3H
New York NY 10036
(212)765-3561
Meets 2nd Monday each month, 6-8 pm in lower Manhattan

Crossdressers Intl (CD/TS/SO)
404 W 40th St, #2
New York NY 10018
(212)570-7389 or (610)759-1761
E-mail: cdinyc@aol.com
Support group

Eulenspiegel Society (CD/TS)
Box 2783, Grand Central Station
New York NY 10163
(212)388-7022
B&D-oriented Support group

Gender Identity Project (TS)
Lesbian and Gay Community Services Center
208 West 13th St
New York NY 10011
(212)620-7310
Support group

Imperial Queens & Kings of Greater New York (CD/TS/SO)
80 Eighth Ave, Ste 301
New York NY 10011
(212)229-1968 days
(212)627-1969 evenings
Open social group

Metropolitan Gender Network (CD/TS)
561 Hudson St, Box 45
New York NY 10014
(201)794-1665 (ext 332)
Support group

Transgender Rights! (CD/TS)
(212)979-8547
Political action group

Transgender Network (CD/TS/SO)
PO Box 1611, South Rd Annex
Poughkeepsie NY 12601-0611
Support group

Rochester CD-Network (CD/TS/SO)
PO Box 92055
Rochester NY 14692
(716)251-2132
Support group

Expressing Our Nature (CD/TS/SO)
PO Box 3586
Syracuse NY 13220
(315)423-4099
Support group

NEW YORK (continued)

Long Island Femme Expression (CD/TS/SO)
PO Box 1311
Water Mill NY 11976-1311
(516)283-1333
E-mail: joed2viola@aol.com
Support group

Transgender Society Of Northern New York (CD/TS/SO)
PO Box 6164
Watertown NY 13601
Support group

NORTH CAROLINA

Phoenix Transgender Support (CD/TS/SO)
PO Box 18332
Asheville NC 28814
(704)253-9882
E-mail: jessicaash@aol.com
Support group

Chi Chi Rho (TRI-S)
Crystal Coast Rose
PO Box 733,
Bridgeton NC 28519
Support group

Alternative Gender-Oriented (CD/TS/SO)
1235-E E Blvd,
Charlotte NC 28203

Kappa Beta (TRI-S)
c/o Corresponding Secy
PO Box 12101
Charlotte NC 28220-2101
(704)565-5034
E-mail: dajones@infoave.net
Support group

Carolina Trans-Sensual Alliance (CD/TS/SO)
PO Box 35378
Fayetteville NC 28303-0378
Support group

Triad Gender Association (CD/TS/SO)
c/o Stephanie Dyla,
PO Box 2265
Jamestown NC 28282-2264
(910)454-1493
Web site: http://www.geocities.com/westhollywood/8607/
Support group

Gdanc Support Group (CD/TS)
PO Box 305
Salisbury NC 28145
(704)642-1914
Support group

A Circle of Children
Rt 5, PO Box 564
Zebulon NC 27579
Chris Allen, (919)269-8698
Support group

OHIO

Cross-Port (CD/TS/SO)
PO Box 1692
Cincinnati OH 45201
(606)581-3711
E-mail: wgbn68d@prodigy.com
Support group

Crystal Club (CD/TS/SO)
PO Box 287
Columbus OH 43068-0287
(614)213-1368
E-mail: cc@stargatge.com
Support group

OHIO (continued)

Paradise Club (CD)
PO Box 29564
Parma OH 44129
E-mail: ParadiseCL@aol.com
Support group

Alpha Omega (TRI-S)
Box 2053
Sheffield Lake OH 44054-0053
(216)556-0067
Support group

Glass City Sisters
PO Box 8532, Toledo OH 43623
E-mail: glassister@aol.com
Support group

OKLAHOMA

Sooner Diversity (CD/TS)
PO Box 575, Norman OK 73070
Support group

Central Oklahoma Transgender Alliance (CD/TS)
PO Box 60354
Oklahoma City OK 73146
Support group

Sigma Beta (TRI-S)
PO Box 42122
Oklahoma City OK 73123
Support group

Cross Dressers International (CD/TS)
c/o Ms. Gwen Pete
PO Box 50192
Tulsa OK 74104
(918)582-6643 or 835-5334
Support group

Desire (CD/TS)
c/o Ms. Gwen Pete
PO Box 50192
Tulsa OK 74104
Support group

OREGON

Salmacis Society/Versatile Women (TS)
PO Box 1604
Eugene OR 97440-1604
(541)688-4282
Service and information

Rho Gamma/Rogue Valley Girls (TRI-S)
PO Box 5551
Grants Pass OR 97527

Intermountain Transgender Outreach (TG)
1524 Monroe Ave
La Grande OR 97850
(541)962-3466
E-mail: keol@eosc.osshe.edu
Support group

Northwest Gender Alliance (CD)
PO Box 4928
Portland OR 97208
(503)646-2802
E-mail: nwga@teleport.com
Support group

The Trans Group (TS/TG/TV)
c/o Phoenix Rising Foundation
620 SW 5th Ave, Ste 710
Portland OR 97204
(503)223-8299
Support group

Trans-Port (CD/TS/SO)
PO Box 66913
Portland OR 97290-6913
(503)774-8463
Support group

OREGON (continued)

Transsexual Peer Support Group (TS)
c/o Phoenix Rising Foundation
620 SW 5th Ave, Ste 710
Portland OR 97204
(503)223-8299
Support group

Capitol City Chapter (CD/TS/SO)
PO Box 3312
Salem OR 97302
Support group

PENNSYLVANIA

Renaissance-Lehigh Valley/Pocono Area (CD/TS/SO)
PO Box 3624
Allentown PA 18106
(610)821-2955
Support group

NE PA Transgender Alliance (CD/TS/SO)
Lehigh Valley
(610)821-2955
Support group

Transfamily (Family)
c/o Deni Scott
692 Rockdale Rd,
Butler PA 16001
Janet, (412)758-3578
E-mail: dscott@pgh.net
Support group

Cross Dressers International (CD/TS/SO)
PO Box 61
Easton PA 18044
S Kristine James, Director
Karen Cioe, NYC Coordinator
Support group

Erie Sisters (CD/TS/SO)
1903 W 8th St, Ste 261
Erie PA 16505
E-mail: eriesister@aol.com
Support group

Travelers Express (CD)
PO Box 150
Falls Creek PA 15840
(814)375-7651
Support group

Renaissance-Lower Susquehanna Valley Chapter (CD/TS/SO)
PO Box 2122
Harrisburg PA 17105-2122
(717)780-1578
E-mail: lsv@ezonline.com
Web site: http://www.ezonline.com/lsv
Support group

Lancaster Boyz (FTM)
Tom, (717)892-4999
E-mail: malesic@prolog.net
(Philadelphia area)

Philadelphia TS Support Group (TS)
PO Box 15839
Philadelphia PA 19103
(215)567-7879
Support group

Philly Boyz (FTM)
Steve, (215)546-6444
E-mail: shock@asc.upenn.edu
(Philadelphia area)

Positive Change (TS)
c/o Pequin Place
201 S Camac St
Philadelphia PA 19107
Joanna Sands, (215)732-0603
Support group

PENNSYLVANIA (continued)

UJIMA
Peer counseling, safer sex demos, and info materials for TG teens. Meets Wed. nights at 6:30 at 1207 Chestnut St, 4th floor, in Philadelphia.

Pitboyz (FTM)
Dan & Michelle
E-mail: windyl@aabe.com

Transsexual Support Group (TS)
6020 Penn Circle South
Pittsburgh PA 15206
(412)661-7030
Support group

Transpitt (CD/TS)
PO Box 3214
Pittsburgh PA 15230
(412)224-6015
Support group

Renaissance-Education Association, Inc. (CD/TS/SO)
987 Old Eagle Rd, Ste 719
Wayne PA 19087
(610)975-9119
E-mail: bensalem@bbs.cpcn.com
Web site: http://www.ren.org
Support group

TENNESSEE

Alpha Pi Omega (TRI-S)
c/o Laury W
PO Box 871
Brentwood TN 37204-0871
E-mail: laurywl@mindspring.com
Web site:
http://members.aol.com/apotris/aponash.htm
Support group

Memphis TG Alliance (CD/TS/SO)
PO Box 11052
Memphis TN 38111-0052
Support group

TV/TS Support Group (TV/TS)
c/o Rev. John Prowett
1517 Court St, Ste 4
Memphis TN 38104-2402
Support group

Tennessee Vals (CD/TS/SO)
PO Box 92335
Nashville TN 37209-2335
Voice mail: (615)664-6883
E-mail: jlove1@ix.nstcom.com
Web site:
http://www.3Dcom.com/tg/tvals/
Support group

TEXAS

West Texas Gender Alliance (CD/TS)
c/o Tami Maloney
5817 Atlantic Dr
Abilene TX 79606
Support group

Tau Chi Chapter (TRI-S)
Box 1105
Alief TX 77411-1105
(713)347-8747
E-mail: jeftris@aol.com
Web site:
http://www.firstnethou.com/brenda/
Support group

Nu Epsilon Tau (TRI-S)
PO Box 14096
Arlington TX 76094
(214)490-5738
E-mail: BobbieR648@aol.com
Support group

TEXAS (continued)

Austin Second Image (CD/TS/SO)
PO Box 15381
Austin TX 78761
(512)515-5460, Wed 7-9 pm
Support group

Boulton & Parksociety (CD/TS/SO)
PO Box 17
Bulverde TX 78163
(830)980-7788, live Tues 6-9 pm CT
E-mail: tx_t_party@aol.com
Support group

WATS (SO)
PO Box 17
Bulverde TX 78163
(210)980-7788, before 9:00 pm CT
Support group

Help Me...Accept Me of Dallas (CD/TS)
6753 Camp Bowie Blvd, #177
Fort Worth TX 76116
Support group

Rosenberg Clinic, Gender Treatment Program
1103 Rosenberg
Galveston TX 77550
(409)763-0016
Medical, psychological care and support groups

Gulf Coast Transgender Community (CD/TS/SO)
PO Box 66643
Houston TX 77266
(713)780-4282
Support group

Helping CDs Anonymous (CD)
68-4 E Hwy 6 S #334
Houston TX 77083
E-mail: brenda@firstnethou.com
Support group

Metroplex CD Club (CD/TS/SO)
PO Box 141924
Irving TX 75014
(972)264-7103
Support group

Wives'/Partners' Support (SO)
PO Box 5304
Katy TX 77036
(909)875-2687

San Antonio Transexual Support Group (TS)
PO Box 12913
San Antonio TX 78212
Support group

Metroplex CD Club (CD)
Bldg 106, Ste 144
7120 Rufe Snow Dr
Watauga TX 76148-1862
E-mail: domiss@flash.net
Web site:
http://www.flash.net/~domega
Support group

UTAH

Alpha Rho, Salt Lake City (CD/TS/SO)
PO Box 571242
Salt Lake City UT 84157-1242
(801)553-8141
Support group

Engendered Species (CD/TS/SO)
PO Box 11897
Salt Lake City UT 84147
(801)364-0136
Support group

UTAH (continued)

Salt Lake Gender Consortium (CD/TS/TG/SO): Genevera Martin, president, PO Box 651073, Salt Lake City UT 84165-1073. (801)576-1416.
E-mail: geneveram@aol.com.
Support group

VERMONT

Trans (CD/TS)
(802)472-8115
Meets 1st & 3rd Tuesdays in Burlington
Support group

Vermont Transgender Support Group (CD/TS)
for information, leave a message at (802)860-8430
Support group

VIRGINIA

Black Rose (CD)
PO Box 11161
Arlington VA 22210
(301)369-7667
Support group

DC Boyz (FTM)
Call Adam, (301)270-0372
E-mail: romandede@aol.com
(Metro DC)

Metro Area Gender Identity Connection (TS/SO)
PO Box 16036
Arlington VA 22215
(301)949-3822
Support group

Trans-Gender Educational Association
PO Box 16036
Arlington VA 22215
(301)949-3822
E-mail: tgea@juno.com
Web site:
http://www.tgguide.com/guide/dc/tgea~ndx.html
Support group

Virginia's Secret (CD)
PO Box 14716
Richmond VA 23221-0386
E-mail: vasecret@juno.com
Support group

Beach Bunnies (CD/TS/SO)
PO Box 64121M
Virginia Beach VA 23467
Support group

VA Boyz (FTM)
Call John, (804)751-0584
E-mail: moojuu@gnn.com

WASHINGTON

Cinderella Circle (CD/TS)
304 W Champin
Bellingham WA 98225
(306)671-7826
E-mail: Starchild@aol.com
Support group

Transsexual Lesbians And Friends (TS/SO)
Seattle WA
(206)292-1037
Support group

Emerald City (CD/TS/SO)
PO Box 31318
Seattle WA 98103
(206)827-9494
Support group

WASHINGTON (continued)

Papillon (CD/TS/MTF/FTM/SO)
Attn: Marianne
PO Box 1365
Veredale WA 99037
(509)624-5358
(Out of Spokane)
Support group

WEST VIRGINIA

The Valley Girls (CD/TS)
PO Box 181
Dunbar WV 25064
Support group

Trans-WV (CD/SO)
PO Box 2322
Huntington WV 25724-2322
Support group

WISCONSIN

Gemini Gender Group (CD/TS/SO)
PO Box 44211
Milwaukee WI 53214
(414)297-9328, voice mail
E-mail:
75261.1443@compuserve.com
Support group

Insitute for Psychosexual Health
Great Lakes Gender Clinic
3250 N Oakland Ave
Milwaukee WI 53211
Charles A Kiley, ACSW, LICSW
(414)332-5407
Psychotherapy

Milwaukee Transgender Program
Pathways Counseling Center
2645 N Mayfair Rd, Ste 230
First Financial Bldg
Milwaukee WI 53226-1304
(414)774-4111
Full service TS facility

Transgender Identity Group
c/o Ivanoff and Ivanoff
Clark Bldg, Ste 1810
633 W Wisconsin Ave
Milwaukee WI 53203-1918
(414)271-3322
Psychotherapy

WYOMING

Central Wyoming TG Support Group (CD/TS)
PO Box 1301
Evansville WY 82636
(307)265-3123
Support group

CANADA

QUEBEC

Club MET (CD/TS/SO)
4113 Dorion St
Montreal Quebec H2K 3B8
(514)528-8874
Support group (Formerly TAM)

FACTT Quebec (TS/SO)
Box 293, Cote des Neiges Post Office, 5858 Cote des Neiges Blvd
Montreal Quebec H3S 2S6
French speaking referrals, medical and psychological services and support group

Transsexuals in Prison (TS/SO)
Non-prisoners contact
Dee Farmer, 23288037
PO Box 4000
Springfield MO 65808 (USA)
Prisoners contact Mrs. Patricia Fisher, Succ 293 Cote des Neiges
5858 Cote des Neiges Blvd
Montreal Quebec H3S 2S6
Information and referrals

ONTARIO

Gender Metaphor (CD/TS/SO)
829 Northwest Rd, Ste 715
Kingston Ontario K7P 2N3
E-mail: genmet@adan.kingston.net
Support group

Canadian Crossdressers' Club (CD/TS/SO)
161 Gerrard St E
Toronto Ontario M5A 2E4
(416)921-6112, 24 hours
E-mail: info@wildside.org
Support group

Patricia Flora (IS)
PO Box 425, Postal Station C
1117 Queen St W
Toronto Ontario M6J 3P5

Street Outreach Services (CD/TS)
c/o W Travers,
622 Yonge St, 2nd Fl
Toronto Ontario M4Y 1Z8
(416)926-0744, 24 hours
Multitude of services for TG youth

Transition Support (TS)
c/o The Church Street
Community Centre
519 Church St
Toronto Ontario M4Y 2C9
Support group

Xpressions (CD/TS/SO)
PO Box 223
Station A
Toronto Ontario M5W 1B2
(416)812-6879
Support group

FACTT Ottawa (TS/CD)
Box 7421
Vanier Ontario K1L 8E4
Support group

Gender Mosaic (CD/TS/SO)
PO Box 7421
Vanier Ottawa Ontario K1L 8E4
(819)770-1945
Support group

MANITOBA

Prairie Rose Gender Group (CD/TS/SO)
Box 23 Grp 4 RR1
Dugald Manitoba R0E 0K0
(204)257-2759
Support group

ALBERTA

Illusions Social Club (CD/TS/SO)
Box 2000, 6802 Ogden Rd SE
Calgary Alberta T2C 1B4
(403)236-7072
Support group

Phi Sigma (TRI-S)
Box 81115
755 Lake Bonavista Dr SE
Calgary Alberta T2J 7C9
(403)271-6247
Support group

Illusions Social Club (CD/TS/SO)
Box 33002 Glenwood PO
Edmonton Alberta T5P 4V8
Support group

BRITISH COLUMBIA

Dream Girls (CD/TS/SO)
PO Box 535
Kamloops British Columbia V2C 5L7
Support group

Cornbury Society (CD/SO)
Box 3745
Vancouver British Columbia V6B 3Z1
Support group

BRITISH COLUMBIA (continued)

Foundation For The Advancement Of Trans-Gendered People's Society (CD/TS)
1-1727 William St
Vancouver British Columbia V5L 2R5
(604)254-9591.

Zenith Foundation
Box 8415 Granville St
Vancouver British Columbia V6P 4Z9
(604)261-1695

Transsexual Support Group (TS)
Dr. Angela Wensley
14905 32nd Ave
White Rock British Columbia V4P 1A4
(604)536-2053
Support group

SOUTH AMERICA

ARGENTINA

Transsexuals for the Right of Life and Identity (TS)
TRANSDEVI
Casilla de Correo 151, CP 1748
Gral Rodriguez, Buenos Aires

BRAZIL

Purpurina (Glitter) Project (TS)
Katia Monteiro
no 55 Rua DA Gloria, #30
Gloria, Rio de Janeiro
02-252-4757
FAX 02-227-5944
Educational outreach, AIDS awareness, referrals

AFRICA

NIGERIA

Transformation Second Self
c/o Jane Enuneku
KM 4 Idiroko Rd, PO Box 1006
OTA, Ogun State, West Africa

SOUTH AFRICA

Phoenix
c/o Desiree Dexter
PO Box 1332, Springs
1560, Gauteng
+27111-362-5247

South African Transsexual Research Unit (SATRU)
PO Box 87283
Houghton, Johannesburg 2041

EUROPE

ENGLAND

(intl telephone code: +44)

Beaumont Society Partners' Group
+44-1223-441246, South
+44-1203-717528, Central and Wales

TransEssex
PO Box 3
Basildon Essex SS14-1PT
+44-12-68-58-3761
Wed & Sun 7-10 pm GMT

Trans-Net
c/o R Floyd
3 St Augustines Rd
Chesterfield Derbyshire S40 2SF
+44-1246-285799, phone and FAX
E-mail: 100764.27@compuserve.com

ENGLAND (continued)

International Gender Transient Affinity
Box 2, 1 Banks Building
School Green Rd
Freshwater Isle of Wight P040-9AJ

Phoenix Centre
12 Barnsbury Rd
Islington N1-1NB.

Friends Merseyside
36 Bolton St
Liverpool L3-5LX
+44-151-709-3181
Fri 7:30-9 GMT

Beaumont Society
Old Gloucester St
London WC1N-3XX
+44-1582-41-2220

Beaumont Trust
BM Charity
London WC1N-3XX

Change (TS)
BM Box 3440
London WC1N-3XX
+44-1303-259543
E-mail: ts1change@aol.com
Web site:
http://users.aol.com/ts1change/private/homepage.htm

FTM Network
(also Press for Change)
BM Network
London W1N-3XX
+44-161-423-1915
8-10:30 pm GMT
E-mail: s.t.whittle@mmu.ac.uk

Gender Dysphoria Trust International
2 School Rd
Hampton Hill, Middlesex
London TW12-1QL

The Gender Trust
BM Gentrust
London WC1N-3XX
+44-1305-269222,
before 9 pm GMT

Overseas Representative
Dorothy Francis,
The Gender Trust
3 Hartington Villas
Hove BN3 6HF

Gender Identity Consultancy Services (TS)
10 Warwick Rd
Earls Court, London SW5 9UH
+44-1071-244-6090
FAX 1071-244-0900
E-mail: gics@aol.com

Mermaids
BM Mermaids
London WC1N-3XX
Group for children and teenagers with gender dysphoria and their families

Seahorse Society
BM Seahorse, Box 6093
London WC1N-3XX

Self Help Association for Transsexuals
2 School Rd, Hampton Hill
Middlesex London TW12-1QL

TV Self Help Group
Box 3281
London E1-6JG
+44-171-289-5240, 24 hours

ENGLAND (continued)

AIS Support Group (IS)
2 Shirburn Ave
Mainsfield Notts NG18-2BY
E-mail:
100572.2376@compuserve.com

Northern Concord
PO Box 258
Manchester M60-1LN
+44=161-236-1311

OUSU Transgender Group
Oxford University Student Union
Little Clarendon St, Oxford
+44-1865-270777

Rose's Club
29 Roundel St
Sheffield S9-3LE
+44-12-68-58-4761
Wed & Sun 7-10 pm GMT
E-mail: roses@argonet.co.uk

N. IRELAND
(intl telephone code: +44)

Belfast Butterfly Club
PO Box 210
Belfast BT1-1BG
+44-585-430408

SCOTLAND
(intl telephone code: +44)

Trans-Trap
c/o Miss Julie Bradshaw
30/1 Halmyre St
Edinburgh EH6-8QD
+44-131-555-6416

Crosslynx
c/o SGLS, PO Box 38
Glasgow G2-2QF
+44-141-221-8372

WALES (intl telephone code: +44)

South Wales Tv/Ts Group
c/o Martina Rees
56a Kinross Ct, Ridgeway Rd
Llan-Romney, Cardiff VF3-9AE

FRANCE (postal code: F-)
(intl telephone code: +33)

Association Beaumont Continental
BP-3, F-68350 Didenheim

Association D'aide aux Transsexuals
Maison des Associations
93 La Canabiere
F-13001 Marseille

Association Devenir Femme
Les Terrasses du Mediterranee
F-13006 Marseille

Association du Syndrome de Benjamin
Relais 59-59 avenue Daumesnil
3 r Keller
F-75012 Paris
+33-1-43-47-21-25

SWITZERLAND
(postal code: CH-)
(intl telephone code: +41)

Selbsthilfe Gruppe (TS)
Postfach 92
CH-9008 St. Gallen

Kontakforum Femme Travestie
Postfach 6788
CH-8023 Zurich

SPAIN (intl telephone code: +34)

Coletivo de Transexuales de
Cataluna (TS)
C. Balmes, 70, 1o 1a
08830 Sant Boi de Lobregat
Barcelona. 08080 3454 6398
Wed 7:30-9 pm
(please speak Spanish)

GERMANY (postal code: D-)
(intl telephone code: +49)

Interessengemeinschaft
Transsexuellegruppe in der Sekis
Albrecht-Achilles-Str 65
D-10709 Berlin
+49-30-892-6602

Sontagsclub e.V.
Rhinover Str 8
D-10437 Berlin
+49-30-208-2035, Fri 6-8 pm CET
E-mail: kasimir@inf.fu-berlin.de

Selbsthilfe Bielefeld (TS)
c/o Praxis für Beratung und
Psychotherapie
Herrn Detlaf Kunert
Karl-Eilers-Str 1
D-33602 Bielefeld
+49-521-63623

Selbsthilfegruppe Bonn (TS)
c/o SEKIS Bonn
Lotharstr 95
D-53115 Bonn
+49-228-221754

CheISI e.V. (TV/TS)
Treff Sachsen
Roesslerstr 9
09113 Chemnitz
+49-371-50094, Fridays
FAX +49-371-55867

Gerede e.V. (TV/TS)
Treff Sachsen
Wiener Str 41
D-01219 Dresden
+49-351-4640220 Fridays

Selbsthilfegruppe Düsseldorf
c/o Stefanie Sander, Pleistr 1
B-4731 Eynatten/Belgian
+32-87852833

Gruppe (TS)
c/o AIDS-Hilfe Thüringen
Postfach 50
D-99001 Erfurt
+49-361-7312233

Angehoerigengruppe AWO-
Beratungszentrum (TS)
Lützow-Str 32
D-450101 Essen
+49-201-312051 or
+49-201-312052

TSH Essen
c/o Claudia Peppen horst
Caesarstr 34
D-45130 Essen
+49-201-786899

FPE Frankfurt
c/o Krucher & Surhoff
PO Box 800442, D-5904
Frankfurt am Main

Selbsthilfe Göttingen
TS in PRAXIS
Dr. Wiedeking
Bühlstr 28a
37037 Göttingen
+49-551-46755

TS Gruppe Hamburg
Chirstian Susan Black
Nubeblerkamp 13a
D-22175 Hamburg
+49-40-754-4323

GERMANY (continued)

Body and Soul
c/o KIBISS KISS
Hanover
+49-511-666567 or Stephanie
+49-511-457347

TVV
PO Box 1148
D-65780 Hattersheim

Selbsthilfegruppe Heidelberg
Andreas Kress
Postfach 103766
D-69029 Heidelberg

Informations Kontakt und Vermittlungsstellefur Transsexuelle Menschen in Baden Wurttemberg e.V.
c/o AOK Karlsruhe
Kriegstr 41
D-76133 Karlsruhe
+49-721-623382, Phone & FAX

Tranidentitas e.V. Selbsthilfegruppe Koblenz
c/o Joana, +49-261-45040

Transexuellengruppe Köln
c/o Karin, +49-2196-1739

Club Neues Leben Nova
PO Box 710232, 80634 München
+49-89-7916643, 6-6:30 pm CET
(please speak German)

Viva TS Selbsthilfegruppe München e.V. (TS)
c/o Peter Reidel
Hirschbergstr 14
D-80634, München
+49-89-134681, 6-6:30 pm CET
(please speak German)
FAX: +49-89-162324

Pro Familia Sachsen
c/o Prof Dr L Aresin
D-04315 Leipzig
+49-341-61530

Selbsthilfegruppe Manheim
Andreas Tremmel
Postfach 1242
D-67370 Dudenhofen

TSH Münster
c/o MIKS
Merwarthstr 2
D-48143 Münster
Claudia Scholz, +49-251-511263

Selbsthilfegruppe Frankfurt am Main
Postfach 10 10 46
D-63010 Offenbach
+49-69-800-1008

Transidentitas
Postfach 10 10 46
D-63010 Offenbach
+49-69-800-1008

AIS Selbsthilfegruppe (IS)
Postfach 7
D-71201 Rottenburg am Neckar
(Fluent in English and German)

Lebensberatung für Transexuelle Menschen in Saarland
c/o Dr. Waltraud Schiffels
Schloßstr 6
D-66117, Saarbrücken
+49-681-583912

Selbsthilfegruppe für Transexuelle
Menschen in Tübingen
Dagmar Kaltenmark
c/o Sozialforum, Tübingen e.V.
Paulinenstr 25
D-72072 Tübingen
+49-7472-6048
E-mail:
100722.3070@compuserve.com

Selbsthilfegruppe
Monika Lusche
Mühlstr 26
74399 Waldheim
+49-7143-33502

Astrid Votz, Forstr 10
71111 Waldenbach
+49-7157-8222
E-mail:
10722@3070@compuserve.com or
10157.1116@compuserve.com

Transsexuellen-Arbeitskreis
c/o HUCH
Westring 278
D-24116 Kiel
+49-431-17090
FAX +49-431-17099

Transidentitas e.V.
WUF-Zentrum
Niggelweg 2
D-97082 Würzberg. jeden4

Transidentitas e.V.
Selbsthilfegruppe
c/o Christoph
+49-391-5614616

AUSTRIA (postal code: A-)
(intl telephone code: +43)

TransX-Verein TransGender
PO Box 331
A-1171 Wien

BELGIUM (postal code: B-)
(intl telephone code: +32)

Franjepoot
Postbox 53
B-2100 Deurne 1

Vervliet Jessica (TS)
Kerkplaats 22
B-2990 Gooreind-Wuustwezel
Place to stay before and after surgery

Genderstichting (Belgium Gender Foundation)
Pluimstraat 48
B-8500 Kortrijk
+32-56-21-9541, M-F 9-11:30 am & 1-4:30 pm, Mon & Wed until 8 pm CET

DENMARK (postal code: DK-)
(intl telephone code: +45)

FPE-NE Denmark
Postboks 361
DK-1504 Köbenhavn V
+45-42-13-9032
Mon & Tues 6-9 pm CET

Transvision
PO Box 280
DK-1502 Köbenhavn V

NORWAY (postal code: N-)
(intl telephone code: +47)

FPE-NE Norway
Box 1968
Vika, N-0125 Oslo

Eurofantasia
Box 442
N-4301 Sandnes
+47-51-66-24-22, phone & FAX
E-mail: jennys@transgender.org

SWEDEN (postal code: S-)
(intl telephone code: +46)

FPE-S Sweden
Box 49029
S-400-64 Gothenburg
+46-8-34-1316

Benjamin (TS)
PO Box 9083
S-102-71 Stockholm
+46-40-611-9923
Tues 7-9 pm CET

Phi Pi Epsilon Sverige
Box 529
S-101-30 Stockholm

FINLAND (postal code: FIN-)
(intl telephone code: +358)

SETA
c/o Trans Center
Box 135
FIN-00251 Helsinki
+358-0-2411-135
E-mail: ekt@seta.fi

Dreamwear Club
Box 159
FIN-80101 Joensuu

ESTONIA (postal code: EE-)
(intl telephone code: +372)

GENDY
Angerja 13-27
EE-0004 Tallin
A small organization with mostly FTM members

LATVIA (postal code: LV-)
(intl telephone code: +371)

FPE Latvia (TV/SO)
Elga Remes, Jurmala, 15
PO Box 17, LV-2015

NETHERLANDS
(postal code: NL-)
(intl telephone code: +31)

AIS Support Group (IS)
+31-38-269845
(fluent in English & Dutch)

Stichting Nederlands Gender Centrum
Borssenburg 24
NL-1181 NV Amstelveen
+31-20-612-4099
Political action group

Genderteam Amsterdam
Prof. Dr. L.J.G. Gooren
Dept. Endocrynology/Andrology
Free University Hospital
PO Box 7057
NL-1007 MB, Amsterdam
+31-20-444-0542 (ext 199)
FAX: +31-20-444-0502

HET Jongensuur (FTM)
Binnenkadijk 178
NL-1018 ZH Amsterdam
+31-20-6221710

Landelijke Kontaktgroep Travestie en Transseksualiteit
Postbus 11575
NL-1001 GN Amsterdam
+31-10-453-18-93
E-mail: R.Hengeveld@inter.nl.net
(Rosalind Hengeveld)

Nederlandse Vereniging Humanitas
PO Box 71
NL-1000 AB Amsterdam
+31-20-626-24-45
FAX: +31-20-622-7367.

Werkgroep Facet (MTF/SO)
Rode Kruislaan 61
NL-5628 GB Eindhoven
+31-40-241-5475

NETHERLANDS (continued)

Werkgroep Transseksualiteit
Groningen (TS)
H.H.Visscher
Eendrachtskade NZ 19
NL-9718 BB Groningen
+31-50-527-35-89
E-mail: francina@worldaccess.nl

ASIA

TURKEY

Sexual Liberties (TV/TS)
c/o Iskendar Savasir
Lao 176/DS, Kultur Je Sanat
Siraselviler, Taksim, Istanbul
Educational outreach for all Islamic countries. DO NOT PUT GROUP NAME ON ENVELOPE.

Travesty/Transsexualle
c/o Demet Demir
Lao 176/DS, Kultur Je Sanat
Siraselviler, Taksim, Istanbul. DO NOT PUT GROUP NAME ON ENVELOPE.

PAKISTAN

Khusra of Pakistan
c/o Muhamid Aslam Khusra
PF-34 Abbotabad Hockey Stadium
Abbotabad
+92-5921-6158 (leave message) or
+92-5921-2858

BANGLADESH

Youth Approach
3, Purana Paltan
Dhaka-1000, Bangladesh
+88-02-7555321
E-mail: yadc@bangla.net

RUSSIA

Ice and Fire Moscow (TV/TS)
Nvo-Alekeeuskaya Str 7, Flat #8
129626 Moscow
Also: Mirninsky r-n Gagarina Str 28, Flat #3, 678190 Aihal Yakutia
Write directly to Margaret Mankevich. DO NOT PUT GROUP NAME ON ENVELOPE.

OCEANIA/ORIENT

AUSTRALIA
(intl telephone code: +61)

NEW SOUTH WALES

Les Girls (CD)
PO Box 504
Burnwood New South Wales 2134

Sex Workers Outreach
Transgender Support Project
PO Box 1453
Darlinghurst
New South Wales 2010
+61-02-212-2600
FAX: +61-02-212-3978

Transgender Liberation Coalition
PO Box 208
Kings Cross
New South Wales 2011
+61-02-358-5664

Gender Centre
PO Box 226, Petersham
New South Wales 2049
+61-02-569-2366

Boys Will Be Boys (FTM/TS)
PO Box 1349, Strawberry Hills
New South Wales 2012
+61-02-319-2034

NEW SOUTH WALES (continued)

Seahorse Society NSW
PO Box 168, Westgate
New South Wales 2048
+61-02-569-6239, Thurs evenings
E-mail: kim@seahors.cv.com

QUEENSLAND

Gender Clinic
484 Adelaide St
Brisbane Queensland 4000
+61-07-839-8262

Seahorse Society of Queensland
PO Box 574, Annerley
Brisbane Queensland 4103
+61-07-38922124

Mary Russell (IS)
PO Box 3371, Logan Hyperdrome
Loganholme Queensland 4129

Australia Transgenderist
Support Association Inc
PO Box 212
New Farm Queensland 4005
24-hour helpline: +61-07-846-3787
+61-07-236-2400
FAX: +61-07-236-2398

Boys Will Be Boys (FTM)
PO Box 212
West End Queensland 4005
+61-07-839-8262

Self Health for Queensland
Workers in the Sex Industry
PO Box 689, West End
Queensland 4101
+61-07-844-4565
FAX: +61-07-844-8840

SOUTH AUSTRALIA

Carrousal Club of South Australia
PO Box 721
Cowandilla South Australia 5033
Lana Allen, +61-08-388-3644
Michelle, +61-08-281-6190

Chameleons Group
PO Box 907
Kent Town South Australia 5071
+61-08-362-1611

South Australia
Transsexual Support
Gayline, +61-08-362-3223
Jenny, +61-08-362-1611

VICTORIA

Gender Dysphoria Clinic at the
Monash Medical Centre
Clayton Campus
246 Clayton Rd
Clayton Victoria 3168
Dawn, +61-03-955-1437

Seahorse Club
Box 2337V
Melbourne Victoria 3001

Boys Will Be Boys (FTM/TS)
PO Box 328
Northcote Victoria 3070

Transgender Liberation and Care
PO Box 1674
South Preston Victoria 3071
+61-03-948-11506, Sharon
E-mail: gayle@melbpc.org.au

Chameleon Society of Victoria
PO Box 500
Williamstown Victoria 3016

WEST AUSTRALIA

WATS Support Unity and Pride
PO Box 771
Doubleview West Australia 6018

Chameleon Society
PO Box 367
Victoria Park West Australia 6163
+61-01-577-1753

Gender Council of
Australia (WA) Inc
PO Box 58
Victoria Park West Australia 6110
+61-09-362-5447

NEW ZEALAND
(intl telephone code: +64)

New Zealand Gender
Dysphoria Foundation
PO Box 2827, Auckland

NZPC/TOPS
PO Box 68-509
Auckland
+64-9-3666-106
Support group and trans-friendly
medical clinic

Intersex Society of
New Zealand (IS)
PO Box 9196
Wellington
+64-4727386

JAPAN (intl telephone code: +81)

Elizabeth Nagoya Shop
1-13-15 Noritake Nakamura-ku
Nagoya-shi 453

Elizabeth Club
1-1-9 Kujo
Nishi-ku, Osaka 550

Elizabeth Club
5-32-18 Kameido
Koto-ku, Tokyo 136
+81-3-3683-6092

FTM Nippon
Adachi-ku
Adachi-nishi-post office
Tokyo 123
+81-3-3683-6092 (Kameido Club)

WEB SITES

For people interested in obtaining information through their computers, there are a number of ways to access the World Wide Web, a giant multi-media encyclopedia made up of thousands of computers all over the world. Unlike the other parts of the Internet, the World Wide Web offers great information resources, often with color pictures. Some sites have sound, all in an easy to use hypertext format. Hypertext means that when you mouse click on a colored underlined word, you will be taken to the reference for that word – another document will be delivered to your computer from a computer maybe thousands of miles away! The Web makes traveling the Internet as easy as point and click. Once you have passed one hyperlink, you can click on another, and get a different document; soon you will find yourself going back and forth across the Internet. The colored underlined words will change color once you have explored their hyperlinks.

Included here are some sites focused on transgender issues—World Wide Web sites to help you explore transsexual information from around the world. The sites that we are suggesting do not imply endorsement, but just resources for you to peruse.

The American Boyz
http://www.NetGSI.com/~listwrangler/

Harry Benjamin Standards of Care
http://www.aa.net/~tomia/hbigda.htm

Deaf Resources
http://www.netgsi.com/listwrangler/deafg.html

Female to Male Guidelines
http://www.netgsi.com/~listwrangler/f2mhealth.html

Center for Gender Sanity
http://www.cris.com/~merkins/index.shtml

The International Foundation for Gender Education
http://www.transgender.org/tg/ifge/index.html

Gender Talk
http://www.gendertalk.com/gtakrad.htm

Gender Web
http://www.genderweb.org

Hormone Therapy
http://www.savina.com/confluence/hormone/m2f.html

Intelligence Engineering
http://www. inteleng.com/gender.html

Ingersoll Gender Center
http://www.ingersollcenter.org

Dr. Anne Lawrence's Transsexual Women's Resources
http://www.mindspring.com/~alawrence

Nu Woman Transgender Cabaret
http://www.nu-woman.com

Planet Out
http://www.planetout.com/

Sex Change Indigo Pages
http://www.servtech.com/public/perette/Sc/sexchange.html

SOFFA Significant Others, Friends, Families & Allies
http://www.netgsi.com/~listwrangler/soffa.html

The Transsexual Menace International
http://www.apocalypse.org/pub/tsmenace

Transgender Community Website
http://www.tiac.net/users/dba/homepage.htm

Transgender Law & Employment Policy, Inc.
http://www.abmall.com/ictlep/

TOPS Transgendered Officers Protect and Serve
http://www.greatbasin.net/~kuryakin/tops

Transgenero (Spanish) Se Habla Espanol
http://www.netgsi.com/~listwrangler/transgenero.html

Transgender articles by request
http://www.netgsi.com/~listwrangler/list.html

TransParent
http://www.critpath.org/pflag-talk/transparent.htm

Note: All web site addresses begin with http://

PRIMARY INFORMATION SOURCES

The Harry Benjamin International
Gender Dysphoria Association Inc.
1300 South 2nd Street, Suite 180
Minneapolis, MN 55454
612-625-1500
612-624-8078
612-626-8311 FAX

This organization provides interaction and communication among a variety of professional groups dealing with research and treatment of gender dysphoria. They sponsor meetings and produce a newsletter.

International Foundation for Gender Education
P.O. Box 229
Waltham, MA 02454-0229
781-899-2212
781-899-5703 FAX

This organization offers a wide variety of printed material for transsexuals. They serve a large group including professionals. They have both regular and specialty publications as well as sponsor conferences.

International Conference on
Transgender Law and Employment Policy
P.O. Box 1010
Cooperstown, NY 13326
607-547-4118

This group deals with legal issues, publishes a newsletter, and sponsors conferences.

FTM
5337 College Ave. #142
Oakland, CA 94618
510-287-2646
E-Mail FTM news @ aol.com

This group serves the needs of female to male people. They have regular meetings and publish a newsletter and sponsor conferences.

A.E.G.I.S.
American Education Gender Information Service
P.O. Box 33724
Decatur, GA 30033-0724
770-939-2128
770-939-0244
770-939-1770 FAX

This group provides information for professionals and individuals with gender issues. They publish a journal and maintain archives and a library. They also conduct seminars and workshops.

COMPLETED SURGERY

Male to Female

Photographed by K.C. Bailey

Female to Male

Photographed by Mariette Pathe Allen, author of **Transformations: Cross Dressers and Those Who Love Them**, 100 Riverside Drive, New York, NY 10024

A FEW PEOPLE'S PHOTOGRAPHS

These photographs, which were furnished by a number of surgeons, show sex reassignment completed surgery. This book does not recommend any physician, but shows the work of a number of physicians who were willing to provide these photographs. All of the information in this book is provided to assist, educate, and enable patients and those who care about them to make informed decisions.

Male to Female Post-Surgery

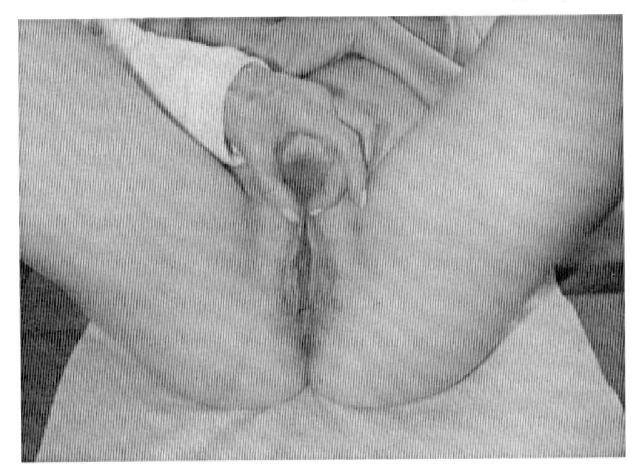

Stanley H. Biber, M.D.

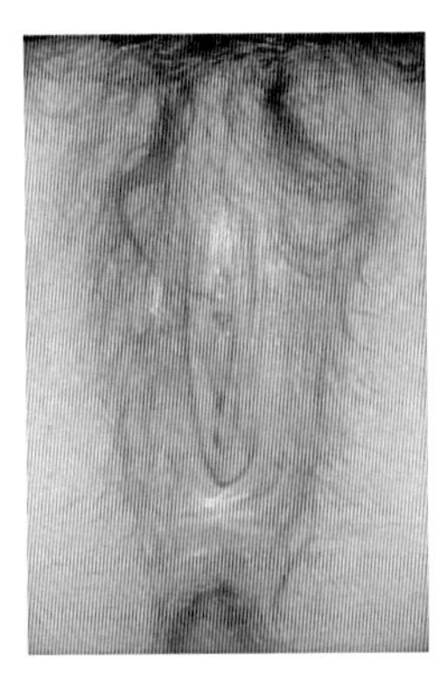

Yvon Menard, M.D.

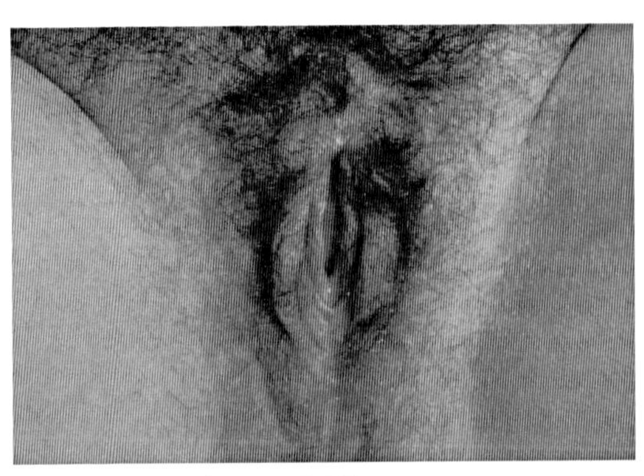

Eugene A. Schrang, M.D.

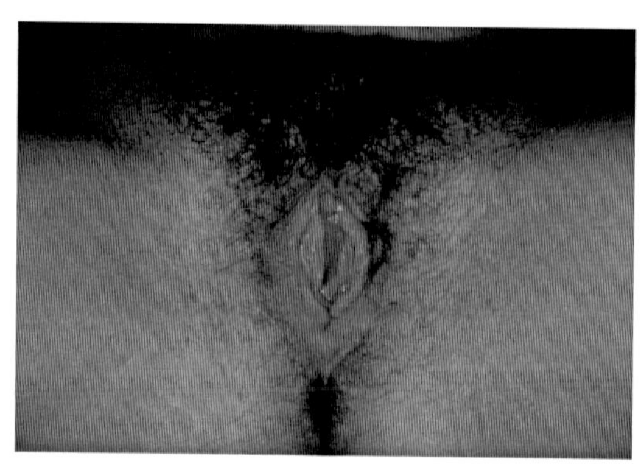

Eugene A. Schrang, M.D.

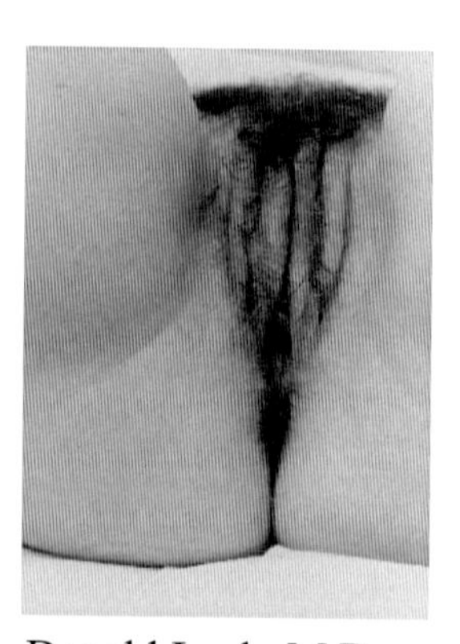

Donald Laub, M.D.
Rectosigmoid Vaginoplasty

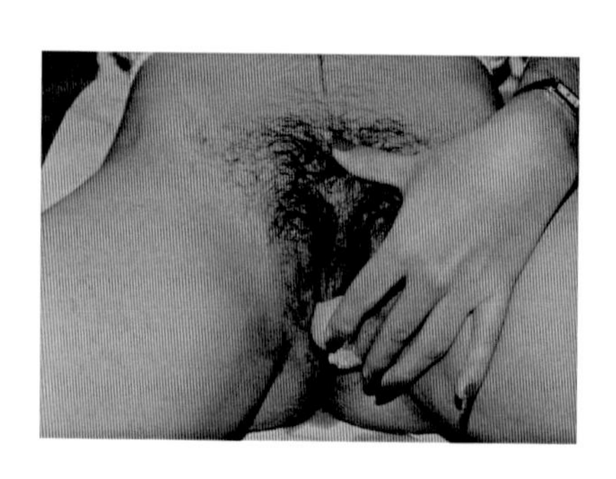

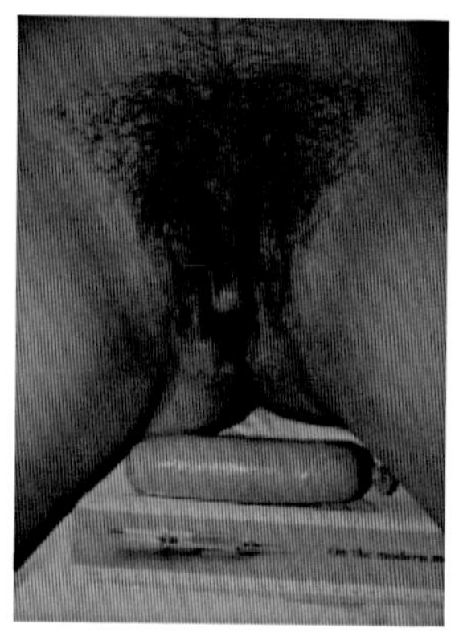

Michael P. Small, M.D.
Removed stent shows depth of new vagina

Female to Male Post-Surgery

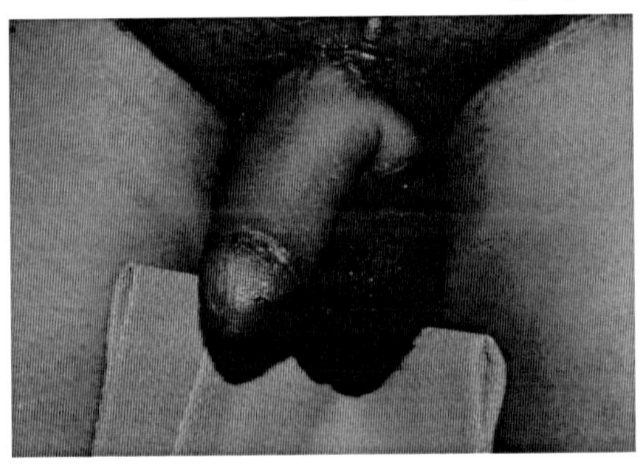

Lawrence J. Gottleib, M.D. and Laurence A. Levine, M.D. (radial forearm flap technique)

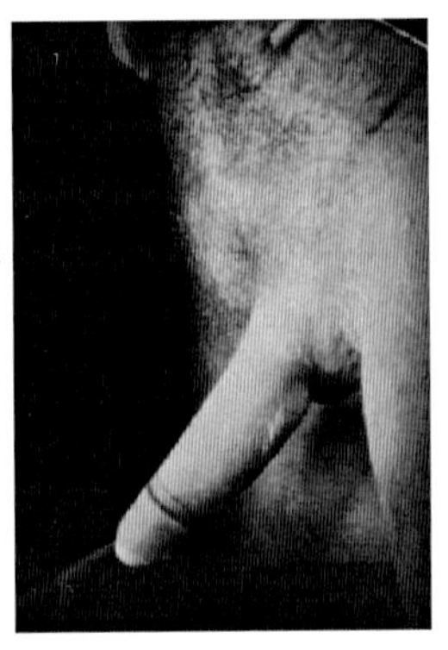

Lawrence J. Gottleib, M.D. and Laurence A. Levine, M.D. (radial forearm flap technique)

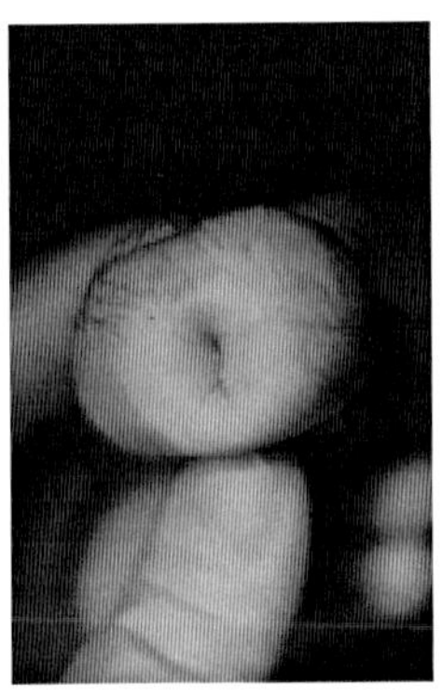

Lawrence J. Gottleib, M.D. and Laurence A. Levine, M.D. (radial forearm flap technique)

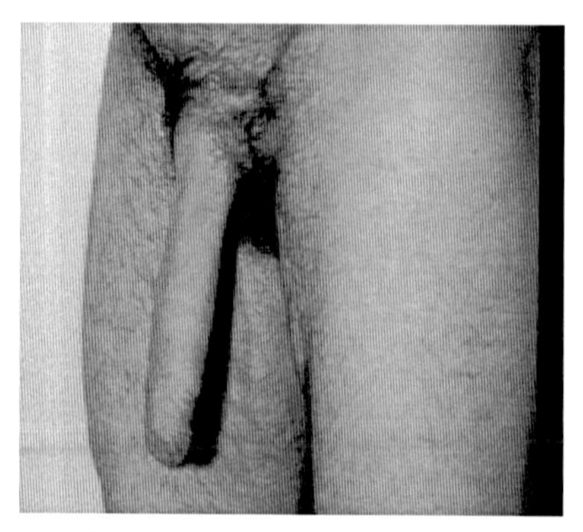

Daniel Greenwald, M.D.

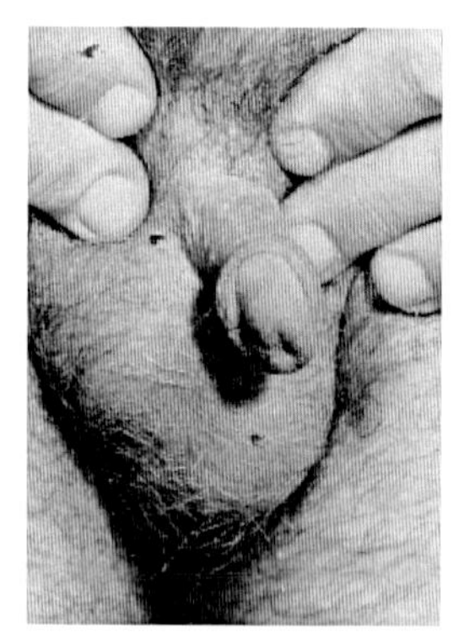

Donald Laub, M.D.
Metoidioplasty

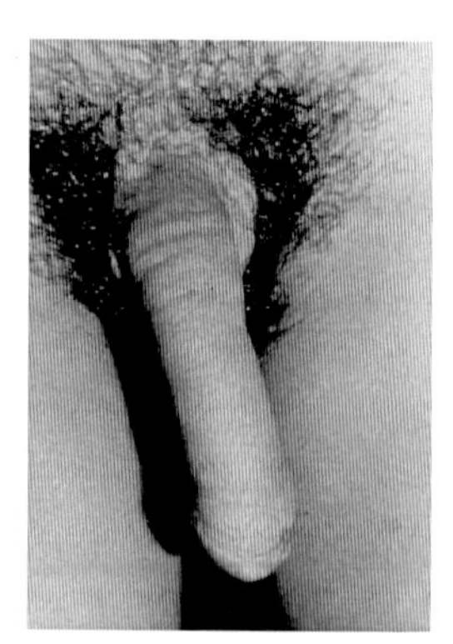

Donald Laub, M.D.
Phalloplasty

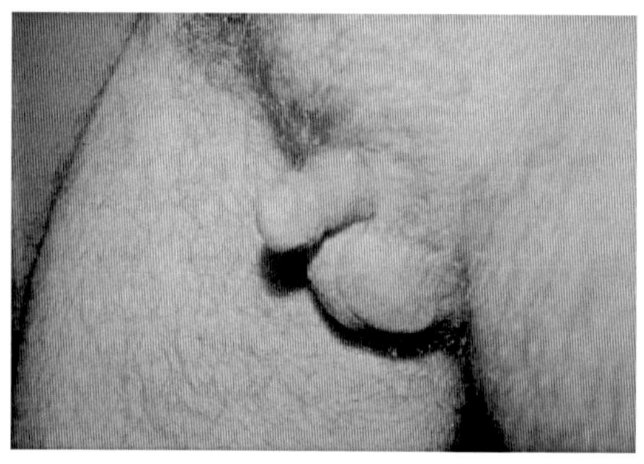

Toby R. Meltzer, M.D.

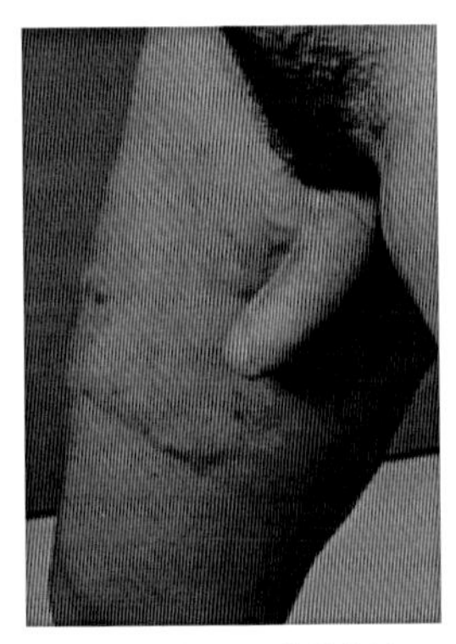

Yvon Menard, M.D.

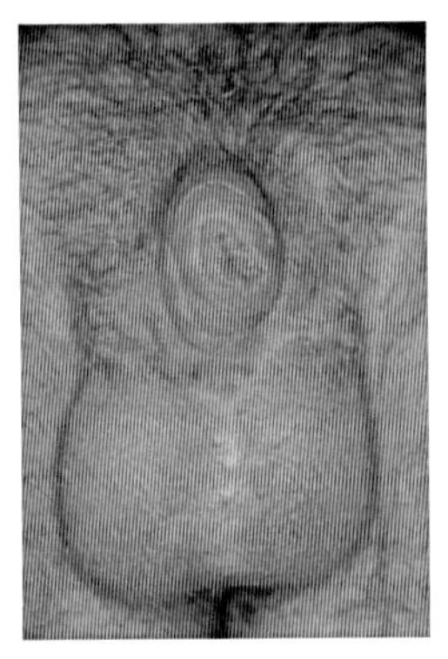

Yvon Menard, M.D.
(metoidioplasty)

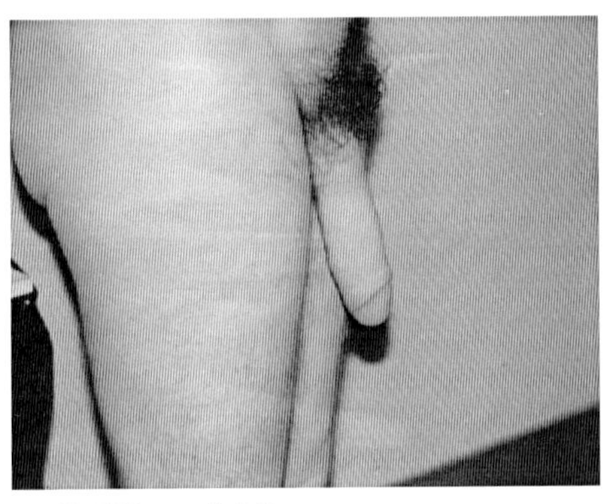

Neil Wilson, M.D.